THE LETTE

MILTO

ERICK

THE LETTERS OF
MILTON H. ERICKSON

EDITED BY JEFFREY K. ZEIG, PH.D.,
AND BRENT B. GEARY, PH.D.

ZEIG, TUCKER & THEISEN, INC.
PHOENIX, ARIZONA

Library of Congress Cataloging-in-Publication Data

Erickson, Milton H.
    The letters of Milton H. Erickson / edited by Jeffrey K. Zeig and Brent B. Geary.
      p. cm.
    Includes bibliographical references.
    ISBN 1-891944-11-8
    1. Erickson, Milton H.—Correspondence. 2. Psychotherapists—United States—Correspondence. 3. Psychotherapy. 4. Hypnotism—Theraputic use.
I. Zeig, Jeffrey K. II. Geary, Brent B. III. Title.

RC438.6.E76 A4 2000
616.89'0092—dc21
[B]

00-033361

Published by

ZEIG, TUCKER & THEISEN, INC.
3618 North 24th Street
Phoenix, AZ 85016

Book design by Kathleen Lake, Neuwirth and Associates

Manufactured in the United States of America

10 9 8 7 6 5 4 3 2 1

CONTENTS

Editorial Note

Our intent in this volume was to let the letters of Milton Erickson and his correspondents speak for themselves so that the reader might draw his or her own conclusions. Therefore, we did not edit the letters per se, except to correct typographical errors and obvious misspellings and to regularize the paragraphing and some punctuation. We also incorporated the writers' corrections and additions so as not to distract the reader. (Note that, to avoid repetition, we are omitting the writers' addresses and affiliations throughout their correspondence.)

Erickson himself wrote with literary flair. He was an artful composer who strove for precision in all of his communications. Our contribution was the interpolation of editorial comments to provide a context or to clarify a particular reference or situation.

INTRODUCTION

"In a man's letters, his soul lies naked."

—*Samuel Johnson (1777)*

Prelude

Who—and what—was Milton H. Erickson, M.D.?

Simply put, Milton Erickson (1901–1980) was the foremost authority on the use of clinical hypnosis in the twentieth century. And there are many who contend that he was the century's premier psychotherapist. What Erickson added to the practice of therapy can be compared to Sigmund Freud's contribution to its theory. Moreover, whereas Freud is represented in the psychiatric literature by only a handful of case descriptions, Erickson detailed more than 300 cases (O'Hanlon & Hexum, 1990).

The Wounded Healer

But Erickson was much more than a singular contributor to the professional literature—his very life was an inspiration, a profile in courage. The archetype of the "wounded healer," he suffered, and overcame, many physical ailments. Most debilitating of these were the ongoing effects of polio, which he had contracted in his late teenage years.

As a victim of the postpolio syndrome, Erickson spent the last 15 years of his life in a wheelchair. With the deterioration of his muscles, he lost mobility. By the end of his life, he had practically no use of his legs and but limited use of his arms. In order to write, he would guide his right hand with his left. Similarly, when eating, he had to use his left hand to support his right hand. Moreover, both his sight and his hearing became increasingly impaired. And by the time he died, he was breathing by virtue of half a diaphragm plus a few intercostal muscles.

Erickson suffered constant pain. When patients came to him, they found a counselor who spoke not hypothetically, but from his own experience. When he talked about enjoying life in spite of—or because of—pain, he was being honest. In affirming his pleasure in just being alive, he would "reframe" his pain, jokingly remarking, "I don't mind the pain. It's better than the alternative." To Erickson, pain was a blessing that confirmed that he was still among the living. Freedom from pain would come only with death. (See Zeig, 1985b, for further information.)

No matter what life-limiting problem brought patients to Erickson, whether schizophrenia or the inroads of cancer, they beheld someone who suffered at least as much as they did. And yet he obviously enjoyed life.

Professional Contributions

Erickson was prolific professionally, and he traveled widely to teach. He wrote more than 140 scholarly papers, most of which appear in the *Collected Papers of Milton H. Erickson on Hypnosis*, edited by Ernest L. Rossi (Erickson & Rossi, 1980). More than 100 books about, or related to, Erickson's psychotherapy are extant, and new works appear regularly. He cofounded the American Society of Clinical Hypnosis and established its journal, *The American Journal of Clinical Hypnosis*, which he edited for the first ten years of its existence.

To honor and advance Erickson's work, The Milton H. Erickson Foundation was established in 1979. The Foundation organizes training programs for professionals and sponsors yearly conferences on such topics as the Evolution of Psychotherapy, Brief Therapy, Sex and Intimacy, and Ericksonian Approaches to Hypnosis and Psychotherapy. More than 80 regional Institutes throughout the world currently are affiliated with the Foundation.

Erickson's professional contributions have been examined through a number of different lenses. Jay Haley wrote one of the most important books about Erickson, *Uncommon Therapy*, in 1973. Here, he focused on Erickson's "strategic" psychotherapy, pointing out that a therapy is strategic when a therapist works to achieve a specific goal.

Notable among the numerous books about Erickson's hypnosis is the four-volume series by Erickson and Rossi: *Hypnotic Realities* (1976); *Hypnotherapy, an Exploratory Case Book* (1979); *Experiencing Hypnosis* (1981); and *The February Man* (1989).

Some of Erickson's students have provided texts explaining his methods for professional readers, including Stephen and Carol Lankton's *The Answer Within* (1983) and Stephen Gilligan's *Therapeutic Trances* (1986). Erickson's unconventional instructional style is explicated in *A Teaching Seminar with Milton H. Erickson* (Zeig, 1980).

Through texts such as these about Erickson as therapist and his methods, one can appreciate—and better understand—the technical wizardry of one of the most innovative practitioners in the history of psychotherapy.

An Intimate Look at Greatness

Beyond the many publications by and about him, however, the letters of Milton Erickson reveal aspects of his life that have not previously been made public. Herein, we are privy to Erickson, the man, in a way that provides new insights into his uniqueness as a clinician, a researcher, a theorist, and, especially, an individual.

As a reader, you will meet the luminaries with whom Erickson interacted, both in the field of psychiatry and in related disciplines, such as anthropology. You will be there with Erickson as he consults on cases with renowned psychoanalysts, exchanges views regarding hypnosis with noted anthropologists Gregory Bateson and Margaret Mead, and discusses research issues with such experts as Stanley Milgram. You will also be able to read, in his own words, his advice to patients, colleagues, and students.

Erickson clearly is someone to be studied, for his personal style as well as his clinical contributions. By reading his correspondence, one becomes familiar with his thinking and its scope. This book should prove of great value to clinicians, historians, and researchers, as well as to the layperson who is interested in his or her own personal growth and development.

Milton Erickson—A Brief Biography

Milton H. Erickson was born on December 5, 1901, in a dirt-floor log cabin in Aurum, Nevada. His family then traveled east in a covered wagon, and he grew up on a farm outside of Beaver Dam, Wisconsin, one of nine children.

A bit of an anomaly in his own family of churchgoing Midwestern farmers, Erickson distinguished himself at a very early age by his extraordinary intellect. He was the only member of his family to go to graduate school, and only one other sibling, a sister, even attended college. As a youngster, he exhibited a precocious interest in language, studying the dictionary to familiarize himself with words and their meaning.

Milton Erickson began his formal studies of hypnosis in the 1920s at the University of Wisconsin, when he enrolled in a seminar taught by Clark Hull, one of the most influential psychologists in the first half of the twentieth century. Hull was a dedicated researcher, especially on learning theory, and wrote one of the early scientific texts on hypnosis, *Hypnosis and Suggestibility: An Experimental Approach* (1933).

After receiving a medical degree from the University of Wisconsin in 1928, Erickson trained in Rhode Island and Colorado. Subsequently, he became Director of Research at Eloise State Hospital in Detroit, Michigan. In 1948, he left Detroit for Phoenix, Arizona, where he took a position at the Arizona State Hospital, After about a year on the staff, he resigned to establish a private practice at his home at 32 West Cypress Street, moving to 1201 East Hayward Avenue in 1970. By maintaining his offices at home, he was able to cope better with his disabilities and to enjoy more frequent interactions with his family.

Milton Erickson died on March 15, 1980. He was survived by four daughters and four sons, 26 grandchildren, and his wife, Elizabeth. A frequent contributor to Erickson's professional work, she still lives at their Phoenix home and is a member of the Board of Directors of the Erickson Foundation.

The Six Streams of Erickson's Heritage

Milton Erickson had many intellectual heirs, and continues to influence upcoming generations of psychotherapists. His contributions to psychology have been described as encompassing six main streams.

1. Strategic psychotherapy. Jay Haley contacted Erickson while in Palo Alto as a junior member of a communications research project headed by Gregory Bateson. A noted anthropologist, biologist, and philosopher, Bateson had previously met Erickson years earlier while married to Margaret Mead.

Haley and his collaborator, John Weakland, visited Erickson numerous times. Some of their recorded dialogues are reproduced in *Conversations with Milton H. Erickson, M.D.*, Volumes I–III, edited by Haley (1985).

Partially as a result of his work with Erickson, Haley devised strategic psychotherapy, which is described in writings by Haley and by Cloe Madanes. Strategic therapy is primarily a family and systems-based approach. Hypnosis per se is de-emphasized in favor of naturalistic procedures; that is, the therapy employs hypnotic techniques, but without the induction of a formal trance.

2. The Mental Research Institute (MRI). Founded in Palo Alto by Don Jackson, the institute spawned the interactional approach developed by Paul Watzlawick, John Weakland, and Richard Fisch. The MRI brief therapy project was created to test offshoots of the methods developed and espoused by Erickson.

3. Solution-focused therapy. Stephen de Shazer and his colleagues at the Brief Therapy Center in Milwaukee, Wisconsin, developed what is called solution-focused therapy. This exceedingly positive Ericksonian approach emphasizes what patients do right rather than their deficits. It is not based on psychopathology; rather, its aim is to elicit patient strengths.

4. The psychobiological approach of Ernest Rossi. Rossi was Erickson's Boswell. He studied Erickson closely, and coauthored and edited a number of important books by and about him, including the *Collected Papers of Milton H. Erickson*. The Erickson–Rossi (1980a–d) four volumes on hypnosis largely represent Erickson's lessons to Rossi on how to carry out hypnotic techniques. Rossi also edited a series of books based on transcripts of Erickson's seminars. In his works, Rossi delineated a number of tactical and linguistic approaches that Erickson employed in his psychotherapy. Later, Rossi developed some of his own theories of mind–body communication and has become known as an expert in psychoneuroimmunology.

5. Neurolinguistic programming. Richard Bandler and John Grinder (a linguist who drew on the revolutionary work of Noam Chomsky) identified linguistic and semantic elements in Erickson's methods in *Patterns of the Hypnotic Techniques of Milton H. Erickson* (1975).

6. The neo-Ericksonians. The neo-Ericksonian group includes Stephen and Carol Lankton, Michael Yapko, Stephen Gilligan, and Jeffrey Zeig. This generation of therapists studied with Erickson when he was in the twilight of his career. Their work tends to focus on Erickson's use of hypnosis, which is de-emphasized in the other schools. More recently, Gilligan (1997) developed a self-relations theory, which may branch into a seventh stream of Ericksonian orientation.

In summary, Erickson's legacy has influenced major contributors to the fields of individual, couple, and family psychotherapy. His heritage endures and his views are being incorporated into the mainstream, including cognitive-behavioral therapy. Moreover, time-limited approaches are a necessity in contemporary practice, and Erickson is considered by many to be the father of brief therapy.

A Therapeutic Touch

Erickson's therapeutic power not only was attributable to the genius of his methodology; it was also rooted in his personal style. We believe that you cannot catalog his skill as a therapist as distinct from his persona. Seven "methods" that can be characterized as generated by Erickson's personality are reiterated throughout his letters: utilization, orienting toward, being experiential, harnessing drama, individualizing treatment, future orientation, and trusting the unconscious.

Utilization

Utilization is not merely a technique; it is a philosophy. Utilization dictates that whatever the patient/family brings to the sessions can be harnessed to effect a psychotherapeutic result. From this perspective, problems, resources, ambitions, and the like are not seen as "grist" for the analytic mill. Instead, they are "rocket fuel" that can be used to help patients propel themselves into a different orbit (Zeig, 1992).

An example of the mind set of utilization (Zeig, 1997) can be seen in the couple who came to Erickson with a presenting problem of the wife's alcoholism. The husband complained bitterly because the wife had a "little hobby." She would spend her weekends gardening, and while digging and weeding, would periodically drink from a hidden bottle of liquor, which the husband could never find. He counseled her, confronted her, and cajoled her about her behavior, indicating that it was detrimental both to her health and to their relationship. However, she did not change.

The wife also had a complaint. She said that her husband had a "little hobby," as well. He spent his weekends reading "dusty old books, dusty old magazines, and dusty old newspapers." She counseled, confronted, and cajoled him about his behavior, indicating that it was detrimental both to his health and to their relationship. However, he did not change.

In their first interview, Erickson learned that the couple owned a camper, but had not used it in a long time, although they enjoyed camping. However, both vigorously asserted that what they did hate about the outdoors was going fishing.

Erickson's initial intervention exemplifies the utilization method. He told the wife to buy a bottle of whiskey and hide it inside the home. Upon returning home from work, the husband was to find the hidden bottle within a specified time. If he did not, the wife could drink with impunity—but only in the house. The wife was delighted with the assignment. She was able to hide the whiskey in a place that no one could possibly find within the allotted time. But after a few days, she grew tired of the procedure.

The couple returned to Erickson, and this time he commanded them, "Go fishing." They protested, but he continued to counsel, confront, and cajole them about the necessity to go fishing. They, in turn, continued to voice their opposition, as they "hated fishing." Finally, they asked Erickson why they had to go fishing. He explained, "It is the only correct therapy for you. If you are in a small boat in the middle of a lake, Husband, there is no way that you can have dusty old books, dusty old magazine, and dusty old newspapers with you. Wife, if you are in a boat in the middle of a lake, there is nowhere that you can hide a bottle of whiskey. Go fishing."

Again, the couple responded by rebelling against the idea, but they did dust off their camper and they took a trip to see more of Arizona. In the process, they rediscovered how much they enjoyed camping—and they also rediscovered how much they enjoyed their relationship. Subsequently, the wife "voluntarily" gave up her "little hobby," as did the husband his. All Erickson had done was establish a context from which they could proceed.

This case is replete with examples of utilization. Erickson utilized the pattern of hiding. He utilized the couple's resistance. They seemed to need something to rebel against. He offered himself. In rebelling against Erickson, they discovered their own road to healing.

Utilization is to Ericksonian therapy what interpretation is to psychoanalysis and what desensitization is to behavior therapy (Zeig, 1992). It should not be considered merely a technique. It cannot be denied that new opportunities for effective therapy become possible when utilization is adopted as a therapeutic philosophy.

Erickson had been familiar with the concept of utilization from an early age. He grew up in a poor family in which it was a necessary coping mechanism. Thus, it was not merely his method, it was his lifestyle. Numerous examples of Erickson's utilization philosophy will be found in his letters.

Orienting Toward

Erickson was renowned for his indirect style, in which he used anecdotes, metaphors, and allusions. His communications were multileveled; he often conveyed more than one meaning with a single message. Technically, this method can be termed indirection, but we prefer to think of it as "orienting toward." Erickson's anecdotal style was a direct throwback to his family of origin. His father liked to describe his experiences as a cowboy and farmer, and the neighborhood children often would gather to hear his tales.

Whereas most letter writers tend to be straightforward, Erickson's correspondence reveals his engaging anecdotal style. His storytelling was not limited to his psychotherapy; it was an integral part of who he was.

One of the reasons for being indirect is to elicit rather than enforce ideas. Through the use of orienting-toward methods, the therapist establishes a context or emotional background, and the patient, by being stimulated into thinking about things differently, can change his or her behavior.

Being Experiential

Erickson was the quintessential experiential therapist. He believed that therapy takes place through direct experiential encounters. His treatment methods were not didactic or analytic. Erickson often took his therapy outside of the consulting room into the patient's life. He also used hypnosis and other techniques to help patients develop constructive internal experiences. He believed that rather than "talking it out," people learn best by doing.

Although one can learn physics in a didactic way, being happy must be learned experientially. Again, Erickson's experiential method was not limited to therapy, as is shown in his letters.

Harnessing Drama

Often, the crucial element in therapy lies not in what the therapist says, but in how he or she delivers the message. Erickson had a dramatic flair. He made simple ideas come alive by presenting them as a playwright would, alluding to the ideas, developing them in small steps, and then leading them to a climax and denouement. His use of drama is amply evident in his correspondence.

Individualizing Treatment

In 1978, the senior editor (Zeig) asked Erickson to provide a quote that could be used to publicize the First International Congress on Ericksonian Approaches to Hypnosis and Psychotherapy, held in December 1980 to honor Erickson's contributions to the field. Erickson wrote: "Each person is a unique individual. Hence, psychotherapy should be formulated to meet the uniqueness of the individual's needs, rather than tailoring the person to fit the Procrustean bed of a hypothetical theory of human behavior."

In a 75th birthday tribute published in the *American Journal of Clinical Hypnosis*, which Erickson founded (he also was a founder of the American Society of Clinical Hypnosis), Margaret Mead (1977) wrote that one of Erickson's distinguishing characteristics was his ability to invent a new therapy for each patient.

Erickson strove to understand the unique nature of a patient's position, style, affect, thought process, and behavior. His therapy was a process of appealing to a patient's dormant resources. And since these resources are highly individual, the personalized approach enhances their effectiveness. His letters contain numerous examples of his flexibility and range in addressing the individuality of his correspondents.

Future Orientation

Life is lived in the present and directed toward a future. The lessons of the past must be heeded in order to live effectively, but the past is fundamentally unchangeable.

In contradistinction to the many analytic approaches that draw upon one's personal history as a primary method of change, Erickson worked to harness structures in the present that could effect a constructive future. He was more a tour guide than a traveling companion. He knew the terrain and how best to get people into fertile fields. He was not an archaeologist searching for "treasures."

Erickson's future orientation was basic to his lifestyle, as reflected in his letters. He was a goal-directed person, a goal-directed therapist, and a goal-directed correspondent. As was his therapy, his letters were vehicles of influence, subtly leading the recipients to thinking differently about future directions.

Trusting the Unconscious

To Erickson, the unconscious was a repository of learning, both physiological and psychological. He viewed inflexibility and myopic perspectives as contributory to psychosocial difficulties. Resources, he maintained, reside in the unconscious and can be unearthed, sometimes with dramatic results.

Effective therapy merges the spontaneity and discipline of therapist and patient alike. Both can benefit from unconscious wisdom.

Students who visited Erickson left with the message, "Trust your unconscious," firmly etched into their psyches. That aphorism had Zen-like qualities that encouraged people to cultivate a "beginner's mind," open to possibility and discovery.

Trusting the unconscious is not a naive proposition. Although "unconscious" patterns often produce the problems that bring people into treatment, most unconscious processes are constructive. Generative patterns can be elicited, to the delight and surprise of their author.

Erickson's faith in the power of these unconscious processes can be noted throughout his letters.

Conclusions

Not only was Milton Erickson a major force in contemporary therapy, he was also an inspiration—in his work and in his life. By standing on his shoulders, so to speak, we can improve our own vistas.

Erickson was a pioneer. He was an explorer, working his way through the jungle of human communication to discover—or uncover—previously uncharted aspects of human responsiveness. His letters illuminate his journey. We hope that they also will illuminate the path of the reader.

I

MARGARET MEAD

"The fascinating thing about Milton Erickson's work is that his originality is not contained in any attempt to differ from others, but simply is a matter of his own pursuit of the new, within his own work."

—Margaret Mead (1977)

When Margaret Mead wrote to Milton Erickson in 1939, she was already known for her contributions to anthropology. She had written *Coming of Age in Samoa* (1928), *Growing Up in New Guinea* (1930), and *Sex and Temperament in Three Primitive Societies* (1939), and had made field trips to Samoa (1925–26, 1928–29), New Guinea (1931–33), and Bali and, again, New Guinea (1936–39). At the time, she was the assistant curator of ethnology at the American Museum of Natural History in New York.

Mead had met Gregory Bateson in 1932 while both were on anthropological assignments in New Guinea. They married in 1936 and their only child, Catherine, was born in 1939. After working together in Bali, they coauthored *Balinese Character* (1942).

The couple was instrumental in establishing the Macy Conferences, which began in 1942 at a meeting on "cerebral inhibition" (a more respectable term for hypnotism). Erickson was a featured contributor, and object of study, at this initial meeting, at which the group tried to determine an identity, and it was the only one he was to attend.

Meetings were held infrequently during the World War II years, but were regularly scheduled once the war had ended. Those convened between 1947 and 1953 were most productive, and it was during this time that the theory of cybernetics was generated.

In addition to Milton Erickson, other notable conferees over the years included Lawrence Kubie, a psychoanalyst who collaborated on papers with Erickson; Heinz von Foerster, the constructivist philosopher who first attended a Macy Conference in 1947, and documented some of the findings; Kurt Lewin, the experimental psychologist; Lawrence Frank of the Macy Foundation; and Norbert Weiner, who is generally credited with inventing cybernetics. The first important paper on cybernetics, "Behavior, Purpose and Teleology" by Rosenbluth, Weiner, and Bigelow, appeared in *Philosophy of Science* in 1943. (For more information on the Macy Conferences, see the interview with Bateson and Mead published in *CoEvolution Quarterly*, Summer, 1976.)

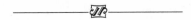

Mead's initial letter to Erickson, dated May 23, 1939, was evidently typed personally on a manual typewriter. The original had a number of typographical errors, and Mead made some handwritten corrections, which have been incorporated in the letter as published here. At the time the letter was written, Mead was 37 years old, as was Erickson.

From: Margaret Mead
May 23, 1939

Dear Dr. Erikson:
Dr. Maslow has let me see some of your materials and my husband, Gregory Bateson, and I are exceedingly interested in them. We have been especially interested in their releveance to the problem of religious trance in Bali, a problem which occupied part of our time during our recent two expeditions to Bali and to which one of our collaborators, Miss Jane Belo, has been giving all of her time. Dr. Maslow was first struck by the applicability of some of your findings to the Balinese trance, after observing some of Miss Belo's Cinema material. Miss Belo is at present in Bali doing some special follow-up work on the personality of her trancers and it is

with the idea of forwarding any suggestions to her, to be applied in the field at once, that I am writing you now.

The special point about which we need your help is the problem of criteria for distinguishing "deep trance" from "sonnambulistic" states. In many forms of trance in Bali, the person "goes in" by some sort of complete seizure, which manifests itself either in limpness and apparent unconsciousness, in a sort of quick convulsive seizure with loss of control over the movement of the body, in a paroxysm of weeping, etc. This is followed by a period of greater calm and control during which the individual trancer, still said to be "in trance" performs series of more or less stereotyped acts following highly stylized procedures, such as: dancing, fitting the steps and gestures to clues given by the tunes of songs, or by the words of the songs; impersonation of a specified God (this may include change of sex, and involves use of special vocabulary the systematic carrying out of a role in regard to other persons, etc.), turning a kris on the self with alternating periods of orgasmic frenzy and rest; making offerings or handling complicated ritual objects; etc. During this period the trancer is in control of his or her body *most of the time*, the control appears to be somewhat unstable, e.g., a small girl trance dancer will sometimes collapse limply into the crowd, or a man who has been turning the kris on himself may fall down in a convulsive state, or a man who has been wearing a mask may suddenly fall, and remain quite rigid for long periods before he is brought out of trance. With these exceptions however, the trancer performs a role and attends efficiently to the relevant stimuli such as: music, songs, appearance of masked figures; offerings of live chickens which have to have their heads bitten off; offers from other officiants to carry them on the shoulders (the small girl dancers), questions from petitioners asking the will of the impersonated Gods; errors in the ritual which need control, stages in the ritual, etc. But they pay no attention, and, as far as our limited opportunities for experimentation permit, seem actually not to have seen or heard irrelevant possible stimuli (such as a cry of "There is a theatrical company coming" which will empty a temple of the audience to which the little girl trance dancers are dancers does not cause them to pay the slightest attention, or alter their rhythm for a second; hot coals which fall on their legs accidentally; the presence of strange Europeans who arrived *after they went into trance*). Nevertheless their attention is not strictly limited to a series of absolutely defined stimuli; they are able to respond to new situations which can be interpreted in the trance context—such as the presence in the crowd of someone who they wish to involve in a temporary plot, or to the possible presence of danger (e.g., our small trance dancers make no observable response when a whole packet of firecrackers are let off at once, BUT after the explosion is all over they will open their eyes and look in the direction of the explosion as if to be sure where the possibly unexploded crackers may be upon which it would be dangerous to step. Another time, when it rained in the temple court, the little dancers insisted—in trance—on being carried to our dining room to dance—something they had never done before, and which was suggested in response to: a. the rain, and b. the fact that a theatrical troop had danced in the dining room the night before. After a period of efficient and stylized performance in trance, which may last from a few minutes—for the violent types—to several hours for the little dancers who merely dance—the trancers are "brought out of trance" by the application of defined rituals—incense, sprinkling with holy water, giving them holy water to drink, singing special songs, presence of the great double animal mask, etc. These rituals for bringing them out of trance may but often are not the same as the rituals which put them in, and "coming out" may, but often is not, be accompanied by seizures, collapses into unconsciousness, etc. comparable to those which accompanied "going into trance."

Now, it seems to us that the period of "going in" might be regarded as comparable to your initial deep trance during which you give your subjects the program which they are to act out during somnambulism, and the period of "acting in trance" might be regarded as comparable to your periods of somnambulism during which your subjects ignore all but specified types of stimuli, and act out highly complicated roles which you have set up. But as I understood your materials, your subjects had to be put back into deep trance before they could regain their normal state. Would the fact that many of our subjects come out altogether at a given stimulus and by some very simple procedure such as clapping their hands once, or taking a drink of holy water, invalidate this comparison? Would you think that the trance state which had an initial state of violent seizure or limpness and apparent unconsciousness, was necessarily incomparable with the trance state where the trancer went in, very quickly and simply, merely by breathing incense while people sang, and giving a few quick jerks, or convulsive trembles? And most important of all, can you suggest any criteria which could be applied to these trance states which would demonstrate their comparability or incomparability to somnambulism. Dr. Maslow suggested hypnotism of the trancers; this is at present impossible due to culture, contact conditions in Bali which would make such methods suspect to government and nativism, and furthermore, although it would tell us whether the trancers could be hypnotised, it would not tell us what their state was when they were in the formal, culturally stylized trance.

I would very much appreciate an early answer as Miss Belo is leaving Bali soon.

Sincerely yours,
Margaret Mead

To: Margaret Mead
May 31, 1939

Dear Dr. Mead:

I appreciate greatly your letter of inquiry, but I am uncertain whether or not I can be of much assistance. However, I shall try to meet your needs by furnishing accounts of various hypnotic phenomena which parallel or illustrate behavior similar to that which you described in relation to the Bali dancers, and then I shall leave to you the task of applying the material to your problem.

Perhaps one of the first points I should make is that the experimental techniques described in my papers were always elaborated for the specific experimental purpose, and hence they are applicable only generally to other forma of behavior.

Concerning the question of criteria for distinguishing the deep trance from the somnambulistic state, I may say briefly that the latter is simply a development of the first. One secures the deep trance by limiting and restricting, through external measures, the subject's processes and patterns of behavior. This then leads to the development within the subject of internal inhibitions and this in turn progresses to a state of complete arrest of behavior, with the substitution for behavior of a state of passive responsiveness. This state of passive responsiveness can then be utilized for the elaboration of desired forms of behavior, provided they are acceptable to the subject. But also it can be utilized effectively only if the hypnotist gives his suggestions in such fashion that they serve only to initiate and to direct the processes of response, with the actual pattern and form and character of the responses entirely dependent upon the experiential acquisitions of the subject. In brief, to be effective in the evocation of valid behavior, the hypnotist's suggestions must constitute the impetus to behavior, the course and development of which must lie with the subject.

Once the deep trance or the state of passive responsiveness has been developed, one can then suggest a state of somnambulism, deafness, color blindness or whatnot, but it constitutes only a measure of utilization of the deep trance. Hence, I do not think you need to differentiate between the two states.

Ordinarily this state of passive responsiveness develops in the highly specific relationship of hypnotist and subject, but not necessarily so, since it can be developed in relationship to any predetermined situation. Thus, one subject with whom I was doing a lot of experimental work became interested in some experimental ideas of his own, and resolved that on the first favorable occasion he would carry them out. Just exactly what would constitute a favorable situation he was uncertain, but he did know that it would be necessary for him to be in a deep trance so that my intense interest in his behavior would serve as the appropriate psychological background for his own experiment. Not for several weeks, despite repeated experimental sessions, did anything unusual occur in my work with him. Then one night my own experimentation was disrupted by remarkable, inexplicable, and elaborate behavior on his part, which finally subsided, permitting me to complete my work.

Some days later, having puzzled over his behavior, I questioned him vaguely and indirectly, only to find that he had no knowledge of the occurrence. As my questioning continued, he developed suspicions to the effect that I had surreptitiously read the outline of his proposed experiment in his notebook. An exchange of questions then disclosed that he had actually carried out his experiment, with many more details than he had actually worked out in his outline, that he had no knowledge of having done so, and that he was astonished to find that his trance performance had been much more complete than he had planned it, and that he had met various experimental angles he had not yet consciously solved and had replaced some of his planned measures with others actually more effective. Despite this exchange of information, it was necessary to place him in a deep trance to give him a full recollection of his activity and to enable him to identify the various psychological elements in the trance situation with me that caused him to seize upon that particular occasion to carry out the experiment, as well as to discover the other elements he had not anticipated and which had necessitated modifications of his proposed plan.

Now, that subject was in a deep trance and no effort had been made to establish the somnambulistic state, yet his behavior was somnambulistic in character and entirely oriented about predetermined attitudes and intentions.

Another example may be cited. A subject, well trained for both deep trances and somnambulistic states, was used to demonstrate to a small group various hypnotic phenomena, during the course of which he conscientiously disclaimed the validity of various items of his performance. This led to extensive questioning, which disclosed that he believed firmly, both in the waking and the trance states, that nobody could be rendered deaf, blind or unresponsive to external stimuli. Careful inquiry disclosed that even when he declared that he could not see a certain member of the group, he would make visual responses. Also, ordinarily the subject in the somnambulistic state is in contact only with that part of his environment specified by the hypnotist, yet this subject demonstrated a full and ready awareness of everything occurring in the demonstration room, recognizing newcomers immediately, responding fully to them, and it was impossible to suggest the contrary to him. Finally, an unexpected visitor from Detroit entered the demonstration room, and was at once seen by the subject, despite the fact that this visitor was totally unexpected. I was at a loss to explain this behavior, since I had full confidence in my subject's somnambulistic state. I attempted to account for it on the basis that the subject's knowledge of the Detroit visitor's occasional calls on me permitted him to include that possibility in his predetermined attitude toward the somnambulistic state. While I was attempting this (so it seemed) rather lame explanation, a totally unexpected visitor from Chicago appeared, whom the subject had met previously. There then occurred an excellent demonstration of the validity of the subject's somnambulistic state and the absolute limitation of his capacity to respond to external stimuli, since, despite earnest effort, the Chicago visitor could not establish any form of contact with the subject. When I made an attempt to establish that contact by direct suggestion, my intentions were misunderstood by the subject as a command to hallucinate the Chicago visitor. The subject disclaimed an ability to do this effectively, declared that his performance would be psychologically invalid, and only a weak visual image. When insistently instructed to see that visitor, he finally responded by weak hallucinatory visualization, uninfluenced and unaided by the actual presence of the visitor. In other words, the predetermined mental set permitted in that somnambulistic state the perception of all reality meeting certain conditions, and any reality without those established qualities could not be perceived. Also, the subject's failure to hallucinate the Chicago man was only another aspect of his predetermined mental attitude, as was demonstrated in subsequent experiments.

Still another example which may bear upon your problem concerns the subject whom I had relive his theater experience of viewing the move "Rasputin," with which he had been much impressed. Having built up the illusion that he and I were at the theater, I had him hallucinate the movie. When he had demonstrated his visualization of this sufficiently, I tried to interrupt the process, but he resented this, announced his intention of not only seeing the rest of the film, but of attending the second show also, and he suggested that I was at liberty to leave the theater any time I chose. Nor could this attitude be altered until I hit upon the subterfuge of suggesting that the projector was getting out of order and that the film was speeding up and being broken. By thus introducing an item from his experiential past, I regained control of the situation.

In relation to the matter of putting my somnambulistic subjects back into the deep trance, this was essentially a function of the experimental procedure. I employed this measure as an additional means for the effective production of an amnesia for the somnambulistic activities. Thus the experiment began and apparently ended in a state of mental blankness with nothing intervening. Under other circumstances, one need only to arrange for a given cue or stimulus which will fit into the somnambulistic reality to effect a ready and prompt awakening. Occasionally, however, some subjects, especially after exceedingly complicated experimental work, find the process of reorienting themselves from the deep trance or somnambulistic state to waking reality so profound a mental reorganization as to be painful, and with them, under those special circumstances, a waking ritual is necessary. Also, many subjects can effect this reorientation apparently instantly, but close observation will disclose definite limitations in behavior responses for some little while.

Now, to comment on various points in your letter, particularly the introductory or preliminary seizures of your subjects. Usually hypnotic subjects, when allowed to go into a trance with a minimum of interference by the hypnotist, develop a rather rigid, highly stylized motor pattern. I myself have capitalized on this tendency by deliberately building up a technique of ideo-motor response which would meet adequately the need for a rigid pattern of motor behavior. Thus, some subjects manifest a peculiar breathing rhythm, others a nodding of the head, others jerking of the arms or shoulders, or tremors of various sorts. If these manifestations are not misinterpreted by the hypnotist—and they usually are regarded as evidence of discomfort, fright and so forth—and allowed to occur without interference, they will aid greatly in subsequent trance inductions, although they do delay briefly the development of the first trance. When a number of naive subjects are hypnotized successively in a group, there is then an extensive patterning after the motor behavior of the first subjects. Likewise, if left to their own natural tendencies, hypnotic subjects usually develop a highly rigid pattern of motor behavior in order to awaken, and this pattern is also susceptible to modification by the observance of waking behavior of other subjects.

However, these patterns of motor behavior tend to drop out with long continued experience or when replaced by established cues, either the cues furnished by the hypnotist or those predetermined by the subject, or selected by the subject while in the trance state.

You comment that the dancers are in control of their bodies "most of the time." I would suspect there a matter of imitation based upon past observations and experiences, although with hypnotic subjects, particularly those of low intelligence or those who are highly neurotic, there occurs fairly frequently a similar cessation in their hypnotic activity and a total unresponsiveness to the hypnotist, as well as to the reality situation. In my experience, however, it has been possible by variations in technique to regain control of the subjects, although often with great difficulty.

You mention the failure of the dancers to respond to strangers who arrive after the development of the trance. This item has been paralleled above, but I will add that the hypnotic subject in the trance state, introduced to the observers, and apparently in full contact with his surroundings, will fail to observe the arrival of newcomers.

The response to fire crackers is precisely what I would expect of a hypnotic subject instructed to perform a dance. Those instructions would imply a protection of the dance act, and there would be no immediate response to the explosion itself, but there would be a delayed realization that there was some unrecognized threat to the dance from some unknown quarter, following which there would be a general avoidance reaction and an incomplete intellectual recognition of the nature of the threat, but there would be sufficient understanding to permit an effective protection of the dance itself.

The insistence upon dancing in the dining room is fully in accord with the utilization of past experiential acquisitions, as I have illustrated above.

The failure of reaction to hot coals can also be readily paralleled. I have had hypnotic subjects so profoundly interested in their somnambulistic activities that, without any induction of hypnotic anesthesic, they have remained unaware of a lighted cigarette placed in contact with their hand by a person they did not know was present.

Concerning the questions in your last paragraph, I believe that I have answered them all, at least in part, but perhaps, for purposes of emphasis, it might be better to reply specifically. The putting back of my subjects into a deep trance was essentially a protective measure for my experiment—they could be awakened directly, but perhaps my experimental results would have been affected. Most of my subjects are trained to awaken, except under special circumstances, to cues so slight that even a keen observer will not detect the cue. A slight gesture, a change of inflection or some similar little thing is all that is necessary. Often I have my subjects select the awakening stimulus.

The trance state prefaced by violent seizures is entirely comparable to one prefaced by some simple act. Thus, one of my sisters first went into trances with a violent shuddering reaction, while another only nodded her head gently three times. While I later altered the first sister's behavior, the trances developed by both were identical in character, and I can cite numerous instances of this sort of thing. I think the preliminary behavior is entirely a matter of individuality and past experiences.

As for criteria to be applied to demonstrate a possible comparability of the Bali trance with the hypnotic trance, perhaps the best thing for me to do is to list some of the things I watch for in hypnotizing a subject who is desirous of being hypnotized and who can be hypnotized readily. Thus, in selecting a possible subject from a group of strangers, I note:

(1) Narrowing of field of attention. (Does the subject tend to watch me or something else with great intensity and to pay attention decreasingly to other things which would ordinarily distract him?)

(2) Development of a paramount interest in the processes of being hypnotized. (Does the subject show an increasing interest in the idea of hypnosis for himself and an ever-decreasing interest in the general topic of hypnosis?)

(3) Limitation of general motor and mental activity. (That is, a decrease in the general physical activity and failure to make adjustment responses when crowded by his seat mates and failure to pay attention to remarks made to him by his seat mates.)

(4) The centering of motor activity upon some one limited type. (The development of ideo-motor responses, the manifestations of any peculiar motor rhythm and the persistence in this even when obstructed.)

(5) The rapid change of facial expression with fleeting conflicting emotions manifested, or the development of a rigidly fixed facial expression.

(6) Unresponsiveness to distractions. (As I discuss the general topic, I am very likely to drop my package of cigarettes, a pencil, or spill an ashtray or something of that sort as a measure of determining their unresponsiveness.)

(7) Time lag in ordinary motor responses. (The prospective subject is crowded by his seat mate and makes only a slow adjustment to it. Or he is asked to move to another seat with a very definite time lag in the initiation of his motor response.)

(8) Time lag in ordinary intellectual responses. (Slowing of my remarks, repetition of my remarks and a slowness of manifestations on the subject's part in understanding what I am saying, or, for that matter, a slowness in his intellectual grasp of remarks made by seat mates.)

Then, upon the selection of my proposed subject, I proceed to intensify the general pattern he has shown, aiding him in developing his motor patterns or aiding him in disregarding distractions or whatever his individual behavior happens to be.

Criteria for the trance state:

(1) The single mindedness of the activity or the general state of absorption in whatever the subject is doing.

(2) The essential purity and intensity of the emotional responses and

the difficulty of introducing a conflicting emotional response. (Actors—good ones—are excellent hypnotic subjects.)

(3) The time lag in perception of and response to alien stimuli intruded into the trance situation. (The subject instructed to walk across the room has a chair thrust into his path, whereupon he demonstrates a definite need for a period of time to react adequately to this.)

(4) The incompleteness of the intellectual handling of intruded alien things. (The subject instructed to walk across the floor and a chair is thrust into his path may demonstrate an intellectual inability to remove the chair properly, or will detour around it so that he can continue his trip in the original straight line, without seeming to realize that he can redirect his walk across the room from another angle than the one originally begun.)

(5) The complete disregard and lack of response to, without avoidance of or provision for, all things that do not enter into the trance situation.

(6) The faulty perception of the passage of time, except where this constitutes an essential part of the activity.

Criteria for the coming out of the trance:

(1) The tendency to reorient in full accord with the original situation and hence a general confusion of orientation.

(2) The persistence of a time lag in all sensory responses for a brief period after coming out of the trance.

(3) Evidence of definite changes in muscular tonus, particularly increased muscular tonus which subsides relatively slowly, and a rigidity of movements.

(4) The tendency to return to the trance state if the motor patterns of behavior during the trance state are reestablished or a significant posture is duplicated. (Thus, if a subject who has been beating time to hallucinated music in the trance state, is, upon awakening, given the task of passing a sheet of paper back and forth before a light in the same rhythm as he beat time, he usually reverts to the trance state. Or if the subject who sat in a particular posture while in the trance state can be induced by casual measures to reassume that same posture shortly after awakening, he is very likely to go back into the trance state. This is a measure I often employ to re-induce trance states.)

(5) The tendency to go back into the trance if external stimuli peculiar

to the trance state are reestablished. (Essentially this is a matter of conditioning and I have often used it by employing a metronome while the subject was asleep, and then induced subsequent trances by merely starting the metronome anew.)

An additional comment I may make is that my reading of accounts of primitive rituals and ceremonies has convinced me on many occasions that there is a profound similarity, if not an actual identity, between primitive trance states and hypnotic trances, and on more than one occasion I have utilized descriptions of native trance motor performances to facilitate trance inductions and hypnotic performances with my own subjects.

I hope that the above material may be of some use to you and I shall be very happy to answer any additional inquiries you might care to make.

I am enclosing a carbon copy of this letter should you wish to send it to your worker.

I appreciate very much your writing to me.

Sincerely yours,
Milton H. Erickson, M.D.

Editor's Note: The following notation was handwritten by Erickson's secretary on Erickson's file copy of the foregoing letter.

"In next letter suggest that hypnosis could be employed on the natives by training the worker to be a good hypnotic subject."

Erickson's reply to Mead's May 23 letter, 14 double-spaced pages, was typed by his secretary. In view of the secretary's notation on Erickson's carbon copy, he obviously anticipated that the letter would be the first in a number of exchanges.

Note that Erickson's emphasis is more on evocation than on induction. He only uses the word "induction" twice; the second mention refers to a particular hypnotic phenomenon, anesthesia, rather than the induction of a trance state per se.

As far back as 1939, Erickson was bucking the trend of regarding the hypnotist as the center of a hypnotic process that enforced the trance state in a "passive" subject. He saw hypnotic behavior as a continuum of normal behavior; the hyp-

*notist elicited hypnosis by appealing to the subject's unique associations, experi-
ence, physiology, learning, and response tendencies. His emphasis, even then, was
on utilization; the therapist would utilize the subject's responses in bringing about
trance. Hypnosis would not be enforced. Rather, naturally occurring behaviors
would be shaped to elicit a hypnotic experience.*

*Notice that Erickson's communication style was narrative, in comparison with
Mead's objective style. He communicated by example, building a patchwork of
understanding. In addition to this mosaic style, he also used linear methods to
convey understanding, but his emphasis was on anecdotes.*

*Mead visited Erickson in Eloise, Michigan, in 1940 and brought with her films
of Balinese trance. Mrs. Erickson was hypnotized and viewed the movies in trance
to better determine aspects of the trance behavior of the native dancers. Erickson
then decided that the staff at Eloise Hospital would benefit from watching the
films, and his wife introduced and showed them in Mead's absence.*

*When the Ericksons moved to Phoenix, Mead made a number of visits to their
modest home there. On one visit, she stayed in the girls' bedroom, and Mrs.
Erickson remembers her commenting on being awakened by the sound of the
caged mice at her feet. According to Mrs. Erickson, Mead was an easy visitor who
fit in with the family's lifestyle. In fact, she viewed her as the older sister she had
never had. (Personal communication, 8/28/97.)*

From: Margaret Mead
June 8, 1939

Dear Doctor Erickson:

Thank you very much indeed for your very helpful letter, and for your
thoughtfulness in sending the carbon. It is exactly the sort of material that
we need and I shall forward it to Miss Belo. Regardless of what use she
is able to make of it in the limited time she has left in the field, it is going
to be of great help to Mr. Bateson and myself in organizing our material
on trance.

If you ever come to New York, do look us up at 253 West 102nd Street.
And would you put me on your reprint list?

With all good wishes,

Sincerely yours,
Margaret Mead

———————— ✣ ————————

Margaret Mead responded minimally to Erickson's lengthy letter. Her invitation for him to come to New York would be the first of two. Erickson had stimulated her interest in learning more about hypnosis and about his work.

To: Margaret Mead
June 15, 1939

Thank you for your letter of appreciation for the material I sent. I am glad that you have a hope that it may be of some use.

Since my previous letter, I have been reviewing some of my data with your problem in mind, and I believe that I can offer a suggestion that may prove of considerable value in future studies of the type Miss Belo is doing. Stated briefly, my suggestion is that the worker add to his general preparation for field work the experience of being a thoroughly trained hypnotic subject. In itself such preparation would not be at all laborious for the worker, and it would serve two important ends, one of making the worker acutely aware of unconscious implications and clues to understanding, easily and frequently overlooked by the consciousness, and the other, that of enabling the worker to make a direct hypnotic approach to the problem under investigation without incurring governmental restrictions, etc.

Before, however, presenting you with case material to clarify these ideas, I would like to state that they are based upon my own use of hypnosis in a similar fashion over a period of years. Also, I feel about hypnotic experience much as the psychoanalyst feels about analysis, namely that subjective experience is of paramount importance in detecting, understanding, and appreciating fully hypnotic phenomena. Often, despite my extensive work in hypnosis, I find my own lack of experience as a hypnotic subject a definite handicap, and frequently, in trying to understand some particular manifestation, I am at a loss. Yet a well-trained hypnotic subject, lacking all of my special training, will unhesitatingly offer an explanation which I can recognize at once as correct and can verify experimentally. Not that there is any enhancement of special insights, nor anything of that sort. Rather, the hypnotic subject, by virtue of his experiential past, is able to single out and to recognize those elements which constitute the hypnotic picture and thus to recognize it, while the observer inexperienced subjectively observes the total picture which is made up of elements both hypnotic and conscious, and, hence, his wide field of attention, as contrasted to the hypnotic subject's markedly narrowed field of attention, results in an inability to detect essential elements, which, however, can be readily recognized when pointed out.

Perhaps the best demonstration of this point is a paper L. S. Kubie and I [Erickson & Kubie, 1940] now have in press for the *Psychoanalytic Quarterly*, which gives an account of how one hypnotic subject, given all the essential data, which were utterly meaningless to me, proceeded to translate cryptic automatic writing by another hypnotic subject, with the translation subsequently verified to the last detail. Should you be interested, I may be able to send you a copy of the manuscript, since the paper probably will not be in print until September.

But perhaps it would be best to present case material now and let you draw your own conclusions as to the possibilities I have mentioned. This I shall give in rather full detail, and I hope it won't be too laborious reading.

* * * *

A medical student volunteered as a hypnotic subject, but in attempting to hypnotize him, I found him so resistive, despite outward cooperation, that I was unable to make any progress with him. One of my prize subjects was watching me with intense interest. After much effort with absolute failure on my part, my trained subject took me aside and suggested that he was confident that he could teach me how to hypnotize that medical student. When I asked him to explain, since he had never tried the role of hypnotist, he stated that he could not explain, that it was simply a matter of "empathy" on his part, that he had watched my efforts and the medical student's behavior intently, and that he felt confident that his own hypnotic experiences had enabled him to understand and appreciate the medical student's behavior, even though he could not put it in words.

His proposed plan was that I hypnotize him and that, as he went into the trance, he would duplicate and elaborate the behavior of the medical student in such a fashion that I could understand it better and that I should, while he was duplicating the medical student's behavior in the trance state, request that he give me explanations of it, and instructions on how I might vary my suggestions to meet the situation.

I promptly accepted his plan, and, as I duplicated with him my hypnotic procedure with the medical student, he offered me instructions, explanations, corrections, etc., as well as clear-cut demonstrations of my difficulties, and then continued until he declared that I was fully prepared.

Then, awakening my subject, we returned to the room where the medical student was still waiting, and I attempted to put him into a trance in accord with my original technique. Again I failed. Thereupon, I made use of the technique suggested to me by my subject, and shortly had the medical student in a satisfactory trance. Giving him an amnesia for the trance experience, I awakened him and then again attempted to put him into a trance by means of my usual technique. Again I failed, but promptly, upon resorting again to the technique outlined by the hypnotic subject, the medical student again went into a deep trance.

Since that experience, I have often utilized trained hypnotic subjects to aid me in understanding the resistances encountered in hypnotic subjects and to reach an understanding of their mental processes and attitudes, and I have found it exceedingly helpful.

Needless to say, in such a situation as the above, one needs to rely upon a highly intelligent hypnotic subject, although many hypnotic subjects not particularly gifted show remarkably clear insight and understanding into the behavior of other hypnotic subjects.

On a later occasion, I was again having great difficulty with a resistive subject, making no headway with him, indeed, only intensifying his resistances. By chance my trained subject dropped in for a visit and I suggested that he take over directly instead of by proxy as he had before. He was most hesitant and reluctant, but finally consented and took over by first intensifying the subject's resistances still more, and then centering those resistances upon a single thing. Thereupon he induced a profound trance easily and effectively. This done, he proceeded to "wash up those resistances" by making various suggestions to the subject without any direct attack upon the resistances, and finally he awakened the subject, telling me privately that I would not experience any further difficulty with that subject. He was right!

The only explanation he could offer was one not helpful to me, namely, that hypnotic experience permits one to have a feeling of the rightness, of the tempo, of the general fittingness of things, that one has an extensive "empathy" that derives from a recognition of the familiar.

* * * *

Somewhat similar to the above was my experience with another hypnotic subject, highly intelligent and with an M.A. in psychology. I worked for a long time trying to train this young woman hypnotically, but failed miserably in my efforts, since I succeeded in inducing no more than a light trance. Finally, when she was in a light trance, I asked her for an explanation of her inability to go into a deep trance. With much hesitance and diffidence she asked me if I would be angry if she gave me an objective evaluation of my hypnotic technique. I reassured her in this respect and urged her to speak frankly.

Thereupon, while still in a light trance, she proceeded to give me an extensive criticism of my technique, pointing out my failure to make suggestions properly impressive for her personality, my failure to utilize the various affective responses she made, stated that the rhythm of my speech was altogether wrong, that at times I was too rapid, at other times too slow, and she explained that, if I would give my suggestions in the terms, the rhythm, and the relationships that she could suggest, she was certain my technique could be effective.

Accordingly, I instructed her that whenever I gave a suggestion wrongly, she was to interrupt me and correct it and explain to me how I should have given it to have better effect. With her aid I was then able to put her into a very profound trance and I used her subsequently in rather rigid experimental procedures.

Not until long afterwards did she remember anything about this matter and then not until I had given her hypnotic instruction to recall that particular session. She apologized for her temerity in undertaking to instruct me, but explained that often when she had watched me hypnotize others she had been much shocked at the "roughness" of my technique and that she had often sensed a feeling of resistance on the part of the subjects, engendered by the defectiveness of my suggestions.

She then called to mind one particular subject on whom I had never had more than fair results, and proceeded to give me a very critical review of my technique in relationship to that particular subject, and she suggested a great variety of alterations in my technique which she declared would enable me to induce an entirely satisfactory trance. I accepted her suggestions and the outcome with that subject was full proof of her contention.

Yet, despite her intelligence and training in psychology, she was unable to verbalize her understandings except to declare rather helplessly that it was essentially a matter of quality, not quantity or variety, that one's unconscious could be best reached by stimuli having certain qualities appreciable to it rather than to the consciousness, that when those qualities were present, the unconscious would respond, when absent, there would be full conscious cooperation and response but nothing more.

* * * *

Another instance concerns the subject H, who had an intense desire to be hypnotized, but also had an exceedingly lively curiosity as to the subjective experience of being hypnotized, with the consequence that her curiosity precluded the effective acceptance of the hypnotic suggestions. After several hours of hard labor on my part, the subject explained that her curiosity prevented her from going to sleep, but that she could give me some suggestions that would enable me to hypnotize her.

Inquiry disclosed her to have this idea: that I suggest slowly and gradually and with increasing effectiveness that she was sitting in a certain chair on the opposite side of the room, watching a young woman go into a hypnotic trance, and she gave me detailed instructions on how to build up this illusion. Acting upon her instructions, I proceeded to do as requested and very shortly had her in a deep trance. After I had made use of her to demonstrate various hypnotic phenomena, she suddenly interrupted me to state that somebody should be reading, but who she did not know. After thinking this over, I secured a book and placed it on the chair on the other side of the room and suggested to her that somebody was reading, was, in fact, profoundly interested in a book and would continue to read indefinitely. This seemed to relieve my subject a great deal. Thereupon she proceeded to tell me of a seriously traumatic experience of her youth concerning which she wished full recollection, insight and understanding, and adequate psychotherapy. By slow degrees I managed to get a complete account of the entire matter and to build up in my subject a good therapeutic background for the eventual conscious recovery of the memory.

After I awakened my subject, a casual conversation took place which was suddenly interrupted by her to give me a detailed account of a book she had been reading the night before, which had entirely absorbed her interest, making her forget her surroundings and which had distracted her mind from a great number of worries that she had, although she explained that her worries were rather vague and general, that she had simply felt unhappy and depressed and worried without knowing why, but that she had felt very much indebted to that particular book because it had so effectively distracted her from her surroundings, that she had read until late in the night without realizing the passage of time—an item of fact I later verified.

At a subsequent session it was possible to bring the traumatic experience into her consciousness and to effect a good, therapeutic result.

Now here, in the hypnotic situation a naive subject outlined to me most completely an effective technique of psychotherapy as well as an effective technique of trance induction and this is all the more remarkable when we consider the unrecognized and underlying motivations in her behavior, the significance of which she did not learn until much later and then only at the expense of much conscious pain and distress.

****

In treating a psychoneurotic patient, I made use of hypnosis. He proved to be an excellent hypnotic subject, but his resistances to therapy persisted even in the hypnotic trance, and no matter what suggestion I gave him, he tended to evade it, or to resist it, or to misunderstand, or to distort it, so that it was invariably without effect. Yet my patient believed, probably as a part of his pattern of resistances, that he cooperated to the nth degree, and he was exceedingly proud in the trance state of his capacity for complete obedience.

Past experience suggested the possibility of meeting this difficult situation in the following fashion. I secured my patient's permission to allow one of my trained subjects to observe his trance behavior, but did this in such a fashion that my patient knew that my trained subject was unprepared for this and that it was actually inconvenient for that subject to be present. Hence, the subject yielded to my insistence on his presence in a hesitant, though gracious, fashion. I then told my patient that I was going to put him to sleep and that the trained subject was merely to watch him. I then proceeded to instruct my trained subject in this fashion:

"As Mr. Jones goes to sleep, I want you to watch him carefully, observing fully everything he does and exactly how he does it. Do not make any attempt to memorize his performance or to remember it. Just watch each step as it occurs and try to understand it fully, and then proceed to the next, and that is all you need to do. I merely want to see how closely you can observe each thing he does as he does it."

Turning to my patient, I then induced a trance and gave him a long series of suggestions of what he was to do, reactions to make and forms of behavior to show, which past experience had taught me would be certain to elicit a great variety of resistances.

As my patient went into the trance, my trained subject at first manifested a great deal of bewilderment and astonishment and then suddenly began manifesting intense amusement and he pantomimed some of the patient's behavior to let me understand that he recognized the resistances. After I had demonstrated my patient thoroughly, I awakened him and told him that he might like to see my subject go to sleep, since it would probably be of interest to him to know how somebody else went into a trance state. My patient wanted to know if my subject could go into as good a trance as he had, and I assured him that the subject could probably do so and that I felt that for him to watch the trained subject go into a trance would be decidedly instructive.

Thereupon I proceeded to hypnotize the trained subject, after first giving him the instructions, "I want you to go into a deep trance. I want you to sleep as soundly and as thoroughly and to obey instructions in as capable and as adequate a fashion as did Mr. Jones. In other words, I want your trance state to be literally a duplication of the trance state of Mr. Jones." As the trained subject went into the trance, I gave him the same series of suggestions that I had the patient and he responded by duplicating to the minutest detail the patient's own behavior. As my patient watched this performance he was at first terribly bewildered and could not understand my subject's peculiar distortion of hand movements and apparent obedience of my commands, that actually constituted a negation of those commands. As he watched, although at first puzzled, he suddenly developed sufficient insight to become exceedingly embarrassed, attempted to protest to me that he hadn't really meant that sort of thing, and, when I silenced him by insisting that he watch quietly, his embarrassment gradually disappeared and he developed an intense interest in the subject's performance.

When I had my subject demonstrate the entire course of events, the patient turned to me and said, "I think I understand perfectly all this; and I have been taking pride and joy in my cooperation, in my excellence as a hypnotic subject. But as I watch your subject here, everything he does, when he lifts his arm I can feel the same sort of movement in my own arm, when he nods his head I recognize the movement as one similar to mine. Everything he does I recognize as the things I do and which I have always misinterpreted. In other words, in watching him, all of this cooperation that I have been giving you, I now realize was nothing less than beautifully disguised resistance, and I realize that your entire purpose has been to let me see this resistance of mine in somebody else and to see it in such a fashion that I could feel it and sense it and recognize it as belonging to me."

Having achieved this, I awakened my subject and dismissed him. In subsequent therapeutic interviews with my patient, I found that he had made an adequate response to the demonstration and that he was able to recognize very clearly any further subtle resistances that he made.

* * * *

Another instance concerns a hypnotic subject who was a very capable crystal gazer. On one occasion, however, he was most reluctant to do crystal gazing and developed an exceedingly faulty hypnotic trance. Nevertheless, because of the general situation, he did crystal gazing in a sufficiently capable fashion that the scientific audience was tremendously impressed and several people who had seen him crystal gaze previously were profoundly impressed by his performance. Nevertheless, a relatively untrained hypnotic subject, who was present and who had never done crystal gazing, watched the performance and came to me later with many denunciations of that demonstration, stating that there was something awfully wrong about it, that it was not valid, that any good hypnotic subject should do much better than that, that it gave the general impression to anybody who had any hypnotic experience of being an intentional deception of the onlookers (as, indeed, it was in large part, since the crystal gazer was desirous only of making a good impression and not desirous of giving a valid demonstration).

When I checked with my inexperienced subject as to why the accusations were made, only the relatively uninformative explanation was given that "when you are in a trance you do things differently than he did them. There was something lacking and I didn't feel myself in agreement with anything he was doing, except for a little thing here and there. Most of it was just made up and I think he was just fooling you and everybody else."

* * * *

At a scientific meeting a friend of mine showed a film depicting various hypnotic phenomena. In the audience were three well-trained hypnotic subjects of mine. After the showing of the film they each sought me out separately to criticize the various parts of the film. I made note of their criticisms and I found that all three of my subjects made essentially the same comments. I myself had reached certain opinions that coincided in large part with those of my subjects. Later I sought out the producer of the film, and told him of my subjects' criticisms of the film and also expressed my own opinions. He confirmed all of the opinions of my subjects, disputed some of my own special views, and suggested that at some future time he and I and some of my subjects get together and produce a hypnotic film that would be much more satisfactory than the one he had succeeded in making.

Later, when I questioned the subjects as to why they had made those criticisms, they were not at all clear in their verbalizations, merely explaining vaguely that there was something wrong in the way the film subject did those particular things the way she did, and the way she responded to certain stimuli, and so on. In brief, it was a very vague, general substantiation of their criticisms, but nevertheless a correct criticism.

* * * *

For another example, I was asked to give a lecture and demonstration of hypnosis before a group of theological students. I reluctantly consented in return for their promise to furnish me with a hypnotic subject.

Shortly after I began my demonstration, I discovered that the subject they had furnished me was actually perpetrating a hoax both upon me and the audience, despite the fact that he was a member of their group. Since this situation suggested various possibilities to me, I proceeded to play up to it by "demonstrating" to the audience a great variety of simple "hypnotic" phenomena, praising my subject's performance highly, and, after having built up a strong situation, I interrupted to explain apologetically to my audience that ordinarily it was my custom as a scientific precaution to test every subject to make certain that he was not faking his performance, but that, since the present subject was a theolog and a member of their group, I would not cast doubts on their integrity but would accept him at full face value. Thus, the situation became one in which the so-called "subject" could not expose the hoax except at great humiliation of himself and the group.

I then continued with the demonstrations, aiding my subject by discussing his performance in such a fashion that I gave him an endless number of cues as to what to do without betraying to him that I was aware of the situation. At the close of the demonstration, I requested of my subject the return favor of a demonstration before a group of my trained subjects, some of whom had never seen another in a trance state. He consented to this somewhat reluctantly, but apparently felt that my enthusiastic acceptance of his behavior warranted full faith on his part in his ability to deceive others.

A few days later I arranged for a meeting at which there were five of my trained subjects, two of whom were decidedly naive in experience. I introduced the theolog to them, explained that I was going to have the theolog demonstrate various hypnotic phenomena for them, and that they were to watch carefully and silently throughout the demonstration.

Following this, I put the theolog through his act with the same enthusiastic discussion that I had given the theological group. Very early in the demonstration I noticed my trained subjects glancing at one another and at me in a very puzzled and bewildered fashion, but they observed my request to maintain silence. At the close of the demonstration, I sent the theolog to an adjacent room and then turned to my subjects and instructed them to write briefly their comments on the entire performance, without discussion among themselves. They were rather puzzled and hesitant about doing so, but finally turned in their written comments, and in all instances they denounced the entire performance as a fraud and expressed their bewilderment at my apparent acceptance of the performance, since it was not genuine in any detail. Upon receiving their opinions, I then informed them of the nature of the situation and that it had been my purpose to see how readily they could detect faking.

After cautioning my subjects not to disclose their awareness of the situation, I recalled the theolog and proceeded to put him through his paces again, but this time asking my subjects to point out what they considered wrong in each demonstration and why they considered it wrong. In this way I secured extensive criticisms of each item, but in going over the criticisms later I found that they were all vague and general in character, with no clear-cut definitive criticisms. Finally, at the close of this session, I asked the theolog to repeat some of the first demonstration. Previously, immediately upon becoming aware of the situation, he had been embarrassed, but he now became exceedingly angry, protested that I had made sufficient mockery of him, that he had been subjected to enough punishment, but he finally yielded to my insistence that his own highly questionable conduct had left him with no choice but to do as I asked. With every outward evidence of anger, the subject proceeded to repeat the desired hypnotic performance. In the midst of his performance my subjects suddenly declared with much astonishment that his performance was now genuine, and testing of the theolog disclosed that he had met the situation by developing his first real hypnotic trance.

In this trance state, I then had him carry out the majority of his previous performances which he had faked, as well as a number of others, and in each instance my subjects agreed as to the validity of the performance.

However, again no clear-cut explanation could be given me by any of them as to how they differentiated between the valid and the faked performance.

****

Now I realize that I have given you a lot of laborious reading, but I think that the material will illustrate both how one can recognize hypnotic phenomena and how one can use his understanding of hypnotic measures to approach and to manipulate other hypnotic subjects. How extensively this could be done in the field, I do not know, but I am quite confident that a great many adaptations could be made of the hypnotic technique. My thinking on the subject has made me feel quite confident that the experience of being a hypnotic subject would prove decidedly valuable.

I shall be glad to hear from you again if this discussion proves of any interest to you.

Sincerely yours,
Milton H. Erickson, M.D.

Erickson's anecdotal style was especially evident in his letter of June 15, where he follows up on the handwritten reminder on his file copy of the original response to Mead in which he indicated that the field worker could use hypnosis as an

investigatory tool. Obviously, Erickson could have expounded on that theme in his first letter, and his failure to do so is evidence that he "knew" that additional correspondence would be forthcoming.

One could make the case that Erickson was proceeding in his customary strategic fashion. His goal may have been to be to get Mead to bring her films to Michigan. He was establishing a context in which she would reach that inevitable conclusion.

Erickson's style was not overtly Machiavellian. Rather, he created emotional "climates" through his anecdotal method. If the recipient of the communications liked the new "weather," he or she could travel into the atmosphere that Erickson devised.

His writing style was similar to his hypnotic style, as was his style of psychotherapy—evoking responses rather than enforcing authoritarian suggestions. Yes, Erickson's method was "manipulative," but not in the negative sense. Manipulation is impossible to avoid. The issue is how to use it. To eat, one must manipulate the food. Erickson's method did not constrict choice; the recipient was free to move in other directions without embarrassment.

Moreover, Erickson's anecdotal style was evident early in his career. In the Mead letters, he responded to a question with a series of anecdotes, thus providing opportunities for the recipient to learn experientially. In A Teaching Seminar with Milton Erickson *(Zeig, 1980), a transcript of a seminar that he conducted in 1979, we see a similar style, in which he responded to questions with experience-inducing anecdotes.*

From: Margaret Mead
July 29, 1939

Dear Dr. Erickson:

Thank you very much indeed for your long letter and for the set of reprints which arrived the other day. I have not had time to read the reprints yet, but I digested the letter very thoroughly. Don't ever apologize for being so cooperative. There are so few people who are willing to give attention to another person's problems and it is a rare privilege to find a good cooperator.

Your letter raised one serious point and one on which I need more illumination. As I understand it you are proposing that we train our students in the technique of being hypnotic subjects rather than in the technique of being hypnotists. Do you consider these two techniques as necessarily mutually exclusive? If so, I can see very great advantage in giving preference to the former technique, as hypnotizing people of unknown culture and background is bound to remain a rather risky business for a variety of reasons. But the problem arises as to what this training should consist of, how many people are adequate to give it, how much time it would take, and what degree of selectivity we should need to exercise among our students. It is possible that inability to attain a trance state might be taken as a criterion of inability to study trance and that students who had failed as hypnotic subjects would, therefore, be advised to center their interest on aspects of primitive religion in which expressions of this sort were not involved.

Would you be able to state the extent to which the capacity to be a good hypnotic subject is limited in terms of personality? The single-handed field worker in a strange cultural has a very heavy demand made upon his whole personality, ability to stand isolation, ability to respond sensitively to an alien ethos and yet not to respond so much that he is thrown off his balance; ability to stand a multiplicity of intimate contacts, and ability to adjust in a strange language and a strange cultural idiom to a wide variety of simultaneous stimulations. Is such a personality type likely to make a good hypnotic subject?

Have you ever met Stewart, the psychologist who has used hypnotic techniques among various Malay peoples? I do not think he has ever published anything.

I have become interested in the course of reading your papers—the ones in typescript that Dr. Maslow has—on the use of hypnosis in therapy, especially in breaking vicious circles. Is there anyone in New York City whom you would recommend as a therapist in cases comparable to the one you quote of the girl whose headaches aggravated her social contacts which then aggravated her headaches, etc.?

We have been having groups of people interested in trance phenomena look at our moving pictures and have found your previous letter exceedingly useful in organizing our impressions. If you should come to New York I hope you will have time to come and look at some of the movies and talk them over with us. With all good wishes,

Sincerely yours,
Margaret Mead

In the foregoing letter, Mead again invites Erickson to New York. Sylistically, this letter was "cleaner" than her previous correspondence in that it was professionally typed and contained only two minor typos and one handwritten correction. It was almost as if she were emulating Erickson's meticulousness.

To: Margaret Mead
August 3, 1939

Dear Dr. Mead:

I judge from your letter that I did not make myself quite clear in my previous statements.

Training qualified students to become good hypnotic subjects does not preclude their becoming good hypnotists. My own experience has been that a well-trained hypnotic subject is fully qualified to become a hypnotist and that he learns the technique of inducing a hypnotic trance much more easily by first being hypnotized than he could if given mere didactic instruction. In brief, the experiential background is of very great value in learning to become a hypnotist, although it is not indispensable, and that it gives the subject more than he can get from just learning hypnotic technique.

With regard to your workers, my reason for suggesting that they be trained as hypnotic subjects primarily, rather than as hypnotists, is that the personal experience of being hypnotized would enable them to use hypnotic techniques indirectly and unobtrusively, while at the same time they would have the experiential background for recognizing and judging any trance behavior in others.

As for suggestions about whom you might call upon to train your students, I really don't know of anybody who has had my particular interest in training subjects to be observers and critics of the trance behavior of other subjects. All of the other hypnotists I know have been interested primarily in utilizing hypnotic subjects for purely academic routine experimental procedures, involving only the subjects themselves.

As for the ability of a student to become a good hypnotic subject, I look upon this as a minor consideration, since, from my experience, practically anybody interested in being hypnotized can be put into a trance if sufficient time and effort are given to the task. However, an item I do consider of major importance is the attitude of the student toward hypnosis. Merely a desire to be hypnotized as a means to the end of studying others would defeat effective training. There would have to be an earnest desire to experience fully, as a personal thing, the phenomena of the trance state, with the application of that experience relegated to the remote future.

Concerning the role of the personality in the development of a good hypnotic subject of a good hypnotist, no general answer can be given. Nor can any general statement be made as to the suitability of the individual, as measured by hypnotic capacities, for the type of field work that he might be able to do. However, my experience in this regard is limited to the fields of clinical psychology and psychiatry.

Failure to become a good hypnotic subject would not necessarily limit the field of observation and study for that particular student, but, on the other hand, the ability to become a good hypnotic subject might easily signify special abilities in certain fields. I think that this question can be answered only by a consideration of all of the pertinent data regarding the student.

Regarding the extent to which the capacity to become a good subject is limited in terms of personality, I can reply only that the best hypnotic subjects are those of good intelligence and who are able to exercise a good control over their mental faculties, although I realize that this statement is so vague as to be almost meaningless. For my own use, I prefer college graduates, of superior intelligence, who have a good capacity for sympathy and empathy with their fellows. I have also found that people with marked histrionic ability are invariably good subjects, if handled properly. Neurotic people may also make capable subjects, but there is the inevitable task of meeting their personality difficulties adequately if use is to be made of them in other connections. The type of personality that you describe as being able to meet the problems of the field worker impresses me as one who should be a good hypnotic subject, although the very stability of such a personality might easily confront the hypnotist with a definite problem of technique in inducing a good trance. However, I cannot be certain of this possibility.

One other consideration is that a purely intellectual attitude toward hypnosis constitutes an almost insuperable barrier to an instructive experience. There is a need for an emotional response to hypnosis and those people who so guard their emotions that they react at a purely intellectual level invariably prove to be exceedingly difficult subjects.

I don't know of anybody in New York to recommend as a hypnotic therapist. I do think very highly of the therapeutic abilities of my collaborator, Dr. L. S. Kubie, of your city, whom you may know. He is a psychoanalyst, but has done some work in hypnosis, and I am certain that he would be glad to recommend someone to you.

I have not met Stewart, nor do I have among my reprints any report of hypnotic work done on Malay peoples.

I wish very much that I could have the opportunity of talking over these matters with you, but I see no immediate opportunity of visiting New York. If, by any chance, you should happen to come to this section of the country, I hope you will look me up, and also bring your films with you. In such case, it might be possible for me to arrange to have certain of my hypnotic subjects view them and criticize them. Also, should you happen at any time to be in the neighborhood of Worcester, Massachusetts, and have the opportunity to do so, I wish you would look up Dr. Arthur Haddad, 18 Wall St., and exhibit your films for his criticism. Dr. Haddad is a hypnotic subject of mine whom I have used extensively and who shows, under favorable circumstances, a perfectly remarkable ability to understand trance behavior in others. In Chicago, (Mrs.) Harriet Lange Rheingold, 907 S. Wolcott Ave., might be prevailed upon to do the same thing, if you use my name. She also is an exceedingly capable critic of the hypnotic behavior of other subjects. Both of these people tend to be unduly modest.

At the present time I am preparing a paper on post-hypnotic suggestion. As soon as it is ready I shall send you a copy of the manuscript, since I feel confident that a number of the incidents I am reporting will be of some interest to you.

Incidentally, you may be interested to know that Mrs. Erickson has read this letter and my previous letter very carefully and confirmed and added to my statements out of her own experiential background as a capable hypnotic subject, mentioning a number of points that I overlooked. I frequently call upon her to assist me in understanding various hypnotic phenomena, of which, in many instances, she has a much better understanding than I have.

If I can be of any additional service to you in your studies, I hope you will call upon me, since it is really a pleasure to be of assistance.

Sincerely yours,
Milton H. Erickson, M.D.

———————— 🙢 ————————

In his August 3 letter, written in an objective style similar to Mead's, Erickson closes by expressing his inability to come to New York. He does, however, invite Mead to Michigan, indicating that Mrs. Erickson would be a good hypnotic subject to view Mead's films.

Note: *Erickson indicated that almost anyone could be hypnotized. He did not subscribe to the notion that hypnotizability is a trait limited to only a small number of people. His position was in stark opposition to that of the Zeitgeist, which postulated that only a few subjects are highly hypnotizable.*

From: Margaret Mead
September 21, 1939

Dear Dr. Erickson,

Thanks very much for your letter answering my question about the difference between training for subject and for hypnotist.

I recently had occasion to show one of your reprints to Mr. Lawrence K. Frank of the Josiah Macy Jr. Foundation, 565 Park Avenue. He was very much interested in this and in the accounts I could give him of your work, and would, I think, appreciate it if you would send him such of your reprints as are available.

Sincerely yours,
Margaret Mead

———————— 🙢 ————————

From: Margaret Mead
January 12, 1940

Dear Dr. Erickson,

I am hastening to acknowledge your kindness in sending me your article, even before I read it, because I have been so very negligent about acknowledging the reprints you've sent me this autumn. I can only plead in extenuation that the complications that the War and a new baby have wrought in our household have made it difficult for me to keep up.

Has Abe Maslow written you about my suggestions about using your "age-regression under hypnosis" techniques to check whether early memories are constructs or accurate? If he hasn't, I will, but he said he was going to, as I think you could make an enormous contribution there in the subject you are interested in, cross-checking psychoanalytic findings.

I am tremendously interested in your work and do hope you'll continue to send me reprints, and manuscripts as you have so generously been doing.

With best wishes for the New Year,

Sincerely yours,
Margaret Mead

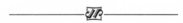

On January 9, 1940, Erickson had sent Mead a copy of a manuscript that he had published in the Psychoanalytic Quarterly, prompting this gracious reply.

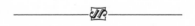

In October 1940, Mead visited the Ericksons in Michigan, where they lived on the hospital grounds at Eloise. As far as we know, this was the first meeting between Mead and Erickson. Erickson had not previously seen the Bali films; Mead knew little about hypnosis. At Erickson's suggestion, his wife was put into trance and watched the movies. Mead's extensive notes (which covered 17 pages) follow her letter.

From: Margaret Mead
October 31, 1940

Dear Dr. Erickson,

Thank you very much indeed for the transcript of your conference over the films and thanks to your secretary for taking her Sunday to make it. I have completed my transcript and I will send you a copy in a few days. Tomorrow we plan to go over the films with all of the Balinese research group, and I am keeping all my copies for use then; after which I'll send one on.

I had an interesting time talking over some of the implications of the double personality research with Mr. L. K. Frank who has a number of useful conceptualizations to apply to the material which I think he looks forward to discussing with you sometime in the future.

The lateness of this letter is no measure of my appreciation of all the time and help that you and Mrs. Erickson and Miss Prindeville gave me.

With special regards to Betty Alice, and all of you,

Sincerely yours,
Margaret Mead

Transcript

October 20, 1940

Dr. E. put Mrs. E. into a trance in the following manner: "Shall we try some hand levitation?" (Mrs E. immediately followed this suggestion and looked intently at her hand. After a few moments of looking at her hand and several further suggestions from the doctor, she was apparently in a trance state). Now, we are going to see some pictures of the Balinese people dancing. Neither you nor I have seen the Balinese people, and we don't know what we are going to see in these pictures, but we are to look at those pictures carefully and we are to try to understand what we see and particularly are you to look. Now it may be that the Balinese people are in hypnotic sleep like you are, and maybe they are not. Maybe they are in a somewhat similar condition, and you, in watching that picture, are to view it with the utmost of critical care to single out anything that is similar or comparable or anything that is definitely contradictory. If there is anything strikingly different that contradicts hypnosis as you know and feel it, be sure to direct my attention to it. Or if there is something that *seems* to contradict hypnosis as you know it, draw my attention to it. Remember fully each and every detail of the entire picture that is shown to you, and be ready to discuss the whole thing in its entirety up to the point at which the showing has been interrupted at any time. Do you understand? (Subject signified "yes" by nodding her head.) Is there anything not clear? (Subject shook her head.) Let me summarize this. Your task is to view this movie and to view it critically and understandingly, as a hypnotic subject, trying to feel yourself into the subject that is depicted on the screen, trying to recognize it as one or as another thing, emphasizing the positive and the negative aspects and trying to give a careful, balanced, judicious criticism of the entire thing. Do I make myself clear? (Subject nodded "yes.") Any questions that you want to ask me? (No.) Now, you are to do this while asleep. You may speak up during the showing of the movie. You may recognize the other people who are here. There are two others here, other than myself. There are Dr. Mead here and Miss Prindeville here. You can call to me to stop the movie at any time. Is everything clear? (Yes.) From time to time I will probably stop the movies and ask you a question, or Dr. Mead may. Is that all right? (Yes.) You want to remember to remain deeply asleep—continuously so. (Started film.)

Dr. Mead: Perhaps I had better say a few words of explanation. These are little girls dancing, and they are not yet in trance. They are part of a theatrical performance. That comes before the trance. They are being taught by the witch to become witches. (Film ran a while with no comments.)

Dr. Mead: You are now going to see a little piece of comedy when the people pretend that they are being driven away from their village by the witch. And a man pretends to be a woman—gives birth to a doll which is stolen by the witches. (Film running.)

Dr. Mead: Now the people have caught this little witch child and in the last scene you will see the witch come out of the temple and a man wearing a mask. We don't know whether this man is in a trance or not. Sometime during the performance he will change to a trance state. He is wearing a mask so that you can only see his legs and arms. He is going to be attacked by the king of the country at the beginning of this.

The king attacks him with the dagger. He cuts him a little on his left foot.

As these angry witches go off, in a minute you will see the dragon come on. The dragon is a mask with two men in it. The man in the head of the dragon will go into trance some time during the ceremony. We do not know when.

These are the men who are going to go in trance. (Reference to a group of young men.) They are the followers of the dragon. They fall down before the power in the eye of the witch. As soon as she looks away they get up again. The dragon is the friend of these men and now comes and brings them back to life. The priest walks behind him and sprinkles holy water on them.

(To Mrs. Erickson) Would you like to make a comment on those men you saw right there? What do you think of those?

Mrs. Erickson: I think some of them were in better trances than others. This first man that fell down looked up several times. He didn't act right at first. I don't . . . that man that was jerking so much. . . . They didn't seem to me right. . . . They seemed more like the Holy Rollers than the hypnotic trance.

Dr. Erickson: Can you think of anything that it might mean—in terms of hypnosis?

Mrs. Erickson: I don't know unless his fighting was kind of lasting over. But it didn't seem like that so much. Some of them went into trances real good and fast. If I were to. . . . I'm not sure of this exactly. . . . but if I were to have to put a finger on the time when the witch went into a trance. . . . I think she has been getting ready for it all along. I think the transition point was when she was dancing with the other witches. I can't explain just what it was. It seems to me there is something different in her movements. It's awfully hard to tell without seeing the face at all, but just from the arms and legs, that is what I would say.

Dr. Mead: There is a different tempo in her movements?

Mrs. Erickson: No. It's not the tempo. It's the way of moving which has a different look.

Dr. Mead: I have some comments to give you on this next film.

Mrs. Erickson: The man that just moved one foot. That didn't seem so funny. . . . But the man that jerked all over didn't seem right at all.

(Film continued with same group of young men lying on ground in stiff poses, as when it was discontinued.)

Mrs. Erickson: They aren't awake yet.

Dr. Mead: No.

Now you will see a group of the women come in with daggers in their hands. They are going to go into trance also. They are not supposed to be in trance yet.

One of the women gives a scream and the others soon follow suit. The Balinese believe that they are now in trance. (An older woman appeared.) Note the face of this woman in particular. You are going to see her later in more detail.

Dr. Mead: Any comments that you would like to make now?

Mrs. Erickson: Most of them seemed to be in very good trances. They all seemed to be cataleptic to a certain degree. One all over and some of them just their arms or their hands.

Dr. Mead: Yes? Did you single out anything in particular?

Mrs. Erickson: Their facial expressions looked like it, too. I don't know exactly what you mean.

Dr. Erickson: It's just your own ideas and not just trying to answer the questions, but to give any particular ideas you have. Have you got anything to add about those foot twitches and muscular twitches?

Mrs. Erickson: They are the only part of it that doesn't seem quite like a hypnotic trance to me, but everything else does. Their expressions—that one woman's expression you could see very clearly, and she certainly seemed to be in a good trance. That man that kept holding his knife so tight, and that one that they carried in. I think especially the women seemed to go into deeper trances. Their movements got more and more the look of it and their expressions, too.

There was certainly an entirely different look about those men just before the witch knocked them down and when they went off with the dragon, even though you could just see their backs. They had an entirely different movement about them.

Dr. Mead: Could you describe what it was about their backs?

Mrs. Erickson: They moved differently. They ran differently and they moved their arms differently, too.

Dr. Erickson: Shall I add a word of explanation? The difference was the same sort of thing as you see in little babies. The baby does not move its wrist and then its elbow. It moves its whole arm from the shoulder. The hypnotic subject moves its arm and fails to coordinate elbow, shoulder and the rest.

Mrs. Erickson: They moved their legs differently. They ran differently. It's slower and a little stiffer in the legs. (Films started again.)

Dr. Mead: When these films begin you will see them inside the temple. Everyone who was in trance is brought inside the temple to be brought out of trance. At the very beginning of the picture you will see a group of people leading a man back who is struggling as if he did not wish to go back.

All of these are boys who were in the trance before. They are being brought out of the trance with holy water and smoke.

Mrs. Erickson: I didn't see a man struggle very much.

Dr. Mead: He was trying to come forward and the others were leading him back to the back of the building.

Mrs. Erickson: Those men were awake then. They weren't the first time but the second time they were.

Dr. Mead: Do you think that girl who is taking the drink there is awake?

Mrs. Erickson: Not all the way. The one before her is though.

Dr. Mead: This is the woman whom you saw before. Why is she making those hand movements?

Mrs. Erickson: I don't know, unless she is just enjoying it. Maybe that's why she takes so long to wake up. Maybe she is just having a good time.

Dr. Erickson: All right. Where did she get those movements?

Mrs. Erickson: She hasn't done them in this dance. They look more like what the little girls were doing at the beginning.

Dr. Erickson: No particular meaning you could put upon it?

Mrs. Erickson: She's just remembering her dance.

Dr. Mead: That woman on the left whose hair is being put up—Is she awake?

Mrs. Erickson: Almost awake. In a minute she will be.

Dr. Erickson: Will you note this as a question for discussion afterward? "What is the usual type of waking up behavior, so far as clearing the face is concerned?"

Dr. Mead: Is she awake now?

Mrs. Erickson: I don't think so. I think she will awaken by herself. I think she was getting ready to wake up as soon as she stretched out her hands.

Dr. Mead: This is going to be the end of the ceremony and they are going to bring over in front of the dragon the man who played the witch and the front legs of the dragon. The man who played the witch has the black bristly hair. The man who plays the front legs of the dragon has white hair, is an old man.

You will see the priest offering a chicken. Holding the chicken up over the incense. Then the chicken is given to the old man to hold and is given to the black-haired man to eat. You will not see him eat the chicken.

Mrs. Erickson: The one with the white hair and the black-haired one are asleep.

Dr. Mead: (After a minute or two pause) Is the white-haired one still asleep?

Mrs. Erickson: Yes. (After a pause.) I think the black-haired man is about awake. (Scene showed old white-haired man against a wall.) But that one isn't. (After another pause.) He's waking up now, though. He's awake now.

The priest did not go to sleep any of the time.

I think that one at the end woke up very fast . . . the old man. He seemed to be still in quite a deep trance, and then he woke up right away.

Dr. Mead: This is a film of little girl dancers, and you will first see a group of people in the temple fastening two little dolls on a string attached to two sticks. The men hold the sticks, the little dolls dance as the men shake the sticks. Then the two little girls come forward and hold the sticks and the little girls are then supposed to go in trance as the dolls come out of trance, and you will see the little girls dressed, you will see them dance in obedience to songs which the people sing. They bow and bend and climb on the shoulders of men in the crowd. And finally you will see them brought out of trance. Do you think these little girls are in trance now?

Mrs. Erickson: I think the one on the right looks as if she is expecting to.

Mrs. Erickson: That one on the right is still much more ready.

Dr. Erickson: I noticed that the little girls had hold of something so that their arms jiggled up and down.

(Mrs. Erickson and Dr. Mead explained that this was the doll and stick arrangement.)

Mrs. Erickson: The girl that's just started to move back and forth . . . when does she take hold of that stick?

Dr. Mead: Well, suddenly they lean forward at a signal in the song and take hold of the stick at exactly the same moment.

Dr. Erickson: It always amazes me to see the Balinese use the same sort of physical sensation technique that I would use myself. (The little girls in the film were now dancing.)

Mrs. Erickson: I think they are both in a trance state.

Dr. Mead: All these different movements that they go through here are told them by the song. Have you anything to say

about the comparison between the children in trance and
the grownup people? (Film stopped.)

Mrs. Erickson: I think the children were better than some of the grown-
ups in that they seemed to be less conscious of themselves. The old man was like that, too. He seemed to
take it entirely as a casual thing.

Dr. Erickson: I think I can explain that. The children were not bothered
by learning. Because what they did was correct. It was
the same with the old man. What he did was correct.

Mrs. Erickson: The little girl on the right at the end seemed to be using
those movements as part of the waking up. The one on
the left did it as part of the ceremony.

Dr. Mead: The girl on the right is always falling down. She falls
during the dance. When she gets on the shoulders of the
man she catches her foot in the hole in her dress and
falls—she gets her dress over his eyes. The girl on the
left never falls.

Mrs. Erickson: I think the one on the left is more in contact with what
is going on all the time. She can look out for the holes
in her skirt and sticks in her path because she is more in
contact with things around her.

Dr. Mead: This little girl on the left is always accusing the other girl
of not being in a trance. When they are dancing she insists that the other girl has not gone into a trance.

Mrs. Erickson: That's not the purpose of the trance for her to watch the
other one.

Discussion After Showing of Films

Dr. Mead: Here's this note you had me make on the use of the
ground for re-orienting purposes.

Dr. Erickson: Subjects coming out of a trance find themselves in a new
temporal situation and a new spatial organization. The
spatial organization is sometimes and sometimes not the
same. If they are in the same chair, for instance, if they
are in the same chair and there has been certain activity
going on within them, it makes them regard the chair as

changed. There have been new emphases placed upon the previous situation. Where previously they haven't noticed a bookcase, they now are aware of it, so it is a physically changed environment. So, in coming out of the trance, they single out first one item of the environment and then another. Usually some simple thing that they can touch or feel or see briefly and which does not require manipulation. That is, you can see the floor and attach a meaning to it, but to look at a bookcase means that you have to place an extensive meaning upon it. Authors of books, and books in a great many varieties—novels and history, etc. The floor is a very simple thing—it is down there or the ceiling is up there. It is a limited "up." A wall is a limited "there." You will see them (hypnotic subjects) look around at some simple object. They will look at it, feel it. Roll themselves back and forth—touch their knee—depending upon their position.

Dr. Mead: And you felt that in that they were sort of orienting themselves toward the ground?

Dr. Erickson: I also noticed that same sort of thing toward the person who was behind them. That there was a very definite jerk of their shoulders. Somebody was switching them back and forth, but it seemed to me that they held their shoulders so that they could themselves establish contact with the other person. In other words, utilizing the swinging motion that was given them in their own way to establish their contact with the people that were establishing contact with them. You see, the process of awakening is one in which they establish contact. Not a process in which others establish contact with them.

Dr. Mead: Now, then, the face clearing.

Dr. Erickson: You have watched newborn babies and babies in the cradle. And how do they behave when they awaken?

Dr. Mead: There's a tremendous amount of that sort of thing.

Dr. Erickson: When they get older they screw up their hands and face and sooner or later that forms a pattern. The hypnotic subject has been asleep in a daylight lighted room and he rouses up without once having closed his eyes except for ordinary blinking. Yet he goes through that face clearing or face rubbing. That's standard for people coming out of trances.

Dr. Mead: We have a man who came out all but his hands. His hands were still rigid, and he woke up and looked at his hands in surprise. Then the people came and pulled at his fingers and straightened them out.

Dr. Erickson: Which is comparable to what I told you about George Millard last night.

Dr. Mead: Another point you said—Mrs. Erickson twice said this jerking looks like the Holy Rollers.

Dr. Erickson: There is something in that type of behavior when you find it in hypnotic subjects that is often distasteful to the majority of hypnotic subjects. You ask a subject to perform such a simple task as picking up that flashlight and putting it over there on that table, and he agrees fully to it, and you tell him to start at once. You watch him and his behavior and you see these little convulsive movements throughout his body. It looks to you as though it were a very unpleasant, disagreeable sight. You wonder what it all means and gradually those minute convulsive movements cease and your subject relaxes.

Dr. Mead: He hasn't put the flashlight on the table?

Dr. Erickson: No, he just sits going through these convulsive movements. By careful questioning you find out that he has executed in fantasy the entire act, and that these convulsive movements are only expressive of the fantasy of the entire performance. Particularly is that type of fantasy likely to develop with these convulsive movements if the subject feels incapable of doing the task or if he objects to it. If he thinks he is not bright enough or strong enough or capable enough to do that, and doesn't want you to know it, he will execute it in fantasy. Or if it is a decidedly unpleasant thing he will take the easy way out.

Mrs. Erickson: Do you think those subjects were acting out something when they were jerking?

Dr. Erickson: I think very definitely that they were acting out part of whatever the rite was. As you looked at that you would see those convulsive movements first in the foot and then a spreading to another part. I would like to see that film in slow motion with a possibility of following it up.

Mrs. Erickson: I didn't think the fellow who was jerking was in a good trance.

Dr. Erickson: Well, did he have a feeling of inferiority about his trance performance?

Mrs. Erickson: What do you think about the Holy churches, then? Where they jerk and leap in the air?

Dr. Erickson: Remember that acting along with those you have tremendous emotional outbursts of an extreme character. In this (turning inquiringly to Dr. Mead) I don't take it that they are so wildly excited.

Dr. Mead: They don't seem tremendously emotionally excited to me. Now you made a note about an incomplete orientation in the old woman when she comes out.

Dr. Erickson: Each time she would seize upon some bit of reality as if to say, "There is the ground," or "There is the wall there." Her vision would cloud over and she would say, "There is a wall there."

Dr. Mead: Did you feel that before she stood up or after she stood up?

Dr. Erickson: Both. She would get an idea and get an amnesia for the idea and remember only that she had an idea and lost its content. My feeling was that she had a limited field of vision in which she could walk freely and then I feel that she was turned aside from that field.

Dr. Mead: In brief, how like do you feel this is to a hypnotic trance?

Dr. Erickson: I think it is very, very like. In their dances one has to discount a lot of their movements because it is a ritualistic practice, but at the same time, just as a baby instead of moving its elbow and shoulder joint moves it all as a unit, so does a hypnotic subject, and they move that way.

Dr. Mead: I always felt that there was something ungraceful and asymmetrical about their movements in a trance.

Dr. Erickson: It's the unitary use of the limbs.

Dr. Mead: (To Mrs. Erickson) One time you said that their backs were different. How did you mean?

Mrs. Erickson: Well, they looked different. It's hard to explain.

Dr. Mead: Is there anything about the head?

Mrs. Erickson: The movements of the head are stiffer and slower.

Dr. Erickson: You expect in a crowd where there is a crowd of people attempting to do something a certain amount of fluidity of the body. Just as you ride down on a streetcar and a total stranger gets on and sits down in the seat and you say, "My word, so he's deaf!" How do you know it? He holds his head in a certain fashion. He makes a response to the screaming of the horn just a fraction of a second too late. His timing is a bit out of order. Somebody brushes past him and the lady next door yells, "How do you do, Mrs. Smith?" He doesn't make that slight turn of the head and response so you can say he is deaf. So when you see these people standing backs toward you, you expect them to depress one shoulder and elevate the other, and a certain fluidity of their back movements and it's only a very, very slight fluidity.

Dr. Mead: Do you think that one could say that these people first went into a trance state and then into a somnambulistic state to perform these things, and then into a deeper trance to come out?

Dr. Erickson: I think a somnambulistic state is the deepest of all trances.

Dr. Mead: But that is comparable to a somnambulistic state.

Dr. Erickson: They go into this deeper sleep apparently. It is only a relaxation period for coming out.

Dr. Mead: Two of them report amnesia only for the period of going in and coming out and have no amnesia for the dancing period.

Dr. Erickson: Hypnotic subjects can have amnesia for any particular part of the trance experience.

Dr. Mead: The culture requires total amnesia and many of them feel it isn't real. So many of them do not admit not having total amnesia and feel guilty when they do admit it. One of the things they used to do, was between these little dancers. One little dancer disliked the other and would pinch her in the trance state. These two little girls used to quarrel and they would bump each other violently in the coming out period.

Mrs. Erickson: I wondered looking at them if they ever crashed into one another.

Dr. Mead: You think that the form of the amnesia is nondiagnostic?

Dr. Erickson: Yes.

Dr. Mead: This old man whom I asked you to see was seen by a good psychiatrist and he took their pupillary reflexes before and during trances, and found their pupillary reflexes very disturbed during the trance and the knee jerks disturbed. He thought that the old man with the white hair was a fake. My sister was there and she took down what he said. He said that he was too extroverted to be in a real trance. But (to Mrs. Erickson) one of your spontaneous comments on him was that he wasn't showing off.

Mrs. Erickson: Maybe when this other man saw him, and didn't like him, he wouldn't go into a trance for him.

Dr. Mead: Yes, that may be.

Mrs. Erickson: Of course, there were times when he seemed to be showing off. For instance, when he put his foot on the wound of the other man. But he seemed to be in a trance. His violent gestures involved his hands when he came out. I think he was very definitely in a trance.

Dr. Erickson: My own experience is that that type of showoff, village busy-body, if you train them to be a hypnotic subject, they are good. If you give them a chance to show off for you. He stood out by himself. Made himself individual.

Dr. Mead: This woman who went into a trance and took so long to come out. She didn't dance in the ballet and she didn't intend to go into a trance that day.

Mrs. Erickson: Maybe that's why she took so long to come out.

Dr. Erickson: She went in against her own wishes, against her intentions. She violated her agreement to herself.

Dr. Mead: One other comment I wanted to make is about Zidietski and his statement that if people think those trance states are painful and people are pitied for them, they themselves ought to see a psychiatrist. There is no question but that in all of those trances the trancers were thoroughly enjoying it.

Mrs. Erickson: Why certainly, they were having an awfully good time.

Dr. Mead: As I see it, the special things that we should watch for are these handling of parts of the body as units, these time lags, and rigidities and the re-orienting gestures. (Gave a lengthy account about an old woman in black.) I think a lot of American subjects are more graceful in the trance state, and these people are more graceful when awake.

Dr. Erickson: One of the cues you can use with American subjects is when all their extra movements start dropping out. But these people don't have them in the first place. Even the Balinese, though, show a greater unity of movement in the trance state. In the waking state if they want to move the hand from here to here they do precisely that. In the trance state they start, then don't make the movement and accomplish the rest of it in fantasy perhaps, or make the movement in a more jerky fashion. Hypnotic subjects use a minimum amount of energy, which carries the hand only so far and then they send out another lot of energy.

Mrs. Erickson: In doing hand levitation, I feel as if there were a cogwheel in my shoulder which moved one cog at a time. It isn't an expenditure of energy.

Dr. Mead: That's a good way of putting it—a cogwheel. Then in people with a different sort of musculature, what would you expect in hand levitation?

Dr. Erickson: You would expect the cogwheel effect to be cut down.

In the following letter, Gregory Bateson makes his first entrance into the correspondence, where Mead refers to her husband rather formally as "Mr. Bateson." Subsequently, the tone of the letters becomes decidedly intellectual.

From: Margaret Mead
November 9, 1940

Dear Doctor Erickson:

We have now had a group session over the notes on our sessions in Eloise, with a great deal of profit to all of us. I am enclosing a copy of the notes I took that day. I am not sending you the notes of our session because in the form I have them they would not mean much in the absence of the films. Instead I am summarizing the principal problem which confronted us after we had gone over my version and Miss Prindeville's version of your interpretations of Mrs. Erickson's reactions.

Mr. Bateson phrases our difficulty as follows:

"The principal problem which arose was an apparent contradiction between two motifs which occur in trance posture, upon which you commented. May we label these 'unitary movement' and 'economy of movement.' As we understand it, the economy of movement consists in the use of only those muscles which are immediately relevant to perform a given act, At the opposite of 'economy' would then be the sort of thing that an athletic trainer tries to eradicate, the linking up of a number of irrelevant contractions with those that are essential, e.g., moving forward the shoulder when all that is required is a movement of the forearm. But as we understand it, the concept 'unitary movement' implies just these things, using the whole arm including those muscles which are irrelevant. We are inclined to think that you are right on both points, but it ought to be possible to work out just how these two contrasting tendencies express themselves."

As I get the picture, the "economy of movement" might be set down to the elimination of irrelevant consciousness of self-response to irrelevant stimuli, such as what the audience thinks, etc., which gives a performance comparable to that of the trained dancer or athlete. The "unitary movement" I see as regressive, as a reinstatement of much earlier, or lower levels of consciousness. In Bali we sometimes see trancers who are almost all one or the other, as well as seeing the mixing of both types of postural adjustment in one trancer.

Mr. Bateson further suggests, "Could we say that the trace state is a sort of razor edge between the state characterized by 'unitary movement' and the state characterized by 'economy of movement?' "

There was one other related problem. In commenting on the similarity between "the old man" who came out of the trance after he went to stand against the wall, and the child trancers, you remarked to Mrs. Erickson that it was because there was no "learning" involved in the performances. Later when we discussed whether the old man was a fake or not, you said that village showoffs of this type are very good subjects when properly "trained." Would you elucidate this apparent contradiction.

Sincerely yours,
Margaret Mead

To: Margaret Mead
November 18, 1940

Dear Dr. Mead:

Perhaps the best way to answer your questions about the apparent conflict between "economy of movement" and "unitary movement" is to state that the first relates to the quantity as a function of the actual total performance, and the second signifies a quality which is a function of the method of performance.

Thus, in moving the hand from position A to position B. the hand travels only the precise distance necessary, thus covering the distance with an economy of movement.

However, the hand is enabled to travel only as an extension of the forearm, the upper arm, the shoulder, and the torso; all of which move in a unitary fashion to permit the most economical trip from A to B. Thus there are both economy of movement and unitary movement.

Perhaps I can give you an illustration of another character. In my paper on dual personality [Erickson & Kubie, 1939], *yes* was written as a vertical line, *no* as a horizontal line. (This finding has been encountered many times with other subjects.) The important definitive movement in *yes* is the up and down movement of the *y*, and once the *y* is written, nothing further need be added to disclose the identity of the answer. In writing *no*, however, this is done on a horizontal plane and the slight up and down movements of the first three strokes of the letter *n* are spatially equivalent to the first three strokes in writing *y*. Any real meaning hence must derive from continuing the writing in the same horizontal plane. Thus, *no* is meaningful only as a horizontal progression and hence can be expressed as a unitary movement free of uneconomical humps and curves, while *yes* can be expressed as a unitary up and down stroke.

If you will reread that paragraph (p. 480 on "yes," "no," "I don't know," "first part yes, last part no," you will find many illustrations of economy of movement by unitary movement. The economy is at the pencil tip where the actual performance is manifested, but the whole body may have moved as a unit to produce that limited performance.

Concerning my comment about village showoffs properly trained, I meant that, once trained to be a subject, they could then give adequate demonstrations by utilizing long-established patterns of behavior without an effort to fit those patterns into the relatively new hypnotic situation. The old man's extensive past experience made him "just know" that his performance would be adequate, that he would not have to make any provision to insure its adequacy and fittingness for the immediate situation. He had passed the period when autocriticism was necessary, and hence did not need to learn, to modify, etc. The little girls, similarly, were essentially free from autocriticism and hence did not need to learn, to modify, etc. The old man's automaticity and the little girls' spontaneity served similar purposes.

The village showoff is always learning, modifying, and improving upon his behavior, since each occasion for showing off is something new. However, train him as a hypnotic subject and he then relies upon basic patterns already learned and the hypnotic limitation of his awareness results in the same type of performance as the old man's, modified only by the old established patterns.

Concerning the significance of unitary movements as possibly regressive, I think that is probably right. The baby moves his whole arm instead of his hand because he does not differentiate between a specific movement and a mass movement, between his hand as a specific object and his body as a mass object. In the trance state there is a comparable loss of differentiation, probably because of the marked loss and restriction of awareness of all things, including the body. Objects cease to be differentiated until attention is directed to them. For example, when BE [Betty Erickson] is told to look at her fingernails or her hand, all awareness centers only on them and they loom so large as to fill completely the entire sphere of awareness. Then, when told to move her hand, because it commands all awareness and its movement is the only thing to be done, a total response is made. Experimentally, I have found that the more simple the response desired, the greater is the mass movement or unitary movement, but that a careful building up of awareness of hand, or forearm, of upper arm, and of shoulder will lessen markedly the unitary movement.

Perhaps the following experiment will shed some light. An empty suitcase of identical appearance is secretly exchanged for a heavily loaded one just set down by the subject. When the subject again picks up the supposedly heavy suitcase the resulting overexertion is regarded as a good practical joke. Under the same circumstances, the deeply hypnotized subject picks up the supposedly heavy suitcase in almost the same manner he would the heavy suitcase. Apparently to pick up the suitcase again is not to pick up a remembered heavy suitcase with a consequent muscle set, but is simply to pick up a suitcase having no other significance, and so he makes a mass response that does not include differentiated patterns of muscle set and balance.

Concerning the pertinency of this example, I am in doubt, but perhaps it does have some. At all events, it does have an interest and meaning you may be able to apply.

I have gone over the record but have noted no particular changes to be made. That rhythmical movement of BE's leg was in response to arterial pulsation.

Also, you did not have much opportunity to see hypnotic technique, since BE is so well trained that it is unnecessary.

I hope this letter is of some assistance.

Sincerely,
Milton H. Erickson, M.D.

II

GREGORY BATESON, JAY HALEY, JOHN WEAKLAND

Bateson

Erickson maintained correspondence with both Bateson and Mead during World War II. They all worked on projects investigating Japanese and German personality structure that were submitted to the War Department. Bateson and Mead divorced in 1950.

After World War II, there was a seeming lapse of correspondence. The first item in Erickson's file on Bateson correspondence is this letter of November 29, 1954. By that time Bateson had begun his communication project in Palo Alto, which included collaboration with Jay Haley and John Weakland.

From: Gregory Bateson
November 29, 1954

Dear Milton,

Here at long last is the letter from me which you predicted. You will remember that Jay Haley, a member of my research project, attended your seminar in San Francisco. This has borne fruit in some experimentation and a good deal of thinking about hypnotic phenomena and their relation

51

to schizophrenia. The project is now on a fairly permanent basis and focussed specifically on schizophrenic communication.

I write to ask you first for reprints of your two papers on the case of ejaculatio praecox: "A Study of an Experimental Neurosis Hypnotically Induced in a Case of Ejaculatio Praecox" [Erickson 1935] and "The Method Employed to Formulate a Complex Story for the Induction of an Experimental Neurosis in a Hypnotic Subject" [Erickson, 1944].

Besides the reprints, there are many questions which we will want to discuss with you. Some of these questions are almost ready but, on the whole, I think it would be best to wait until our ideas about schizophrenia are riper. Is there any likelihood of your coming to this neighborhood to give the seminar again or for any other purpose? If so, we would like to hold you here in Palo Alto for a day or two as a consultant. Would that be possible? Alternatively, one of us might come to Phoenix some time next year to work you as a consultant.

We shall meet again one day,

Yours sincerely,
Gregory Bateson

To: Gregory Bateson
December 6, 1954

Dear Gregory,

I am delighted to know that your research project is continuing and that you are pleased with the results being obtained.

Concerning reprints, unfortunately my supply of the one on Ejaculatio Praecox is exhausted, but I am sending you the other one requested and, in addition, several other reprints that may interest you. There is also included one by Linn Cooper and myself which may offer you some ideas about time in connection with schizophrenia.

Williams and Wilkins of Baltimore have published a book by Cooper and myself, entitled *Time Distortion in Hypnosis* [Cooper & Erickson, 1954]. The first part of the book is by Cooper and is devoted to experimental work and the second part is the clinical application of the concept of time distortion.

I doubt very much if I shall be in the neighborhood of San Francisco in the near future. At least I have no expectation at the present time of making such a trip. However, I should be delighted to be of any possible service, should any of you come to Phoenix. I hope that can be arranged and I hope it will be possible for you personally to come.

I shall continue to hope that in some way or other I may be able to visit San Francisco some time in the summer and be free enough to visit the surrounding territory.

Yours sincerely,
Milton H. Erickson, M.D.

The following letter of May 24, 1995, is of historical importance, and is one of the most important pieces of correspondence in this book. Bateson set the stage by initiating consultations with Erickson for Haley and Weakland. He then outlined one of the major projects of his research team, namely, the double bind, indicating structural similarities between the operations of the hypnotist in inducing hypnotic phenomena and the operations of "schizophrenogenic" parents in inducing symptoms in schizophrenic offspring. The paper on the double bind, "Toward a Theory of Schizophrenia," was published in the October 1956 issue of Behavioral Science. *It was written by Gregory Bateson, Don Jackson, Jay Haley, and John Weakland.*

Two of Erickson's experiments are mentioned in the original article. The Bateson team contended that similarities between hypnotic communication and schizophrenogenic communication were collateral to the main theme of the paper. Erickson's findings were presented because they shed light on the nature of the development of schizophrenia.

"Toward a Theory of Schizophrenia" presented the "theory of logical types." The Bateson team examined schizophrenic patients and their parents and posited the existence of a pathogenic double bind, a situation in which no matter what the recipient does, he or she cannot win. The paper discussed how and why the double bind exists in families and provided clinical and experimental observations.

Bateson's letter covers five single-spaced pages. It appears that he typed it himself. There are a number of corrections (e.g., letters changed or deleted to correct spelling, punctuation marks) made after the text was typed. The changes are incorporated here.

Erickson replied in a handwritten letter of May 28, 1955. In a letter of June 24, 1955, which is not included, he indicated that he enjoyed the time he had spent with Haley and Weakland in Phoenix and requested transcriptions of the consultations.

There is no evidence that Erickson commented on the Bateson team's premise in print.

From: Gregory Bateson
May 24, 1955

Dear Milton,

I write to you because at long last my research project seems to have reached a theoretical position where we know some of the questions we would like to ask you about hypnosis. Two members of my project, Jay Haley and John Weakland, have been doing some minor experimenting with hypnosis since Jay attended your seminar in San Francisco. It has become more apparent that a better understanding of hypnosis would carry us forward in our work.

Is it possible to arrange a conference with you? I am unable, because of my V.A. duties, to leave here right now, but Mr. Haley and Mr. Weakland are ready and willing to go to Phoenix and confer with you. They can leave any time after the first of June, and if you can conveniently arrange two or three days with some free time to talk with them, it would be of great benefit to us, and I think of interest to you. In this letter I shall try to give you some idea of the sorts of things we are interested in.

During our previous project, a general investigation of the formal characteristics of communication, we became interested in hypnosis because it seemed to us to bring sharply into focus many of the problems involved in interpersonal communication. Since then we have begun a project concentrated primarily on schizophrenia and communication, and I shall try to suggest how we believe hypnosis is related to our point of view.

It soon became apparent to us that many of the manifestations of schizophrenia can be produced in trance. I refer to such manifestations as hallucinations, catalepsy, analgesias, and so on. One of our particular interests is a similarity in the literal-metaphor problem. Schizophrenic patients often seem to take metaphorical statements as literal and vice versa. For example, a patient might feel lonely and then say he is a wallflower—

but he will then spend his time standing against the wall. Similar thinking seems to occur in the hypnotized subject. There is the example of the woman in a deep trance playing bridge who became dummy and was asked to show her hand—so she held out the palm of her hand.

I'm sure you have thought about the similarities of these manifestations, and perhaps you have decided whether they are similar and whether they might have similar mechanics. It has seemed to us that if various kinds of schizophrenic phenomena can be induced in normal subjects by hypnotic trance, then if we could discover more about that induction, we might discover something more about the etiology of schizophrenia. Of course, we are concerned with *formal* similarities rather than specific details.

To discuss this further, it will be necessary to tell you some of our ideas about the etiology of schizophrenia. This is difficult because we are still working in the preliminary stages and our ideas have not sufficiently jelled to make a rigorous statement of our hypothesis. But I shall try to suggest the kind of thing we are investigating.

We assume that at least one species of schizophrenia is nonorganic and that it is a product of a particular kind of family situation. It is our hypothesis that a child raised in such a situation spends a period of years faced with what we call *"double binds."* That is, his relationship with his mother is such that he is continually in a position where he cannot get himself accepted by her, cannot win, cannot succeed, and so on. Characteristically the father supports the mother in the situation and confirms for the child the idea that he is wrong and Mother is right.

The precise nature of the double bind is something we are in the process of trying to define more clearly. The flavor of it runs throughout the monologues and dialogues of our schizophrenic patients, and occasionally we find an example that is reasonably clear. I shall cite one in an attempt to give you an idea of what we mean. A schizophrenic girl in therapy was consistently giving her age as a year younger than she actually was. She discovered her reason for this. When her mother put her in a private school, her mother (for her own personal reasons) gave the girl's age as 17 when she was actually 18. This act placed the girl in a bind situation. If the girl didn't lie about her age and say she was 18, then she was announcing that her mother was a liar. If she did lie about her age and say she was 17, she made herself a liar and her mother hated liars—never letting her daughter forget it. Whatever she did, her mother would reject her. This is what we have in mind by a double bind.

We believe it is a matter of messages of multiple meaning with a primary meaning contradicted by a secondary meaning in the same message. Given such a message, the receiver is faced with a problem of discriminating between two contradictory levels of message. If the receiver *must* discriminate, when it is a matter of life and death importance, the problem becomes so extreme that a breakdown is possible. Given an entire childhood faced with such a crisis, we hypothesize that a person will develop an elaborate system of defenses as a way of dealing with messages and that these defenses and ways are the symptoms of what is called schizophrenia. (The patient, in defense, can assume that messages only have one meaning, as in paranoia; or that they are meaningless [or must be reacted to as meaningless] as in hebrephrenia; or that they are insoluble as in extreme catatonia, and so on.)

The core idea in our hypothesis is the notion of "levels": (a) that the painful *double bind* is constructed out of messages of contrasting levels, and (b) that the syndromata of schizophrenia are an expression of the patient's resulting confusion regarding levels. He cannot be sure what sort of a message any message is (Is it kidding? Or dream? Or metaphor? Or literal? etc.). As we see it, the link between etiology and syndromes lies in the fact that the signals which tell what sort of a message it is are of a different level from the message itself.

I hope this oversimplified discussion will give you some idea of what we are trying to investigate, and I shall now try to suggest to you why we feel your work in hypnosis is related to this. I don't mean to imply that hypnosis is schizophrenia and vice versa, merely that certain aspects of trance induction seem to have the flavor of double binds.

You are continually working with the multiple meaning aspect of messages. This is particularly apparent in your ejaculatio praecox paper. You consistently emphasize the use of cue words to shift the level of meaning, or order of message, in the story you are telling the patient. That is, you work with *three* types of message: a. the story of the ashtray; b. the underlying story of a sexual nature; and c. signals which hint that b. and not a. is what is *really* being discussed.

It also seems to us that the extraordinary skill you demonstrate in handling resistance is somehow related to making use of the resistance by shifting levels of message to create *double binds*. This is particularly apparent in those cases where you have induced trance against the subject's expressed preference or challenge. For example, I have heard it said that when a medical student insisted that you couldn't hypnotize him, you invited him up before the class. When he came, you said, "I want you to stay awake, stay awake." I don't know the details of this incident, but assuming that something like this happened, then it appears that the student was placed in a kind of double bind. He assumed that if he obeyed your suggestions, he would go into a trance, and therefore he refused to obey your suggestion to stay awake. Yet if he had accepted your suggestion to stay awake, he would have been accepting your suggestions, which would have put him in danger of going into a trance.

You will notice that two levels, at least, are involved in this incident. The level of the specific suggestion "stay awake," and the level of "obey my suggestions." A double bind seems to occur when these two levels of message, or classification, are put together in a certain way. The subject is then caught in a situation where not obeying the specific suggestion in order to not obey the more general suggestion leads him precisely into obeying the more general suggestion.

To us, this incident resembles the situations our patients seem to report—it is as if in their relationship with Mother they found that their mother was saying, "If you obey me, I will love you," and within that frame she was saying specifically, "Do that which will make me hate you." The result is a patient unable to discriminate levels of message and unable to trust those messages, such as context or tone of voice or gesture, which qualify verbal messages. In other words, his discrimination of types of messages gets screwed up so that he doesn't know when someone is kidding him, bluffing him, deceiving him, and so on, because this requires a correct discrimination of levels.

We wonder if trance might not be defined in terms of some kind of screw-up of levels of messages—in the case of a negative hallucination, for example, it might be said that the messages from an object are interpreted differently from the interpretation made during the waking state so that the object isn't seen. In any perception the internal discriminating signal which must be significant is that neurological event which labels the datum as coming from a sense organ. Is it possible that this label is somehow sidetracked in negative hallucination? Are there any cases in which the negatively hallucinated object is perceived but discounted as imaginary? When a hypnotist is putting a subject in a trance, he seems to be constantly watching for cues from the subject as to the depth of trance and these cues seem largely to be indications as to what sort of meaning the subject is assigning to the hypnotist's messages, i.e., on what "level" are these messages being received?

Further, we wonder if trance doesn't occur at the moment of a shift in the subject's discrimination of levels, i.e., when the subject accepts or agrees to a shift of discrimination. I have in mind another induction statement you have used (we have a recording of your demonstration in San Francisco). You said to a girl, a resistant subject, "Are you in a trance *now*?" This seems again a bind—if she attempts to resist by answering "no," she is answering "no" to the question "now" and accepting the more general level of a possibility of going into trance, i.e., of agreeing to shift her discrimination of messages.

We would like to know if something like this double-bind phenomenon is characteristic of many aspects of both trance induction and trance phenomena. If it is, I think it might be possible to better understand the manifestations of schizophrenia by better understanding the processes involved in hypnosis. Of course, a hypnotic manifestation, such as a hallucination, is of brief duration and whatever pressures or binds the subject might be undergoing are within a benevolent frame. But one can imagine a childhood spent with a mother not so benevolent who imposed a consistent pattern of binds which would later produce the persistent and distressing manifestations of schizophrenia.

This, roughly, is the kind of thing we'd like a conference with you to discuss. As a further idea of the kinds of questions we have about hypnosis, I shall list a few for your consideration. I don't expect answers to these in a letter, but I mean them to suggest the kind of discussion we're interested in having.

In general, we are concerned with (1) the relationship between hypnotist and subject, (2) trance induction, and (3) waking from trance.

1. We are interested in comparing the hypnotist–subject relationship with both mother and preschizophrenic child and therapist and schizophrenic. We wonder, for example, if the therapy of schizophrenia is not related either to the patient's insight into his discrimination of levels of meaning, or his being caught in binds by the therapist, or both. For

example, what happens when a patient who cannot admit he is wrong and cannot admit he ever hated anyone is asked "Was it wrong of you to hate your brother?"

2. We wish to compare trance induction and the etiology of schizophrenia. This includes such central problems as the nature of resistance, the multiple levels of meaning involved in hypnotic suggestions, and what is *formally* common to the various induction techniques.

3. Waking from trance seems to have had less emphasis than trance induction, and we wonder if there might be something in it relevant to "waking" the patient from his psychosis. There seem to be direct and indirect means of waking from trance as well as "spontaneous" waking. Why is waking commonly achieved by means of a message within a message? "I am going to count to 3 and when I say '3' you will be awake. One, two, three!"

We are also interested in certain trance phenomena, such as:

a. The shift in interpretation of messages by subjects, such as the literal-metaphor problem as well as the increased emphasis on words as cues, and so on. (For example, why is it necessary to be so precise in the wording of suggestions?)

b. Can the so-called word salad of schizophrenia be produced by hypnosis in a normal subject, and if so how? Is this related to the obscurities of automatic writing under hypnosis?

c. The problem of "as if" behavior under hypnosis, which is related to the literal-metaphoric problem. For example, the subject feeling "as if" he is awake, or the use of such suggestions as "imagine yourself on an escalator."

d. We wonder if there are any irreversible phenomena which occur in hypnosis—schizophrenic manifestations seem almost irreversible. Would it be possible to suggest to a subject the impossibility of waking? Or to so organize suggestions that all the waking cues which the hypnotist gives will act in a contrary direction?

One of my difficulties is that I do not know how much you have worked with schizophrenic patients or how much investigation of schizophrenia you have done. To us it is fascinating, and so is hypnosis. I'd like to send my two staff members to discuss both with you. Please let me know if and when such a discussion is possible.

Yours sincerely,
Gregory Bateson

To: Gregory Bateson
May 28, 1955

Dear Gregory:
Question No. 1—My experience with schizophrenia—4 years of intensive work on schiz. on the Research Service, Worcester State Hospital—Continued intensive [work] for the next 14 years in Michigan in teaching psychiatry, using the schizophren as the most informative teaching material.

I shall be delighted to see your assistants and to spend time with them. I hope they can come so that I can spend an entire Sunday with them as well as time during the week.

The questions for discussion that you have listed are of much interest to me and have been for a long time. Also, I'll dig out some of my special material on schiz and psych concerning communication and discuss that with them. We should have a marvelous time.

Hastily,
Milton

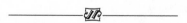

The correspondence between Bateson and Erickson continued. The initial part of the following letter discussed billing (Erickson was paid $300 for 20 hours of consultation) and is omitted here. Subsequently, Bateson poses a philosophical question. Erickson did not reply directly to the problem that Bateson posed.

From: Gregory Bateson
June 27, 1955

Dear Milton,

... There is a more general subject which I hope we may one day explore with you. It seems as if the human mind (with certain limitations) is capable of such flexibility that it can function as if it were a mechanism of many different types. If expected to work with images, it will work with images. If expected to work with words, it will work with words. If expected to be conscious, it will be conscious. If expected to behave like a computer, it will behave like a computer. And so on.

But the limitations of this are quite obscure, and so is the word "expected." Expected by whom? By the thinker? By the parent or hypnotist? As a result of training?

What I'm getting at is the notion that there can be exceedingly abstract instructions or programming of mental operations. To use an analogy, if an engineer is programming for an analogic computer (i.e., one which uses images), he will program the operations in a way appropriate to this characteristic of the computer. But if he is dealing with a digital computer (i.e., one which uses numbers), he will suit his programming to this characteristic. But the human mind does not seem to be like either of these. Rather, it seems that it can receive programming of a still higher order which would tell it to be either digital or analogic.

If this be so, then there must be pathologies related to conflict at this higher level. And the etiology and psychotherapy and symptomotology of these conditions should be investigable.

I think that this idea is one which you have thought about in other phrasings. I am only trying to focus it a little so that we might one day get together and discuss it. Someday when our present wealth of material has been assimilated. Please give my best greetings to your wife and family. Jay and John join me in these greetings.

Yours sincerely,
Gregory Bateson

Erickson's letter of September 4, 1956, perhaps refers to the fact that he had not received remuneration for his consultations. Bateson replied to Erickson's anecdotal request with a pun. Obviously, Haley and Weakland were planning a book, which was never written. Correspondence continued between the Bateson team and Erickson.

There was some additonal related correspondence that is not included. On September 21, John Weakland wrote to Erickson, referring a friend with arthritis. Also, in the letter he mentioned a medical problem and asked Erickson for a personal consultation. Erickson replied on September 24, indicating his willingness to help both the referral and Weakland.

To: Gregory Bateson
September 4, 1956

Dear Gregory:

Once upon a time two humpbacked whales, who had been lifelong friends, and who had traveled the seven seas together, decided to tour the continents. They agreed to part company, but with the hope that they eventually would meet somewhere, and meet they did, indeed, in the middle of the Arizona desert. Said the one to the other, upon meeting, "Long time no sea."

Now I know there must be some way of paraphrasing that story, but for the life of me I can't think how to do it, except by paraphrasing the punch line and letting it read, "long time no hear."

My best regards to John and Jay.

Sincerely yours,
Milton H. Erickson, M.D.

From: Gregory Bateson
September 24, 1956

Dear Milton,

Your obscure letter about whales crossed an indirect communication from me to you in which I instructed Stanford University to send you a check. You are not forgotten, but were I think entitled by my lack of communication to send me one or two "wails."

John and Jay and I continue to labor on the formal problems of schizophrenia. At the next get-together, we shall try to get your comments on our films of what we think are schizophrenogenic relationships between parents and children. But I don't know when this will be. John and Jay first have to do the next stage of editorial work on the schizophrenia–hypnosis book.

With best greetings from all of us,

Yours sincerely,
Gregory

Editor's Note: This book was never written.

Bateson's letter of July 26, 1957, was typed on the stationery of the Veterans Hospital in Palo Alto, where Bateson served as the Staff Ethnologist. It seems that Erickson's consultations to the Bateson project were quite meaningful.

From: Gregory Bateson
July 26, 1957

Dear Milton:

This is to tell you that you will get a check from Stanford for $175.00 in exchange for ten hours of recorded consultation with Jay [Haley].

I want also to say how valuable the working with you has been to Jay and John [Weakland] and therefore how much it has helped me.

My best greetings to you and all yours.

Sincerely yours,
Gregory Bateson
Ethnologist

Haley

To: Jay Haley
February 16, 1956

Dear Jay:

After a hasty reading of your letter, I felt most enthusiastic about your suggestions. After a second reading, I felt more enthusiastic. Being naturally calm, I have postponed a third reading.

I shall be in San Francisco April 27 to 29 and will hope to see you. The day of my arrival will probably be April 26 and I expect to be staying at the Sir Francis Drake Hotel.

Sincerely yours,
Milton H. Erickson, M.D.

From: Jay Haley
May 3, 1956

Dear Milton:

Unless we hear from you otherwise John and I will arrive in Phoenix and call you on Saturday, June 2nd. We hope for about ten hours of your time in the following days, preferably before Friday.

Enclosed is a copy of an article which I send you for several reasons.

One, because I hope it will ultimately be published, and since it mentions some of your work I think that should be cleared with you.

The main reason I sent it, however, is because some adaptation of this will preface the book we have in mind and I hope this will give you a better idea of the point of view from which we are working. We hope to get you interested in this hypothesis, if not in agreement with it, because we feel that if you assumed that the parents of a schizophrenic are exercising certain strategies which the schizophrenic reaction is appropriate to, then you would be able to see more clearly than anyone we know what sort of strategies are involved. This article attempts to state the hypothesis that the mother—or the family situation—of the schizophrenic entraps the child in a double bind, and it defines a double bind. We are now particularly concerned with *how* the mother does this, and the article deals only briefly with this question.

We find, for example, that when studying recordings of patients and parents, we can see various gambits which the mother, or the father, takes when the child says something that makes them anxious. Some of these gambits seem reminiscent to us of hypnotic techniques, although we assume they are involuntary on the parent's part, persistent over long periods of time, and motivated by fear and anxiety, so they are different in purpose from the hypnotic situation. The mother may, for example, distract the child's attention when he starts to say something to her that is important to him. Or she may "drift rapidly away" from the subject while appearing to be interested and concerned. Or she may act hurt or helpless as the child begins to develop his point, thus preventing him from developing it. Or he may tell her something indirectly, using an example or a story, and she will accept literally the example or story and ignore what he is telling her indirectly. In general these are ways the mother obfuscates the situation so the child cannot get clearly expressed what he wants to express. We are more concerned with *patterns* of the mother's behavior which induce in the child either a lack of desire to express himself with reasonable directness, or an inability to do so, thus requiring him to talk in a metaphoric, disjointed way, or give up trying altogether.

Our basic argument is that the mother presents contradictory messages to the child which provoke in him a habitually screwy response. A very nice example of the *situation* which we believe exists is the incident when you blocked John when he was drawing a picture at our previous conference. You suggested he draw a picture, and then you said "Now draw another one." John felt on the spot and was unable to tell whether he was to draw a specific picture or merely draw a picture, and he blocked. However, he was able to ask what you meant. Suppose he had been forbidden to ask you what you meant, and yet was forced to respond? We feel that it is a situation like this that the preschizophrenic constantly faces.

Therefore we are basically interested in the kinds of situation in human life, or in the hypnotic situation, where the individual feels himself caught in a situation where he must respond but he is unable to know what he is responding to and he cannot comment on the situation. Our assumption is that the result of such a situation is often an individual who experiences "involuntary" shifts in perception, or type of message, such as those experienced by hypnotic subjects in some situations and by schizophrenics. In the enclosed paper an example of yours is mentioned; the one where you suggest that a hand remain where it is and yet move. We would be most interested in any similar examples you might have, since we want as many examples as possible of obvious double binds producing shifts in perception.

We also wonder how you prevent the subject whose hand is to move and yet not move from commenting on the situation. Our main generalization about the schizophrenic is that he is forbidden to meta-communicate, or talk about what the other person says. We assume that in his experience his mother used various devices for preventing his commenting on her statements. It seems to us that in many hypnotic situations it is necessary to block off this meta-communicative level so the subject merely responds without commenting on, or perhaps even noticing, what was said to him. The strategies you use to prevent a subject from commenting on what you are saying, particularly the indirect strategies, would interest us very much.

We plan to bring you excerpts from tapes of patients and their parents to see if you agree with us that the schizyness of the patient's responses is appropriate to the moves of the parents.

Along with this basic interest, we will have other questions to fill in some of the things we missed in the previous conference. For example, we would like more information on the ways of inducing auditory hallucinations. The area of "voices" we didn't discuss then, and there are some other similar areas we would like to cover with you. If it is possible, we would also like to have a recording of you inducing a trance in a naive subject.

We enjoyed seeing you here, and we are looking forward to visiting you in June.

Yours sincerely,
Jay Haley

Jay Haley had written a profile of Erickson for possible publication in the New Yorker; *however, it was rejected. Also of historical interest is the fact that Haley asked Erickson to publish his (Erickson's) collected papers. Erickson declined, saying that he was working with a junior colleague, Dr. Christenson, on that project. Bernie Gorton, M.D., a psychiatrist who eventually practiced in Phoenix, took over the task with the help of another junior colleague, André Weitzenhoffer, Ph.D. But Gorton died prematurely, and the undertaking subsequently was completed by Haley. He published the collection of Erickson's papers entitled* Advanced Techniques of Hypnosis and Therapy *in 1967, and included a short biographical piece, just as he had promised in his letter of December 6, 1956,*

From: Jay Haley
December 6, 1956

Dear Milton,

After receiving the manuscript of the Profile back from you, I reorganized it, polished it up, sent it to the *New Yorker*, and they have rejected it. On reading it over afterwards, I could see why. It's not a good piece of work, certainly not good enough for the *New Yorker*. When I get up strength to work on it again I shall cut about a fourth of it out, rewrite the remainder, and send it off to my agent to see what he can do with it.

While thinking about what to do with the Profile, I recalled something I've been planning to write to you about for some time. I think it very important that your papers be collected and published. It would please me very much if I could be the editor of your papers, and I hesitate to suggest this because I know your wife has, or had, plans to edit and collect them. I don't wish to tread upon her ground, but if she has abandoned the project, I would like to put in my bid. I don't know how you wish your work organized, but as I remember there was an outline made up along some kind of theoretical line. Perhaps that would be an appropriate way, but in my mind any kind of organization, even along the line of a simple division between hypnotic experiments and therapy, would be satisfactory just so the papers get in print and are accessible to readers. Perhaps some modification of that Profile could serve as a biographical sketch to accompany the collected papers.

At any rate, I would like to offer to edit and collect your papers and perhaps include a biographical sketch as a preface to them. I have not read them all as yet, but I think I could make a collection suitable to you. If you agree to this, we will have to handle it by mail. I would like to use it as an excuse to visit you again, but I doubt if I could swing project financing for that. Please let me know what you think of the idea.

Yours sincerely,
Jay Haley

To: Jay Haley
December 19, 1956

Dear Haley

    I am very much flattered by your request to edit my papers, but I have some time ago broached the subject to Dr. Christenson, a student of mine, who is exceedingly well acquainted with all my publications, has already done some work in this regard, and has a genius for collating material. I expect to see him at some length during January, but I am pretty certain my plans with him will be continued.

    Many thanks for you offer and, with Season's Greetings to everybody there.

Sincerely yours,
Milton H. Erickson, M.D.

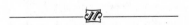

Haley's initial consultations with Erickson seemed to focus around the communications research project. The letter of March 18, 1957, represents a change in direction. Haley was moving away from research and into the clinical domain. He asked for Erickson's consultation and assistance in understanding the process of psychotherapy. There is no reply in the Erickson file, but obviously Erickson responded favorably. There were many years of Haley's visits to Erickson in Phoenix to discuss cases.

From: Jay Haley
March 18, 1957

Dear Dr. Erickson:

I think I may have found another excuse for visiting Phoenix to consult with you.

Three months ago, the chief of psychiatry at the local clinic, a consultant on our project and a friend of mine, suggested that I go into part-time private practice as a hypnotherapist. He was being referred quite a number of patients who did not need, or could not afford, long-term psychiatry and he thought I could provide quick therapy to relieve symptoms. Since I am not an M.D. or a psychologist, I hesitated over the matter, but I finally plunged in. A couple of other psychiatrists have referred patients to me, so I have been about as busy as I want to be what with holding this full-time research job at the same time.

When I entered practice, it soon became clear to me that if I was to provide brief therapy, it was going to have to be directive, and I would have to know what I was doing. I've been doing psychotherapy with schizophrenics here at the [Veterans Administration] hospital for four years, but working at quick symptom removal is quite a different matter. What has helped me most I find are some of the things I've learned from you during our conferences even though we weren't conferring specifically on the techniques of psychotherapy. Although I've had reasonable success with my patients, I have the uneasy feeling that I don't know really why I succeeded when I succeeded. This is as uncomfortable as not knowing why I failed when I failed.

At any rate, I would like to know more about what I'm doing and I think I could learn some of the things I need to know if I could consult with you and discuss the cases I've had. You have a way of working with patients which I would like to absorb. Talking about what I have done, and what I should have done, with particular patients would be very helpful to me.

I would like to spend a week in Phoenix some time in the next couple of months, and confer with you an hour or so a day if you can arrange the time and are willing. When would be the most convenient week? What would your fee be for such consultation? The project may help pay for my visit since it is relevant to an investigation of the nature of psycho-therapy which we hope to get started on soon.

I hope all is well with you and I look forward to hearing from you.

Yours sincerely,
Jay Haley

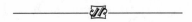

The following outline was probably prepared by Weakland and Haley, perhaps with assistance from the Bateson project team members.

Erickson Consultation—November 1959

Matters to Cover:

I. Pathology and Therapy

Basic plan of discussion—To start with some central questions about individual treatment, and move toward comparable matters for couples, and, to the extent possible, families.

Schema of Erickson's procedure appears to be:

Categorize the essential problem

Accept the patient's behavior

Utilize this behavior—that is, begin a shift based on it, and go on to

Shatter old neurosis

Peg change

Terminate and dismiss

A. Individuals

1. How does he really classify pathologies—i.e., when the patient enters, how does Erickson categorize the basic difficulty?

2. Same problem on what level of patient's behavior to accept and utilize; in some cases, seems to be the overt behavior (e.g., pacing); in others, an underlying pattern. Basis of choice?

3. How is the shift from accepting to utilizing and redirecting made?

    3a. How to handle patient who is hard to get to do what you ask?

    3b. What is really crucial to producing change, anyway? "Expressing feelings," "insight," different actions, what?

4. How is change pegged, stabilized, made to stick?

    4a. How to handle patient who insists he's not getting any better?

5. Decisions on time and manner of termination of therapy?

Moves to promote further improvement after termination?

B. Couples

1. In dealing with individuals, it is often obvious how much a spouse is involved in a problem. What is basis for choice of trying to affect relationship through the one individual, or seeing both parties?

2. If choice is to see both, how to handle bringing the second in—how to get acceptance by the original patient, and by the new one.

3. Choices involved in seeing the two together, separately, or both.

If separately—what about freedom of communication; handling of "secrets" revealed by one party?

4. Classification and categorization problem here: What goes wrong with marriages?

    4a. Goals, and what is a good relationship?

5. Acceptance and utilization—With couples, does Erickson handle their existing relationship, and promote it toward an

alteration, as he does with an individual's main behavioral theme or symptom (in relation to himself, of course)? How?

6. How does he obtain and retain change when couples tend to be so reciprocally reinforcing of their interaction pattern?

    6a. Alternatively, how to control how they get together when change is produced, so they don't panic over it.

C. Families (parents and children)

The questions here largely parallel those under "B" above.

1. Choice of seeing parents and child, or only one or the other.
2. How to frame the inclusion of whole family.
3. If to see both, then when separately and when jointly? Handling of private or secret communications.

4. What causes difficulties in children?

    a. E.g.—Suppose Erickson wanted to create a disturbed child, what would he have parents do?
    b. Function of child in a pathological marriage—how used by the parents?
    c. Goals in dealing with families.

5. What about acceptance, utilization, and change in this situation?—A complex interaction in which the differences between parties are so great that it is hard to see what exists to accept overall, yet a system that is very self-reinforcing and resistant to change.

II. Ideas on Experiments to Discuss

1. What sort of experiment to separate good and bad hypnotic subjects?
2. What sort of experiment to differentiate various kinds of families?

III. Separate Points

1. Therapy failures.

How much follow-up information does he have?

2. Want recordings of actual work with patients—especially couples or families—if these exist or can be made.
3. Get reprints of his more recent articles, particularly several in the *American Journal of Clinical Hypnosis.*

In an exchange of correspondence in December 1959, Erickson and Haley discussed their perceptions of a book about the clinical treatment of a patient through hypnotherapy. Haley did not like the book as much as Erickson did. Subsequently, Erickson offered an expostulation about the nature of psychotherapy.

On December 7, 1959, a letter from Erickson to Haley described a review by Haley of a clinically oriented book. Perhaps the review was for the American Journal of Clinical Hypnosis, *which Erickson edited.*

To: Jay Haley
December 7, 1959

Dear Jay:

I am grateful to you for your comments on F's book. Neither fish, flesh, nor fowl—but the patient responded and in relation to the procedures related. I interviewed the psychoanalyst who "analyzed" him extensively and wrote him off as a total loss. I followed the course of therapy. I'm very curious about it. I have seen the patient and the girl—interviewed the patient.

All I know is therapeutic results were obtained by a "mongrel approach." I value the book because it illustrates this matter not only of *thinking, knowing, understanding, feeling* and *believing* but also illustrates the tremendous importance of *doing*, perhaps first safely at the fantasy level and then at a progressive reality level.

I know personally three other patients, two women and another man, treated by F. by essentially the same type of procedure, varied to fit them and the therapeutic results were excellent.

I sometimes wonder what psychotherapy is—certainly not the involved psychoanalytical theorizing, certainly not any organized body of thought. Rather, it is a human relationship in which patient and therapist by a complexity of interreactions strive toward a common goal, the patient's thinking, feeling, and doing within his frame of reference as he currently understands it and with freedom to alter current understandings.

Thanks greatly.

Sincerely yours,
Milton H. Erickson, M.D.

————————————— *JC* —————————————

Haley indicated that he was interested in further popularizing Erickson's approaches, and in his February 21, 1962, letter proposed the idea of writing TV scripts based on Erickson's cases. Erickson declined, and it seems that Haley never pursued the project.

From: Jay Haley
February 21, 1962

Dear Milton,

As you may have guessed from my papers, I am inclined toward writing as a career.

Recently I have been attempting some TV scripts based on psychiatric cases. Most psychiatry on TV is both phony and dull, and I think I can do better.

As I have been working up some of my own cases, I recall one of yours which I think would make a delightful script. Since I know you are sensitive about publishing your cases unless they are thoroughly disguised, I write you now for permission to use the story if I can disguise it appropriately.

The case I refer to is the one where the mother sits upon the misbehaving little boy. The format I have in mind is a young psychiatrist and an older one, with the young one attempting to solve a boy's behavior problem when faced with a helpless mother and a father who won't enter therapy. The older psychiatrist suggests he should be able to solve the problem quickly, and the younger one places the problem in the older psychiatrist's lap. The mother is told to advise the father that he should come in for therapy, and if he does not, she is to make an agreement with him that if she can make the boy mind, he will enter treatment with her and have Family Therapy. The father agrees, not believing it possible, and the psychiatrist instructs the woman to sit upon the little boy, which she does, and the father enters therapy.

The problem in the case is to make the situation more dramatic, since the idea of sitting on a boy is entertaining but after a few minutes it would begin to get a bit dull. So it needs a format like this one around it with her sitting on the boy as part of a larger plot.

Of course, if the script sold, I would pay you a story fee, which is usually $150.00 for source material for scripts. Payable if and when it appears on the screen.

I think a psychiatric series would make a good TV package and I might ultimately sell one. I would have to present reasonably orthodox psychiatry and much of your stuff is rather far out, but if I ever get such a series going, I will use it as an excuse to come and see you and discuss which of your cases might be appropriate.

Let me know what you think about my using this case, and whether you would be interested in letting me dramatize some of your other cases if ever I become a big wheel in television.

Best regards,
Jay Haley

To: Jay Haley
February 26, 1962

Dear Jay:

I really hesitate to give permission. I don't like TV presentations, and so many of the presenters are more interested in the "art" than the values involved. Sorry to be such a wet blanket.

Wish I could get up there but I'm too darned busy.

Yours,
Milton H. Erickson, M.D.

———————— 𝒥𝑅 ————————

In May 1970, Jay Haley worked at the Philadelphia Child Guidance Clinic, which was directed by Salvador Minuchin. Haley had served as editor of Family Process *and was attempting to publish a collection of papers on family therapy. As he described in his letter to Erickson of May 7, it seems that there was competition between Haley and Nathan Ackerman and John Bell, who also wanted to publish a compendium on family therapy. Neither of the books was published.*

In Erickson's reply, he described how he used his strategic method not only for hypnosis and therapy, but also in handling political situations in professional organizations. Erickson closed with a note about his new home. In 1970, the Ericksons moved approximately six miles northeast in Phoenix, from Cypress Street to Hayward Avenue. The new home was equipped with special fixtures to facilitate Erickson's wheelchair-bound lifestyle. There was also a small guest house, which became his office and the site for Erickson's teaching seminars. (See Zeig, 1980, for a description of Erickson's seminars from that period.)

From: Jay Haley
May 7, 1970

Dear Milton:

This is likely to be a long letter, so make yourself comfortable. It should not be too tedious since it is about a controversy.

I am sorry to tell you that I must cancel publication of the collection of papers on family therapy in which your article was included. It is painful to me to drop what I think would be a good book into which I put many months of labor. It is also embarrassing to me to inform you that this must be done after you granted permission for publication of your paper (and some of you did extra work to prepare it for publication). I feel obligated to give you the background that forced this decision.

Since there was not a good collection of articles on family therapy in book form, and many of the better papers were published some years ago, I decided to make a selection that would represent the wide variety of views in the field. Grune & Stratton agreed to publish it. The work was to be called *Changing Families* and the royalties were to be shared among the contributors.

Besides obtaining your permission to re-publish your article, releases had to be obtained from the journals where the articles were first published. All of the journals granted this permission. Several of the articles, nine out of twenty-one, had been previously published in *Family Process*. As Editor of *Family Process*, I granted myself, as Editor of the collection, permission to reprint articles from that journal. I assumed this was right and proper. The Board of Editors of *Family Process* had established a policy that permission to re-publish papers would be freely given by the Editor to any Editor of a collection, asking only that the written permission of the author be obtained and the journal cited. We felt that an author should have the basic right to re-publish his own article since a scientific article is essentially a gift to a journal by the author. We also felt that it was good public relations to have articles from *Family Process* included in collections. Over the eight years I was Editor, I granted this permission to Editors innumerable times and articles from the journal have been well represented in collections.

While I was putting together this collection, I was involved in another enterprise. For some years we had talked about putting out a *Family Process Reader*, which would contain the better articles from that journal. Nathan Ackerman said he was working on it, but the years passed and nothing was done. When I corresponded with Ackerman about including one of his papers in *Changing Families*, he suggested we should get going on the *Family Process Reader* and he and I should edit the collection. I agreed and suggested that he send me whatever list of articles he had been working on. Several months later I received his list and it was not a practical one. He wanted to place the book with his publisher, Basic Books, and they had asked for 300 pages. His list totalled 750 pages and just seemed to be a list of everything he liked. We corresponded, trying to reach agreement on the selection and he sent a shorter list. I could see there would be difficulty because we disagreed on the organization and differed markedly on what we considered the better articles.

Since I was resigning as Editor of *Family Process*, and since I had endured eight years of dealing with Ackerman on that journal, it seemed to me a graceful way to avoid further difficulty was to suggest that John Bell replace me as co-editor of the collection. I recommended this, and it was accepted. The two Directors of the two Institutes sponsoring the journal would be responsible for the *Reader*, and I cheerfully offered my wise advice should they need it.

At this point, a problem appeared. *Changing Families* had reached the contract stage with Grune & Stratton. I had all the authors' permissions, including that of Ackerman, except from John Bell for a paper by him. He raised a question whether the collection I was editing would conflict with the *Family Process Reader*.

I did not take this issue seriously enough, apparently. To me, the *Family Process Reader* had been years in the making and looked like it would take more years to complete while *Changing Families* was ready to go to press. I also saw no conflict. Collections of papers are regularly appearing and there is room for them. The *Family Process Reader* was also to be only one-third on family therapy and two-thirds on other aspects of the family. The family therapy collection was quite different and would have little interest for research people. I went ahead with the collection and the book entered the production stage with the publisher.

At this point, I received an ultimatum from Drs. [John E.] Bell and Ackerman that I could not publish papers originally published in *Family Process* without special permission of the Directors of the two Institutes holding copyright, namely them. Permission of the Editor was not adequate. They also said that even if I had their permission, I could not publish until six months after the *Family Process Reader* had come on the market. They had only started their collaboration, had not made a final selection, and had not even begun correspondence to receive the authors' permissions, so this meant asking me to delay publication until six months after some indefinite date. Since there had been several years of delay on the Reader by Ackerman, I could not see immediate publication in the offing.

I suggested to Drs. Bell and Ackerman that their request was unreasonable. I pointed out there was really no overlap between the two collections, and if there was, this could be changed. The last list Ackerman had sent me included only two articles which might appear in both collections, and one of them was by me. The other was a paper by Ross Speck. I offered to shift articles so that there would be no overlap and the two collections would not duplicate a single paper.

Drs. Bell and Ackerman responded by saying that whether the same papers appeared in the two volumes was not the issue. *No collection which contained any papers originally published in Family Process* could be published until six months after the *Family Process Reader*. I have never heard of a scientific journal establishing such a rule, with all the implications it has for authors. They said they must establish this rule to protect their two Institutes which would receive the royalties. (One would think that vast sums of money hung on this decision. Even though both Institutes are in desperate financial straits, they overestimate what can be made with a Reader like this. The royalties from such a collection are hardly worth bickering about, far less violating the obligation of a scientific journal to distribute ideas widely.)

So I was faced with a complex and exasperating problem. Legally I was probably on good grounds since the permission of *Family Process* to reprint the articles had been obtained from the Editor, namely me, in the proper manner. (If someone else had been Editor at the time, there would be no problem, which is the curious situation.) However, to sort out the legal issue could prove quite difficult. *Family Process* is owned by the two Institutes, but the policy-making power resides with the Board of Editors. The powers of the two Institutes in relation to the Board have not been defined because the two Directors have not been able to agree with each other enough to make a legal contract. The Board has the power but rarely meets, and now it is an almost new Board which has not clarified its authority. Where final decision-making power resides is totally unclear.

I could have avoided the issue by dropping the *Family Process* articles, but this would weaken the collection because so many valuable ones came from there. I should know, I recruited many of these articles by persuading the authors to publish them in *Family Process* instead of elsewhere.

Recently Drs. Bell and Ackerman have shifted their approach from a legal one to a moral one and have become increasingly rude. This has both irritated and puzzled me. I really have not wished to do *Family Process* any harm. After spending eight years of my life sweating over that journal, I would like to see the better papers published in book form. I also think the two Institutes have benefited by the journal and my labors and might let this matter ride as a courtesy. Instead the correspondence has been increasingly insulting, which puzzles me. I can understand that John Bell is finding it impossible to fill Don Jackson's shoes at the Mental Research Institute, which is failing, but why he would behave this way to me is not clear since we have always respected one another. With Ackerman, it is another matter. When Jackson and I founded *Family Process* we got off on the wrong foot with Ackerman. We invited him to jointly sponsor the journal, partly for financial support, and also because we wanted a broader representation than one Institute. Ackerman's terms for joining us were that he be Editor, and since we didn't want that we dismissed him and sought another Institute. At this point Ackerman said he would give up wanting to be Editor and could come up with some money, so we let him back in. Even though Don made him Chairman of the Board so he would feel better, there was always resentment from Ackerman. We managed to work together on the journal but it was difficult and apparently still is.

The final end to this controversy came on the moral issue. Drs. Bell and Ackerman wrote to me that they considered my granting myself permission to republish articles from *Family Process* was "misusing my office for self dealing." As they knew it would, this accusation left me no alternative except to cancel the collection and sever what little relationship I have with *Family Process* and the two Institutes.

I regret this whole affair and particularly regret involving you in this childish struggle. The field still needs a good collection of articles on family therapy, and if any of you would like to edit one, perhaps you can have better luck with the owners of *Family Process* than I have had.

Yours sincerely,
Jay Haley

To: Jay Haley
May 16, 1970

Dear Jay:

I am sorry to receive the news of your May 7 letter. All controversies are not necessarily limited to the campus or legislative halls. Petty behavior can be found most expected at the least expected places. I have always looked forward in every instance to such possibilities and only found myself pleasantly surprised when no grief was encountered. I also took care of matters by granting permission while Editor and thus had properly dated permission which would require a legal effort to block. I should have thought of so advising you.

I do not know how to offer you comfort since the lot of an editor and the lot of an author are never very happy ones. Dr. [John] Hartland of England did not believe me when I told him he was headed for trouble but he has written to me his amazement of the behavior of one of his closest friends. I succeeded in having Bill Edmonston succeed me as Editor [of the *American journal of clinical Hypnosis*] by finding a corner into which my seemingly good friends could back me into in a most painful fashion and I convinced them it was a proper place to corner me by reducing to tears three of my genuine friends. I knew my genuine friends would survive and that I could eventually clarify things for them but you should have seen the mountains of scorn and accusations of practically everything undesirable that were leveled at me. Incidentally, the Professor of Internal Medicine at the University of Wisconsin nicknamed me "nemesis" because of the way I had of dealing with my classmates. I always let them shove me viciously into what they thought was surely the wrong direction and I enjoyed that greatly.

Our new home is taking shape very well. Betty is taking her time in arranging things and I think she is doing an excellent job.

Sincerely yours,
Milton H. Erickson, M.D.

From: Jay Haley
March 30, 1971

Dear Milton and Betty:

I was in Pittsburgh this week and spent some time with Kay Thompson. In the conversation, I mentioned how little there was of the Ericksonian approach on film and how you should have a video set up in that fine office in the guest house. While discussing how inexpensive this would really be, Kay pointed out that the Education and Research Foundation of the ASCH would undoubtedly finance it and she pushed me to apply for the funds.

I am writing to you now to see if this would seem to you to be a sensible procedure. I could obtain from the ERF a grant to buy a small, $1,500 videotape setup which would remain the property of the Foundation and could be used at workshops and such ultimately. The additional costs would be for videotapes, and for my travel to come down and set it up and to check to see how it is going from time to time.

As I see it, I could bring in the equipment, put the camera unobtrusively in the wall, and have the recording equipment outside in the waiting room. Then, Betty, when you wheel Milton into his office, if it is an interview he wishes to record, all you would need to do is put on a tape and flip the machine on. It is a simple piece of equipment, rather like a tape recorder. As tapes pile up, I could come down and go over them and possibly edit out pieces and put them together around different themes. The tapes could be of a single case seen over several sessions, or they could be different types of induction or different types of interventions that Milton would like to have on tape. Any tape he doesn't like is erasable and reusable. Once set up, it could stay there for months and be used only when Milton is in the mood for it with an appropriate patient.

I can't emphasize enough how important it is to get some visual record of Erickson at work, and even though this should have been done years ago, it still seems feasible to me. Does it seem so to you? Let me know and I'll start filling out forms to see if I can raise the money.

Best regards,
Jay Haley

Editor's Note: Kay Thompson, D.O.S., was a student of Erickson's, an accomplished teacher of the practice of hypnosis, and one of the presidents of the American Society of Clinical Hypnosis.

To: Jay Haley
April 10, 1971

Dear Jay:

However good the videotape sounds to you, I hesitate very much to encourage it. Very seldom do I feel free enough to see patients in the presence of someone else. The private practice of psychiatry is very different from clinical center practice. Also, at the present, hungry lawyers are seizing upon every possible opportunity to sue some doctor for malpractice.

I have had three patients recently that I could have used video with but on the occasion of one, my speech was terribly limited. The fact that I use hypnosis frequently leads patients to check my office to see if I have someone listening in.

I received a letter asking for a reference for you and it is being typed and mailed today.

Yesterday I had a 15-year-old girl to work on. At the age of 3 she was state champion in ice skating. Recently she had developed a great deal of stage fright. Her mother and her coach came with her. I had to reduce the mother to tears and the coach to tears and the girl to tears in order to get psychological commitment to therapy and then everything developed beautifully, exactly as I wanted it to. A videotape of such a case would be very difficult for observers to understand because it would be an objective presentation of something where it was necessary to have a purely subjective view. Also I am going to have to see that girl and her parents and coach next Thursday to make certain that the parents are not going to develop a hostility toward me because I have emancipated the daughter so that she can skate for her own satisfaction. I was thinking about a video all the time I was working with her and seeing, along with the positive aspects, how other people, in trying to empathize, would get an extremely false impression.

T. E. A. Von Dedenroth [a close colleague who at that time was also Erickson's personal physician] recently gave a rather extensive account to me about C. S. [Erickson names a renowned medical practitioner of hypnosis]. C. S.'s perfect imitation of me, even copying of my mannerisms, the tone of voice to such an extent that when he closed his eyes he actually had the feeling that it was I who was speaking and not C. S. and a videotape would give a lot of novices an opportunity to imitate me without securing the effects I can.

Margaret Mead is coming here May 22, and I will ask her concerning the writing of an introduction for your book. [*Editor's Note: Uncommon Therapy* (Haley, 1973).] Incidentally, there are a couple of case histories that I want to change. The one about the girl with the automobile accident lawsuits and a year's treatment by a psychiatrist has to be changed so the setting is in Minnesota. The case of the February man, I am having Betty look up, and the case of the philoprogenitive couple, I want to send you a complete and accurate account. Betty will probably look those up this weekend.

I am writing a new paper and I will send you a carbon copy of it as soon as I get through it.

Roxie [Erickson's daughter] is home for Easter and my grandson, David Elliot, is here for Easter also. Roxie and I and the maid are having a tremendous amount of allergic difficulties.

I am very glad that the taco sauce was satisfactory. It was a pleasure to send it.

Sincerely,
Milton H. Erickson, M.D.

———————————

There was a great deal of interest in videotaping Erickson's work in the 1970s, and a number of students recorded Erickson. For example, Herb Lustig, M.D., attempted videorecording in Erickson's office, but because of interference from radio signals, the sound was poor. Zeig, in 1974, accomplished some videotaping; Marion Moore, M.D., amassed the largest collection of videotapes of Erickson working in his office. Lustig (1975) produced high-quality videotapes in a television studio. Videotapes of Erickson are included in the archives of the Milton H. Erickson Foundation in Phoenix and are available for viewing by professionals.

Margaret Mead did not write an introduction for Uncommon Therapy. *Instead, Haley wrote about his experience with Erickson and gave a brief account of Erickson's background.*

Weakland

From: John H. Weakland
December 11, 1959

Dear Milton:

Among the reprints which Betty supplied us during our visit last month was one entitled "Pediatric Hypnotherapy." I found this so interesting in several ways that I took it home so that Anna could have a change to read it. However, before she was able to get a chance at it, Alan and Lewis did. Judging from the state of the fragments we recovered later, they have probably digested your article rather thoroughly. Perhaps even in this way it might have the effects I was thinking of, but I do think that Anna should still have a chance at it herself, at least for the benefit of the third.

Would you, therefore, please send another copy? With best wishes,

Yours sincerely,
John H. Weakland
Ethnology Section

———————— 𝒥𝑅 ————————

An additional turn in the consultations between Erickson and members of the Bateson project is seen in the October 26, 1961, letter to Erickson from John Weakland. Obviously, Haley and Weakland had become interested in treating couples and families and requested Erickson's assistance. From his reply, it seems that Erickson was treating families and family units. He simply had no cases available to record in the period Weakland outlined.

In the second paragraph of his letter, Weakland refers to Erickson's induction of Ruth and his subsequent discussion of the event with Weakland and, presumably, Haley. There is no record of this discussion. However, a transcript of Erickson's and Ernest Rossi's commentary on the induction appears in Experiencing Hypnosis *(Erickson & Rossi, 1981).*

From: John Weakland
October 26, 1961

Dear Milton,

Jay and I would like to make another visit to Phoenix soon, to see you and confer about your ways of handling problems clearly involving couples or families (parents and children). We would be particularly interested in how you deal with two or more family members together in the same interview, since most of our own interest and experience with families has been of this sort, at least in our research project, if not so much so in private practice. But we would also be interested in cases where you would instead choose to see two or more family members separately rather than together, or to see only one and work through him to influence a spouse as necessary.

We would like to approach this subject in the same way that was so successful in understanding your hypnotic induction methods better. That is, if it would not be too difficult for you to arrange it, what we would like is for you to make a tape recording of an interview with a family or couple before we come to Phoenix. Probably an initial interview with a family whose members are all previously unknown to you would be best of all; we are not especially concerned about the nature of their problem. Then on arrival we would like to begin by hearing this record, getting your comments on what you did, and questioning you about it, very much as with the record of Ruth's hypnotic induction. (We could wait until we get there and then persuade you to record a session with a couple or family, but it would be nice if you could do it before we arrive.) We will also arrive with some general and particular questions in mind, but they would be secondary and subsequent to this.

We are thinking about the weekend of December 1 as a possible time, with the idea that between Friday evening and sometime Tuesday we could get eight or ten hours with you. Will you let us know if this is feasible for you, and suggest an alternative if it is not?

Sincerely,
John H. Weakland
Ethnology Section

To: John Weakland
November 21, 1961

Dear John:

I have read your letter with much interest this A.M. It arrived while I was in St. Louis for a week—since then I have been in the East for a week. Your letter was in the accumulation I want to work on for the next two weeks besides the April issue of the Journal.

Awfully good of you to assign such a "simple" task to me: As I look over the schedule, there isn't a single family unit listed. Mother–son, daughter but parents in East, etc. Maybe I'll be able to get hold of something, but Thanksgiving week and Christmas shopping time always cause a letdown in new patients.

I'm sorry my reply to your letter is so delayed.

Regards to everybody.

Sincerely,
Milton H. Erickson, M.D.

III

PSYCHOANALYSTS:

Lewis Wolberg, Lawrence Kubie, Ives Hendrick

Wolberg

Lewis R. Wolberg, a preeminent psychodynamic theorist, was considered one of the fathers of modern medical hypnosis. He published his seminal work, Medical Hypnosis, *in 1948, only six years after the following exchange with Erickson. This two-volume set at the time was considered a landmark achievement in the theory and practice of hypnotherapy. That Wolberg would consult him in this manner shows the respect that Erickson engendered in his colleagues.*

The correspondence begins with a continuation of discussions Wolberg and Erickson had had at an earlier meeting, where they talked about referrals, and then Erickson responded to a survey that Wolberg conducted. Subsequent exchanges revolved around books, and Wolberg credited Erickson with stimulating his initial interest in hypnosis.

From: Lewis Wolberg
June 11, 1942

Dear Dr. Erickson:

First I want to express my appreciation and gratitude for the time you spent with me at the American Psychiatric Convention listening to my amateurish questions regarding hypnosis. I have been stimulated into reading more of your articles, which are very complete and inspiring. I am herewith plaguing you with a couple more questions and seem to have struck a snarl in my own technique.

(1) I wonder if regression to a six-year level during hypnosis approximates in any degree the condition in a six-year-old child. By this I mean are the symbols used by the adult who believes he is at the six-year level like those of a six-year-old child? For instance, in hypnotic regression the type of art seems childish, but is this because the person recapitulates the six-year level or is he merely trying to act the way he thinks a child of six should act?

(2) Can one assume that a person who cannot be hypnotized always shows a resistance either to the type of technique or to hypnosis itself and if so, could any person be hypnotized if their resistance to the hypnotist or hypnosis were resolved?

(3) Is amnesia always present in a deep hypnosis and is this an infallible criterion of a deep hypnosis?

May I again thank you for your previous courtesies.

Very truly yours
Lewis R. Wolberg, M.D.

To: Lewis Wolberg
June 15, 1942

Dear Dr. Wolberg:

In the October issue of the *Psychoanalytic Quarterly*, 1941, on page 592, I have a footnote which constitutes an answer to your first question.

In reply to your second question, I can give you only a dogmatic statement to the effect that every normal person can be hypnotized but not necessarily by any one hypnotist or by any set technique. Removal of resistance to the hypnotist or removal of resistance to hypnosis as such should not necessarily mean that hypnosis can be induced.

Concerning your third question about amnesia always being present in a deep hypnosis and as an infallible criterion of a deep hypnosis, the answer is positive but necessarily qualified. The mental life of some people requires that they do not have amnesia and so they recover the amnesia material or enough of it to satisfy their personality needs. In other words, the amnesia is present but the subject can go through a spontaneous process of recovering fully the amnesic material or recovering it in part, whatever is necessary to him as a person.

I trust this answers your questions.

Sincerely yours,
Milton H. Erickson, M.D.

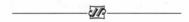

The 1941 article to which Erickson referred in his June 15, 1942, letter was the successful treatment of a case of acute hysterical depression by a patient's return, under hypnosis, to a critical place of childhood. Its coauthor was Lawrence Kubie. The footnote he cites was a two-paragraph explanation in which Erickson differentiated two forms of reliving earlier events. The first, which he termed "regression," was defined as "a half-conscious dramatization of her present understanding of that previous time." The other form involves "an actual revivification of the patterns of behavior of the suggested earlier period of life in terms only of what actually belonged there. The present itself and subsequent life and experience are as though they were blotted out." (Erickson & Rossi, 1980c, p. 129).

Erickson's forceful use of the word "dogmatic" in the second paragraph indicates that he was making a general statement that brooked no exceptions. His reply to Wolberg succinctly summarized Erickson's belief that hypnosis is a natural phenomenon, disagreeing with the prevailing tenet that only some people are hypnotizable. For Erickson, successful hypnosis was a matter of technique. He was mindful of the idiosyncracies of response, and insisted that an individualistic approach be used in hypnosis. Individualizing, in Erickson's estimation, was the key to eliciting a constructive response.

From: Lewis Wolberg
June 20, 1945

Dear Dr. Erickson:

I enjoyed your last paper on hypnotic techniques. Since communicating with you last I have worked considerably with hypnoanalysis and have completed a volume which is to be published shortly. May I express my appreciation for all the suggestions you have given me of a personal nature and take this opportunity to say that your own work was largely responsible for the stimulus that originally interested me in hypnosis.

I have a second volume on medical hypnosis in mind which deals with a more general use of hypnosis in psychotherapy than that restricted to psychoanalysis. I have completed about two-thirds of the book—the historical, theoretical, and dynamic aspects, as well as some therapeutic phases. Would you be interested in collaborating on this book with me? Your own experiences in therapy and methods of hypnotic induction would make your contribution invaluable. I am quite sure we could get this published by the same publisher who is publishing my present volume, that is, Grune and Stratton.

Recently I had conversations with Drs. Fisher, Gill, and Brenman in which we talked about instituting some research in hypnotherapy. Do you plan to be in New York City in the near future? Another question is, would you be interested in leaving your present position and setting up practice in New York, working with hypnotherapy? Around August 1st, I am to direct the New York Consultation Center, a new clinic which will utilize many types of therapy, including hypnotherapy. If you are at all contemplating settling in the East, I should like to talk to you about work in our Center.

Very truly yours,
Lewis R. Wolberg, M.D.

The Drs. Fisher, Gill, and Brenman to whom Wolberg refers in the third paragraph of his June 20 letter were all prominent psychoanalytic writers. Fisher wrote extensively regarding suggestion. Two of his principal works were: "Studies on the Nature of Suggestion, Part I: Experimental Induction of Dreams by Direct Suggestion" (Fisher, 1953a), and "Studies on the Nature of Suggestion, Part II: The Transference Meaning of Giving Suggestions" (Fisher, 1953b), both published in the Journal of the American Psychoanalytic Association.

Gill and Brenman were leading exponents of hypnoanalysis. Two of their major publications were: Hypnotherapy. A Survey of the Literature *(Brenman & Gill, 1947) and* Hypnosis and Related States: Psychoanalytic Studies in Regression *(Gill & Brenman, 1961).*

Wolberg eventually published a two-volume compendium on medical hypnosis in 1948, but without Erickson's collaboration. He had founded, in 1945, the Postgraduate Center for Mental Health in New York, which must be the organization he asked Erickson to join.

To: Lewis Wolberg
July 2, 1945

Dear Dr. Wolberg:

Thank you greatly for your letter. It was very pleasing to me and I am glad to be credited with your interest in hypnosis.

I wish I could see your book on hypnoanalysis in manuscript form with the possibility of offering some helpful comment. But I judge it is now in the printer's hands.

As for collaboration on another book, I would like to greatly. Unfortunately, I cannot give a definite reply yet, since the recent death of one of our senior psychiatrists plus the depleted state of our staff and the ever-increasing amount of work make the future a bit uncertain. However, we hope to secure a certain man to fill the vacancy, in which case the present load on my shoulders will be lessened.

At all events, I would like to see the manuscript, if you have a copy to spare, of the part you have completed of the second book.

I do not expect to be in New York until December, and I am not sure of that yet.

I appreciate your offer of a new position, but my present one, despite the work, is still attractive to me.

I hope to hear from you again.

Sincerely yours,
Milton H. Erickson, M.D.

The page numbers cited in the August 17 letter to Wolberg refer to the proofs of his book Hypnoanalysis, *which was published by Grune & Stratton in 1945. It is apparent that Erickson took great pains to provide a meaningful critique of Wolberg's work and to polish it via his editorial comments.*

To: Lewis Wolberg
August 17, 1945

Dear Dr. Wolberg:

I have, despite the flu and everything else, completed reading the manuscript. To say the least, it was a delightful experience and I can only wish we were neighbors so that we could talk things over.

Briefly said, your book is a most significant contribution and I am tremendously pleased to see how much in accord are your findings from one background with mine from another background.

It is delightful to see how thoroughly you appreciate hypnosis as a means by which to establish interpersonal relations and to set into action intrapersonal processes by which the personality can reveal itself. Practically everybody else I know places too much emphasis upon himself as a hypnotist and what force the hypnosis he is inducing can exercise, instead of realizing, as you have, the absolute reality of the person who is hypnotized, his personality, his attitudes, wishes, etc.

Before I go further, there are a number of minor errors I would like to call to your attention. Throughout the book you use the phrase "toward myself" when I believe you ought to say "toward me."

Second, on pages 56 and 57 in pencil, or 37 and 38 of Chapter 2, you speak of "a spontaneous hysterical dual personality." I know what you mean but those aren't the right words. "A spontaneous hysterical dissociated state somewhat resembling a dual personality" is better, I believe.

On page 38, "a dual personality who communicated . . ."; a dual personality cannot be produced so simply—rather one brings about a certain dissociation so that the patient can view himself in a detached, dissociated, dispassionate manner, but that is *not* a dual personality.

Page 50, same chapter, or page 69 in pencil, bear in mind that the most dogmatic and critical writers are those who have little or no clinical experience. In the regression of subjects to infantile levels, too many people forget that the subject really regressed to an infantile level does not know how to talk. One subject of mine, regressed to an infantile level while sitting in a comfortable padded trick chair which fell backward when a trigger was pressed, quite properly wet his pants and squalled, but showed none of the balance reflexes.

On page 178 in pencil you have used the word "contemptuous" instead of "contemptible."

I made a number of other notations, but as I continued to read the book, found that you had answered my questions. One point I believe you overlooked is this:

When you instruct the hypnotic subject to forget a newly recovered traumatic experience, and he does so, in accord with both his needs and the hypnotist's instructions, he thereby unwittingly but effectively gives over a goodly share of the forces that affect the repression of that material. It is my common practice to help repress material that the patient needs to repress— that means I control it and have both the responsibility of keeping it repressed and permitting him to recover it as fast as he can stand to recover it.

Another item concerns the fact that a patient in the waking state can be mute. In the trance state he can easily be induced to talk about "harmless" things. Muteness in the waking state is often an insurmountable barrier, but the muteness itself is not important—it's simply a barrier. One can by hypnosis eliminate that barrier and still leave the patient with all of his necessary defenses and thus not violate him.

Also, in hypnosis, when the patient tries to be too communicative as a measure of building up defenses by releasing too much, the hypnotist has an excellent opportunity to limit or restrict the patient so he won't go too far, which you cannot do in the waking state, or perhaps better said, not so well in the waking state.

Concerning the utilization of hypnotic techniques such as automatic writing, crystal gazing, hypnotically induced dreams, etc., you do not make quite clear how often the patient welcomes such measures because they free him from conscious effort. In the waking state the patient often feels that he would like to communicate but is tired of conscious methods. Also, these special methods remove him by one step from the material and thus make it safer for him to tell. Thus, in recovering seriously traumatic material, I can have my patient crystal gaze and see a horrific scene concerning an unknown person, get full details, his ideas of how that unknown person might react, should react, what could be done later about it by a therapist, and then when my clinical judgment indicates, I can let him know who that unknown person really is.

To close, you have done a marvelous job and I feel tremendously grateful to you.

Sincerely yours,
Milton H. Erickson, M.D.

From: Lewis Wolberg
August 20, 1945

Dear Dr. Erickson:

I am the one who is really grateful to you for your pioneering work in hypnosis which really opened up a new vista for me. Without your extraordinary intuition into human personality—which led to an entirely different dynamic use of hypnosis—none of us secondary workers could have elaborated on your methods.

It was most pleasing to me, therefore, to get your enthusiastic response which I appreciate no end. Also your appropriate criticisms will help me correct the proofs. May I add that Dr. A. Kardiner, who is writing the introduction, thinks along with myself that you have in your contributions done psychoanalysis an enormous service.

If you could write a review for *Psychosomatic Medicine*, as well as *Psychiatry*, I should appreciate it, since there are so few people qualified to voice their opinion on the subject.

Sincerely,
L. R. Wolberg, M.D.

From: Lewis Wolberg
September 1, 1945

Dear Dr. Erickson:

I was very pleased to receive your letter indicating your interest in collaborating with me on a book on medical hypnosis. Grune & Stratton have expressed a desire to publish a volume on the subject by myself next year, but I am sure they would consent to our joint authorship. In my book *Hypnoanalysis* reference is made to this new book, *Medical Hypnosis*, by myself. Since the book is in press, it is too late to change the authorship to include yourself. I hope you will not mind this too much, but it could not be helped.

I am mailing you a number of chapters which I have completed, along with a table of contents of possible other chapters to be included. The chapters I have completed must be brought up to date and there are a number of inserts that I have not included. For instance, in the "History of Hypnosis" the booklet "Hypnotherapy" by Brenman and Gill may be included and some of the material on history utilized; also my new book. The chapter on induction methods is weak and I am sure you can vitalize it materially. We should have something on narcoanalysis, and if you have not done much with this method, I can offer some material from my own experience.

I have completed the chapter on hypnoanalysis, i.e., "Hypnosis and Psychoanalysis," which I will send you when I get it typed up. I also have material for the chapters on "Hypnosis and Psychobiologic Therapy" and some for "Limitations, Dangers, and Drawbacks of Hypnosis." I am sure you could do much for the latter chapter.

I thought a chapter on "Self-Analysis" and one on "Group Analysis" would be good to include, but I know little about these methods.

I should like to get your reactions to the manuscript. Do not hesitate to change things and add them as you see fit. You may perhaps have a different idea about what to include in the book.

Please do not feel obligated to collaborate with me if, after considering my outline and manuscript, you feel you are unable to go through with it.

Sincerely,
Lewis R. Wolberg, M.D.

P.S. Could you review my forthcoming book for the *American Journal of Psychiatry* too? That would make three journals, but apart from Fisher, Brenman and Gill, and Kubie, there appear to be no other M.D.'s qualified. The latter are reviewing it for other journals.

To: Lewis Wolberg
October 19, 1945

Dear Dr. Wolberg:
I have been going through the manuscript with great care, and find it difficult to give all the time and effort necessary. We still remain completely understaffed with an ever-increasing number of new patients, and so far no relief in sight.

Concerning the manuscript, I have grave doubts about my ability to collaborate on such a text as you have outlined. You have paid such scholarly and exhaustive attention to hypnotic literature that you actually present to the reader an account of the growth and development of hypnosis and also give an account of the various hypothetical and theoretical speculations covering the various contributions. However, from my point of view, I could not do this at all. Many of the past contributions to hypnotic literature are outmoded, actually false and misleading, improperly oriented, and faultily developed. From a purely comprehensive point of view, it is desirable to summarize all of this material, and to give the student an adequate understanding of past developments and present understanding is a most legitimate purpose. However, I find myself taking exception repeatedly to much of the material you include.

For example, you quote from Winn, and one only needs to glance momentarily at Winn's book to realize that it is an armchair product by someone who is biased and uncritical and actually unconcerned about scientific matters but merely desirous of being an author.

Another instance is Messerschmidt's experimental work on dissociation, which is actually a single clear example of Hull's errors, oversights, and misjudgments. Messerschmidt had no real understanding of how to set up her problem. Having set it up and having secured the results, she nevertheless propounds dogmatically, with total unawareness, that her experimental study was so organized that it absolutely precluded the experimental results she desired. Hence her findings are without any real validity except for demonstrating how not to do her problems.

Hull's book is another instance wherein Hull, with a full awareness of experimental methods and experimental controls, never did realize the difference between an inanimate experimental subject and a living, thinking, feeling human being. I have Hull's textbook extensively annotated on the margin as a comprehensive demonstration of how hypnotic experimentation should not be done. Hull's real contribution is his recognition that hypnosis should be investigated experimentally.

I note also that you have referred to Hollander. I went through his book when it was first published, at which time I was trying to establish an acquaintance with the literature. I threw the book aside without finishing it because it is so grossly an effort on the part of the author to be erudite and to be exhibitionistic of himself.

The main reason I liked your book on hypnoanalysis was that it was essentially a straightforward, comprehensive, and understandable presentation of actual hypnotic phenomena as they occurred under such-and-such conditions. My feeling is that any textbook on hypnosis or hypnoanalysis ought really to be oriented about adequately described hypnotic phenomena, without any effort to try to fit those phenomena to theoretical elaborations of such-and-such contributors to the literature. I think all of our "knowledge" of hypnosis is top-heavy with theoretical elaborations, and I know that a large portion of the papers published by academic psychologists are oriented about hypnosis as a miracle performer, taking neither time nor effort but only magical hypnotic commands, and that results so obtained are offered as scientific findings.

You can go down the long list of "contributors" to the literature only to come up with an almost equally long list of those who base their experimental investigations upon limited, circumscribed, dogmatic opinions, and successfully prove their opinion, or those who, in five minutes' time, plus the magic of hypnotic suggestion, can produce results based upon profound psycho- and neurophysiological changes and processes which, were it not for the magic of the hypnotist, would take a much longer time to develop. Nevertheless they get their results, positive or negative, and dogmatically proclaim the finality of their findings for which some armchair philosopher will propound an elaborate superstructure.

I wonder how you feel about this sounding-off of mine? If I am all wet, please let me know.

In the meantime, I'll read the rest of the manuscript.

Sincerely yours,
Milton H. Erickson, M.D.

Editor's Note: Erickson's copy of Hull's book is in The Archives of The Multon H. Erickson Foundation.

From: Lewis Wolberg
October 22, 1945

Dear Dr. Erickson:
Thank you very much for your letter of October 19th. The manuscript that I sent you is merely a rough draft outlining a number of aspects that

I desire to cover, without a complete evaluation of the particular works cited. I appreciate your comments on the inadequacy of the work of some of the persons quoted, and I entirely agree with you. Your own experience is invaluable in being able to winnow out whatever grains of worth there are in the contributions, if there are any at all. I have mentioned a number of people whose works I certainly do not consider of positive value, merely to make the historical account complete. Perhaps some of these can be eliminated or at least the negative aspects of their work can be enlarged upon.

I appreciate the fact that you may be quite busy and therefore unable to work on the manuscript. Grune and Stratton are anxious to get this as soon as possible. Should you be unable to arrange your own time, please do not hesitate to tell me this and I shall understand fully. Even though you should be unable to act as a collaborator, your comments would be appreciated enormously by myself, since you are probably the only person in this country who can offer an authoritative opinion.

If, on the other hand, you are prepared and willing to go ahead with the project right away, I shall send you the completed chapter, "Hypnosis and Psychoanalysis." Again may I thank you for your cooperation.

Very sincerely yours,
Lewis R. Wolberg, M.D.

Erickson did not serve as coauthor of Wolberg's (1948) influential two-volume Medical Hypnosis *and there is no further correspondence to indicate whether or not Erickson reviewed the manuscript. Wolberg autographed a copy of* Medical Hypnosis *for Erickson as follows:*

To: Dr. Milton H. Erickson whose monumental work in diagnosis made these volumes possible. In appreciation, Lewis R. Wolberg

By the 1940s, eminent clinicians had begun to send their difficult cases to Erickson. One such example is the case referred in the following correspondence from Wolberg. (During a 1984 meeting between Zeig and Wolberg, Wolberg re-

*counted sending a patient whom he had been unable to hypnotize to see Erickson.
Erickson worked many hours with the patient, finally effecting a trance through
a confusion technique. Whether this is the case referred to in this January 5, 1946,
letter is unclear.)*

*In his November 11, 1946, letter, Wolberg referred to the hand-levitation
method, which Ernest Hilgard credited Erickson with inventing as an induction
approach. (See Hilgard, Crawford, & Wert, 1979.)*

*Wolberg's suggestion to Erickson to detail a complete trance induction seems
to be one that Erickson took to heart, publishing an example of such an induction
in the* American Journal of Clinical Hypnosis *(Erickson, 1964b).*

*Wolberg referred to a forthcoming book by Erickson, but Erickson did not
publish any books until* Time Distortion in Hypnosis, *which he coauthored with
Cooper (1954), and the* Practical Application of Medical and Dental Hypnosis
with coauthors Hershman and Secter (1961). Practical Applications *contains transcripts of inductions.*

*Apparently, Erickson returned the favor of referring patients to other clinicians,
as the November 11, 1946, letter mentions.*

*The file contain no response from Erickson to Wolberg's January 5 or Novem-
ber 11 letter.*

From: Lewis Wolberg
January 5, 1946

Dear Dr. Erickson:

I cannot tell you how much I enjoyed talking matters over with you
during your recent visit to New York. I hope you were able to get comfortable reservations back to Detroit.

The young man you inducted in a trance is capable of entering deeper
trance states with your technique and he follows posthypnotic suggestions.
There are certain personality needs, however, which reflect themselves in
the tendency to remember trance events. We are making somewhat better
progress, nevertheless. Do you employ any particular techniques in facil-
itating posthypnotic amnesia?

I hope you will follow through with the suggestion I made to have typed
in detail a complete trance induction, both in a susceptible and in a resis-

tant patient. I believe these would be valuable in your forthcoming book, and I shall be very pleased to do whatever I can to help you. As soon as you get the induction techniques typed up, send them to me.

May I wish you and yours a happy and prosperous New Year.

Sincerely yours,
Lewis R. Wolberq, M.D.

From: Lewis Wolberg
November 11, 1946

Dear Dr. Erickson:

I had intended to write you several times to thank you for the referrals. I am also most grateful for the techniques of hypnosis through the medium of hand levitation that you taught me on your last visit here. I have been using it extensively and find that it produces excellent results in compulsive-obsessives who have failed to be hypnotized by any other method; there hand levitation succeeds splendidly.

Mr. H., whom you hypnotized, began showing such remarkable improvement that he himself decided that his therapy was complete. He started heterosexual relationships, enlisted in the Army, and at the present time is in Japan. The letters he writes me indicate that he has never been so well-adjusted and happy.

I should be grateful if you would inform me of when you are coming to NYC again. I trust that this time I will not have an upper-respiratory infection.

I went over the manuscript, "Hypnotism Today,"* for Mr. Stratton, found it to be an excellent book and recommended it for publication. I note that you are writing the Introduction.

Sincerely yours,
Lewis R. Wolberg, M.D.

Editor's Note: See LeCum & Bordeaux, 1947.

From: Lewis Wolberg
May 26, 1955

Dear Dr. Erickson:

The section on psychotherapy of the American Psychiatric Association is planning publication of the proceedings that took place in Atlantic City on May 10th. I have been asked to contribute a short chapter on current thinking in the field of hypnotherapy as part of a supplementary addition in the book of representative techniques of psychotherapy. Toward this end I am writing to those who have made a significant contribution to hypnotherapy, or who have in the past published important material on theoretical or practical aspects of the subject. Since you are one of the people whose clinical judgment I hold in the highest esteem, I am particularly anxious to get your present ideas on hypnotherapy. Answers to any of the following would be helpful:

1. Do you have the same faith in the value of hypnosis that you had previously? If not, what has caused your change of opinion?
2. Could you estimate in what percent of your present patients you employ or have employed hypnosis for one or more sessions?
3. When you employ hypnosis, what technique of induction do you find most effective?
4. Do you believe that in selected cases hypnosis can shorten the therapeutic process?
5. Do you have any opinions on the kinds of conditions in which hypnotherapy is (a) the *preferred* therapy, (b) of potential adjunctive help to the therapeutic process, (c) neither of particular value nor detriment, (d) contraindicated or dangerous?
6. Do you believe that hypnosis can contribute to psychoanalytic treatment under certain conditions?
7. Do you believe that hypnosis helps or hinders the following aspects of the psychotherapeutic process: (a) the working relationship with the therapist, (b) the unfolding of transference, (c) the resolution of resistance, (d) the acquisition of insight, (e) the utilization of insight in the direction of change, (f) the working-through process, (g) the termination of therapy?
8. Have you ever used or do you now occasionally use hypnosis for the palliative removal of symptoms? If so, which symptoms have

responded most effectively? Have you observed in any of your cases any bad sequellae as the result of the removal of symptoms through suggestion? Do you endorse the traditional dictum that there is actual or potential danger in hypnotic symptom removal?

9. Do you believe it safe to employ hypnosis in a supportive way to calm and reassure a frightened individual who is about to undergo an operation? Do you believe in the use of hypnosis as an anesthetic in obstetrics, minor surgery, plastic surgery and dentistry! If not, why not?

10. Do you utilize any of the following techniques under hypnosis?

 (a) free association
 (b) dream induction and exploration
 (c) induction of experimental conflicts
 (d) play therapy
 (e) mirror gazing
 (f) drawing

11. Recently the British Medical Association appointed a commission to investigate the virtues of hypnosis in medical practice. The report was favorable and a recommendation was made to teach hypnosis in medical schools so that it could be practiced by the general practitioner. Do you believe this recommendation to be a reasonable one?

12. Do you believe there are any dangers to an individual's being hypnotized by an untrained operator? If so, what dangers?

13. Have any of your patients exhibited rape fantasies or sexual delusions as a result of the trance state?

14. Have any of your patients exhibited a dependence on hypnosis, or excessive dependence on you as a result of hypnotherapy?

15. Do you have any opinions as to the quality of present-day writings on hypnosis?

I should personally appreciate answers to any or all of these questions, as well as any other comments you would care to make about the positive or negative utilities of hypnotherapy. Your statements will, if you so desire, be held in confidence.

Cordially yours,
Lewis R. Wolberg, M.D.

To: Lewis Wolberg
Comments on Your Letter [of May 26, 1955]

Item 1. Increased faith and more critical judgment.

Item 2. For nearly all of my patients, I employ hypnotic techniques in one form or another, directly or, more often, indirectly. I follow no rigid procedure, but try to meet the patient's needs in each session.

Item 3. Usually an indirect technique of induction, shifting from one technique to another for the same patient at different times. The same is true of direct techniques. I use all the techniques I know, trying to fit the choice of technique to the patient's needs for the particular session. Hence, the effective technique I find to be the one the patient responds to best at that particular time.

Item 4. I feel that hypnotic techniques invariably shorten psychotherapy. In those few patients on whom I do not use hypnotic techniques, usually because of their superstitious fears of hypnosis and their demands that hypnosis not be employed, invariably therapeutic situations develop where hypnosis could be employed advantageously.

Item 5. This question is too difficult to answer dognatically, and the patient's needs at the moment are the determining factors. Hypnosis can be the *preferred* therapy; it almost always can be an *adjunctive* help, and can be of no particular help in certain types of organic or alcoholic cases, and it can be detrimental, not in itself, but in the patient's subsequent utilization of hypnotic insights, in certain psychopathic personality problems, drug addiction, and homosexuality. For example, a pedophile definitely seeking therapy to achieve better social adjustment wanted hypnotherapy so that he could learn a better technique of seducing prepuberty boys. This instance illustrates the need of orienting hypnotic therapy so that the patient is blocked in any personal utilization of it toward others.

Item 6. Yes, under most conditions.

Item 7. Hypnosis facilitates and speeds and improves every item listed in your question.

Item 8. I often employ palliative symptom removal, but I make it contingent upon the correction of the underlying process. Or I do as described in my recent paper on "Special Techniques of Brief Hypnotherapy" (Erickson, 1954).

I do not endorse the traditional dictum of potential danger from hypnotic symptom removal, but I do recognize that practically anything can be done stupidly and thus result unfortunately, not because the measure was wrong but because it was not appropriately used. An example is the professionally trained man who asked me to abolish his compulsive drinking of two cans of beer before dinner and two cans immediately after dinner. Even when invited out to dinner, he had to take his four cans of beer with him. This was essentially his alcoholic history except for one or two cocktails a year on appropriate occasions. Except for this one compulsion, adjustments were good.

He insisted that I remove the compulsion. I expressed reluctance until I had talked to his wife. In my interview with her, I told her that I could meet his and her wishes, but that the outcome would be unfortunate and would entail further therapy. I presented her with a sealed envelope, which I assured her was an account of my ideas of the nature of the unfortunate outcome and that she was to hold the envelope unopened until she herself recognized the unfortunate outcome. Also, in that envelope, I outlined my procedure in handling her husband.

I then removed his compulsion. For a week he rejoiced each evening over his freedom. Saturday night he ran out of cigarettes and stepped out to get some. He returned Sunday morning thoroughly intoxicated. He was horrified by this on Monday, could not understand what had happened.

He repeated the next Thursday, then on Monday, and again on Friday.

His wife then called me and asked permission to open the envelope. She read the contents and brought her husband into the office for therapy.

I had removed his beer-drinking compulsion, explaining carefully to him that I was removing it from him, that I was taking it away from him, that he no longer had it, that it was in my possession, to be discarded by me into the wastebasket or to be placed *wherever I chose.*

When he arrived in the office, I rehypnotized him, reminded him that I had removed his compulsion with the understanding that I could dispose of it *wherever I chose*. Thereupon I gave it back to him.

A month later he came in for therapy—not symptom removal—and therapy has been successful.

The tip-off to me that led to this concealed type of limited-in-time symptom removal was the detail with which he described his somatic response to the alcohol content of the beer, rather than the flavor or taste or smell or brand of beer, or its coolness or wetness. Rather, he emphasized the feeling of inner warmth, of vascular dilatation peripherally, of relaxation, etc.

In other words, an unintelligent symptom removal would have been detrimental, but only because of unintelligent use.

Item 9. Not only safe but should be regarded as an essential part of the art of medicine. And it should be used in any medical procedure where the patient can be given intrapersonal peace and comfort.

Item 10. I utilize all of the enumerated techniques, many others, and with variations of all of them.

Especially do I like time distortion and pseudo-orientation in time and place.

Item 11. The action of the British Medical Association is most commendable and also long overdue. But then, medical progress is always unduly tardy.

Item 12. Untrained operators are dangerous in that they promulgate misconceptions, encourage false hopes, and delay the intelligent use of hypnosis. It is much the same as the harmless cancer nostrums that give cancer patients false hope and delay them from seeking competent medical aid. Other dangers I doubt.

Item 13. Rape fantasies and sexual delusions arise from the patient's past experiential life and not from the trance. A trance may uncover them, but offers an opportunity for an intelligent control of such problems, a control far more meaningful than blind repression which permits such unexpected and difficult uncontrolled manifestations.

Item 14. Any undue dependence is indicative of the operator's incompetence, and would be manifested because of that, even if hypnosis were not used. Too often the undue dependence is not recognized as a personality problem unrelated to hypnosis.

Item 15. Present writings are improving constantly but are overweighted on the nonclinical academic side—not a defect but merely indicative of the need for clinical writing to keep pace with psychological academic work.

Although most of Erickson's replies to Wolberg's questions are concise, they nonetheless contain good illustrations of the principles outlined in the Introduction. For instance, his answers to items 2 and 3 demonstrate Erickson's belief that treatment should be tailored to the particular needs of the patient. His response to item 3 also contains a reference to his preference for working indirectly.

The principle of utilization is particularly clear in Erickson's reply to Wolberg's item 8. Erickson referred Wolberg to his 1954 article, in which he put forth the notion that neurotic symptoms can be constructively transformed to meet particular needs in patients' lives. This notion ran counter to the prevailing approach of the day, which sought to correct causal factors underlying clinical complaints. Erickson's focus on symptoms in his utilization approach gave therapists a new way to view symptoms—as leverage points for enhanced adaptation to life rather than as nuisance behaviors to be discarded.

In the matter of the beer-drinking compulsion, Erickson's future orientation in psychotherapy is quite evident. Erickson often predicted the outcome of cases, a practice that kept him thinking ahead as to possible patient responses to therapy. Developing a predictive response orientation is valuable in utilizing hypnosis because it keeps the therapist looking forward, with the therapeutic focus on solutions rather than on etiology.

The compulsion case also illustrates the Ericksonian technique of concretizing and displacing the symptom. This tactic rests on a primary dictum of Erickson's utilization approach—that any technique a patient uses to produce a symptom can be utilized by the therapist to promote effective treatment (Zeig, 1988). For example, Erickson utilized concretizing with a woman whom he had write out her psychotic episodes (Haley, 1973). Displacement also was used in a case where Erickson moved a woman's flying phobia from her body to a chair (Zeig, 1980).

On the surface, these specialized techniques may seem bizarre or illogical. Ac-

tually, however, they simply employ a different logic, the logic of the unconscious and of hypnosis. Since rational and objective logic is sometimes ineffective in solving a problem, Erickson often utilized the "emotional" or subjective logic of the patient. Patients would not be in treatment if they could solve problems by objective logic. Therefore, the judicious use of subjective logic can prove beneficial because it speaks the experiential language of patients. Everyday examples of concretizing and displacing are common. Both children and adults have the capacity to be quite literal and to concretize aspects of their environments. For instance, the child who is admonished to "get lost" to stop disrupting parental activities might disappear for hours, much to the dismay of the parent. Conversely, one might have a worry churning in the mind that could cause gastric distress. This would be an example of displacing. In the hypnotherapeutic context, such personal strategies that are employed to maintain symptoms can be utilized therapeutically to ameliorate them (Zeig, 1988).

Kubie

Lawrence S. Kubie, M.D., was an eminent psychoanalyst, highly respected in analytic circles. He collaborated with Erickson on a number of scholarly articles and the two became close friends. It seems that Kubie assisted Erickson greatly in the latter's early career by introducing Erickson's thinking into the mainstream of contemporary psychiatry.

To: Lawrence S. Kubie
November 16, 1942

Dear Kubie:

I can send you no significant references on the interrogation of criminals under hypnosis. However, I do know from personal experience and from the experience of some of my friends who have attempted such interrogation that it is completely unreliable. The hypnotized subject can lie as easily in the hypnotic trance as he can in the waking state and often more effectively. Two of my friends carried on a systematic investigation of this project. For a long time they were very pleased and happy about their results and then they discovered that they were actually being played for suckers, although the other hypnotic work that they did with these same criminal subjects proved to be reliable. The only condition under which it works is when the subject himself is consciously interested in giving information but is unable to do so consciously. In the trance state he has better access to his memories, but even so one has to be very critical of what he relates. On the whole, my experience, and that of my friends, makes me consider hypnosis an undesirable instrument for the interrogation of criminals.

I trust this is the information you wanted.

Sincerely yours,
Milton H. Erickson

Although the letter from Kubie to Erickson was not found in the file, he obviously had queried his associate about the efficacy of interrogating criminals under hypnosis. Erickson was cogent and clear in his reply.

From: Lawrence Kubie
February 26, 1954

Dear Milton:

A lifelong friend of mine, a man in his middle fifties, has recently been helped by one of our colleagues to skirt safely by the edge of a rather acute involutional depression. In the course of it, it developed that he had suffered from partial potency difficulties for years and that in the course of those years he had come to depend more and more on "massage" parlors and the like, of which he is deeply ashamed. Now that he is out of the depression he wants desperately to find a shortcut to help with his sexual maladjustment, and has asked about successes or failures with the use of hypnotherapy in such problems.

Would you be willing to venture any generalizations about this, based on your own experience or that of others?

Cordially,
Lawrence S. Kubie, M.D.

To: Lawrence Kubie
March 20, 1954

Dear Larry:

My general experience with that type of patient is that they can be helped.

My usual procedure is to give them a very elementary, but progressively more complex, discussion of the biological significance of sex, the biological development within the individual, its meanings and significance, and the response is usually pretty good. My last patient in this regard was in his mid-sixties. His sexual activity has stabilized at four times per week.

Here's hoping all is going well with you.

Sincerely,
Milton H. Erickson, M.D.

A fuller discussion of Erickson's approach to sex therapy is contained in the Friday morning section of A Teaching Seminar with Milton H. Erickson, M.D. *(Zeig, 1980). His March 20, 1954, letter to Kubie once again highlights the incremental and naturalistic style that was such an outstanding characteristic of his method.*

The December 27 reply from Erickson to the December communication from his longtime colleague and friend exemplifies his meticulous and giving nature. Kubie requested referral to a private school in Arizona, and Erickson replied in great detail, providing abundant background and justification for his recommendations.

Erickson was dogged in his pursuit of the charlatanism and misrepresentation that sullied the reputation of hypnosis. But he was an exceedingly loyal friend,

and he championed those whom he knew were ethical and performed good deeds.
Note the esteem in which he obviously held Father Rene!

From: Lawrence Kubie
December 3, 1969

Dear Milton:

I hope that this information will help you help me in finding an appropriate school for this twelve-year-old step-grandson of mine. On the basis of your initial information I will write for further data myself.

Best greetings over time and space for the holiday season,

Lawrence S. Kubie, M.D.

[Note that, to protect their privacy, names of particular persons have been deleted from the following exchange, as well as the names of the places and schools to which the memo refers.]

Memo
From: Lawrence S. Kubie, M.D.
Subject: Schools

I need information about [two particular schools] in Arizona or any other school that has a freely exploratory approach to the emotional problems of bright youngsters.

This concerns a youngster whose twelfth birthday was on October 13th. He lives in Minnesota where his father is full professor in the Department of Chemistry at [the college]. His mother is the daughter of the former head of the Department of Physics there. (Her father is now retired and lives in Arizona, where for some time he was consultant and is doing some teaching.)

My interest in the situation arises because the mother was married to my stepson, until his death when the child was only four months old. The father died from sudden and fulminating Kimmelstiel-Wilson complications of a long-standing and previously well-controlled diabetes. Two or three years later, the mother remarried, and had a son, who will be nine in April. Last summer they adopted a little half-Negro girl who arrived when she was three weeks old, and is now about six months old. Both of her parents were college graduates. So much for the general structure of the family. [The second husband] has adopted his stepson legally, but admits that he does not have an easy time accepting him emotionally. (v.i.)

The boy is a bright and gifted youngster. He is a little shy in his relationship to adults and even more so to his age peers. In general he prefers to read or draw or write or play by himself, showing a great deal of creative originality in such activities. He is body-shy and physically timid in sports. The only ones in which he can indulge freely and with confidence are swimming and skating. He is tense and a little jerky in his facial expressions and his movements are a trifle "swish," although not too disturbingly so for his age. These give us hints of problems that may lie ahead and strengthen the impression that he needs therapy. As a matter of fact, with this in mind, his parents and I have conferred with the lay therapist who is associated with our colleague in Minneapolis. There is no psychotherapeutically trained and experienced advisor close at hand. (Minneapolis is 400 miles away.)

The younger boy has some problems of his own but these can wait until we can lay the rails for his stepbrother's.

I have been visiting the family, and am dictating this in the presence of the mother and also at the request of her husband. In short, we are working together to try to explore the possibilities of bringing the youngster some help.

This brings me back to my inquiry about schools, and the related question of whether there are any schools in your neighborhood where we can find the flexible and creative schooling that he needs, i.e., a more creative environment than the local public school provides (if it seems advisable for him to go away to school) and also where he can have some concurrent therapy.

All of us would feel indebted to you for any suggestions which occur to you. It would be helpful at this stage to use me as a clearinghouse for information and to distribute it to the family. Ultimately, however, you may want to know how to reach them directly.

Lawrence S. Kubie, M.D.

To: Lawrence Kubie
December 27, 1969

Dear Larry:

In reply to your urgent letter concerning possibilities of finding out about schools or getting help for [the child], I am afraid I shall have to disappoint you. I doubt that there exists anywhere in Arizona any possible private school that can be of benefit to your stepson . . .

. . . While the [existent Arizona] schools are well-intended, their enrollment is pretty well dominated by ultra socially conscious parents who reject their children and prefer social activities to parental guidance of their children. Thus they get rid of the children by a pretense of giving them an opportunity. A large number of these children at various private schools feel they are rejected and are resentful, and there is a rather frightful amount of disturbance in students' adjustments to life.

I have had many patients from a great number of local private schools. The following quotes from some of my former patients can be used to illustrate the situation. A 12-year-old girl from one school said to me, "I am rejected, my father doesn't want me around because it interferes with his drinking and my mother finds it difficult to have me around because she is so socially conscious of her parties that she wants me here to free herself of responsibility. I am just a rejected only child. The only happiness I have ever really had in life was with the horse wrangler at the school and somehow or other, this was discovered and the school authorities sent me to you; but what the school authorities don't know is that there are a lot of other things going on there. If they did know, you would have a lot more patients."

In other words, this 12-year-old girl was having an affair with a horse wrangler, and she had been so very lacking as far as discretion was concerned that the school had to take some action. The action did not include discharge of the horse wrangler. However, this 12-year-old girl's story was already known to me because a 14-year-old patient from the school had demanded of the school authorities that she wanted to see a psychiatrist, the school authorities reacted by informing her parents and the parents gave permission and she was sent to me. The girl told me about the 12-year-old girl before I ever saw her, thereby confirming the story in advance.

I have known some very stable students in various private schools but it was not because of the school. For example: A 14-year-old boy from a boys' military school in New Mexico who was sent to a private school here because he had been expelled from the military school for striking an upperclassman. The upperclassman had made homosexual advances; then he had struck the upperclassman instead of reporting him to the school authorities, and so he was expelled because of his inability to respect authority in others. Always, the attitude is to cover up the situation for the socially prominent parents. The boy was sent to a local school here. He learned that I was seeing his brother and one of his close friends and he himself called for an appointment. He was advised he would have to get parental permission and that he should then take the matter up with the superintendent and make arrangements for the superintendent to call me to ask for an appointment for him. The patient was a very badly disorganized boy, a boy who demanded an appointment for himself and his friend whom I had seen previously and both of those boys were equally intent on doing anything unacceptable that would make it possible for them to get "out of that hell hole." This private school is so widely advertised, and many of the children had no choice and were forced to go there by parents who are unwilling to investigate the place. I know the place very well; the superintendent and his wife have both been my patients. In other words, I advise strongly against the local private schools.

However, I do have a suggestion for you and I hope it will be possible for you to make arrangements. There is a Catholic priest up in Canada, 400 miles north of Minnesota, whom I have had a long correspondence with. He is Father René le Major, O. M. I. I knew him through his letters and then later on when I was conducting a serious of lectures on hypnosis, psychosomatic medicine and psychotherapy at Winnipeg. Father René attended through my invitation and I met him personally. This was several years after his first letter came to me inquiring about the techniques of dealing with people. He had come across my name in his reading and had written to me for reprints and he had been delighted to meet me at Winnipeg after several years of correspondence. I was delighted to get acquainted with him and his views on life. Father René is primarily a religious counselor, but he has had training in psychology and some medicine. In his isolated location, he is the only source of counseling, and often the only source of medical care as well. His parishioners consist, in general, of prospectors, hunters, and Indians. He works hard in meeting the needs of the community and he does this exceedingly well.

I have had a direct report on his work from an internist in St. Paul, who sent his wife to me as a patient after we had been acquainted for several years. After I had been seeing her for sometime, her husband came to see me. When he finally acknowledged the nature and character of his wife's problem and the effect it would have upon his children, and his own distress, I suggested that he take his plane and fly up to see Father René so that he could get some sense of relief. Now this Minnesota doctor was a Catholic who had married a divorced woman, with a child (his stepchild), and they had five additional children. He was a good physician, had a very happy, outgoing disposition, and in his practice he employed five widowed or divorced nurses who were all supporting children. He had just about the best practice in town, so extensive that he could support literally six families of children. He was so distressed about his children and the effect their mother had on them, I advised him to see Father René. Since the first visit by this doctor with Father René (there has been additional contact by mail and personally), the physician has reported to me extensively upon the results of his visit and all the details of Father René's work. He was markedly impressed with Father René's counseling, by his guidance of the children in the mining camp, and the young Indian children, and how Father René emphasized the need for constructive adjustment in this poorly organized social community. My doctor friend reported recently that he had been up to see Father René again, but that his divorce had resulted in his former wife's securing custody of the children, and thus he could not send his own children to Father René. He inquired of me what adjustment should he make to the maladjustment that was developing in his children because of his former wife's personal problems. He also stated to me that his stepdaughter was very earnestly on his side and he had his oldest son, who had reached the age of military service, stop in and see me in Phoenix on his way to Camp Pendleton, California. I had a long talk with this boy and he gave me a very reliable picture fully in accord with my own knowledge, and as the children become old enough, they want to be allowed to return to their father. The boy now in military service is making a very markedly good adjustment. I had visited in this doctor's home repeatedly and I had observed that the children, and his stepdaughter, as well as the other children, are all beginning to show signs of discontentment with their mother and are becoming increasingly rebellious.

For the first time, the doctor is now aware that his ex-wife is set upon ruining him financially and he is very busy distributing his patients and securing employment for the widows who worked for him because he and I both know his ex-wife will bankrupt him. Before that occurs, he wants to take good care of all his patients by distributing them to other physicians best qualified to meet their needs. When this is completed, he is going to set up practice in Phoenix. On the doctor's last visit to me he said, "I should have believed every word you said to me ten years ago when everything you discussed openly with my former wife and me is coming to pass." His ex-wife is one of five sisters and all five sisters have ruined the lives of five men and the lives of their children. The doctor reported, "The children have been awarded to my former wife and I don't think they are going to have much chance in life and there is nothing I can do about it. Her own daughter has rejected her, and I think that my ex-wife will join her four sisters in their destructive path. If I had any way of doing it, I would take the children to Father René and let them live with him in that mining camp community. I think they would get over all the damage that has been done and I don't anticipate any difficulty in establishing a practice in Phoenix and I will be able to meet all my job needs."

Now this is a rather long story but my personal knowledge derived from correspondence and from personal contact and this physician friend of mine indicates that if you can make arrangements with Father René, I think that you might find it a very desirable placement for your stepson. His location is a small town called Cranberry Portage, Manitoba, Canada. Cranberry Portage is about 50 miles from the larger city called The Pas, which has an airport with jet service. In his many invitations to me to visit him, Father René has informed me that there is helicopter service available from The Pas which lands next to his church. In establishing contact with him the use of my name in making arrangements is readily granted. I hope very much that Father René is now permanently located at Snow Lake where this coming spring he will enjoy his passion for growing roses.

The only other suggestion I have for your stepson is through some of the limited circumscribed efforts being made by the Episcopal and Methodist churches to establish small centers in which dedicated counselors and paramedical students in the congregations of these various churches participate. The groups are small and I do not know the location of any of these groups. I am enclosing one such brochure, but it is for older boys. The primary problem of these small groups is monetary assistance since most of the children they deal with cannot afford to pay for the help they receive; the churches contribute the support and the people working there are usually dedicated young men and women who take positions with the church as a matter of getting training in the field. Sometime, possibly a year or two, ago there was a nice write-up describing the efforts of these individuals. How these individual efforts are working out now, I do not know nor do I have any idea where you can learn about them.

Now coming to the matter of Larry Kubie. Betty and I wish you a very Merry Christmas, Happy New Year, and we do hope that what I have written to you will be of some value and I would be delighted to know the outcome of any requests made to Father René.

Sincerely yours,
Milton H. Erickson, M.D.

From: Lawrence Kubie
January 9, 1970

Dear Milton:

What a wonderful fellow you are to take so much trouble to give me so much helpful and detailed information.

I will share all of this information with [the parents] and let them carry the ball from there. They will have to make the ultimate decisions and the ultimate contacts. I will let you know the outcome.

I also want to wish you a very happy New Year. There is a chance that I may come to southern Arizona south of Tucson sometime in late February or early March. I cannot be sure of this but I am going to try to, because I want to bake my legs in the sun and swim and exercise in order to regain some strength. The tendonitis seems to have subsided but it has left the legs much weaker than they should be.

If I do get to the Tucson area, you can be sure that I will also get in touch with you and will fly up to Phoenix for a visit.

In the meantime every good wish,
Lawrence, S. Kubie, M.D.

To: Lawrence Kubie
June 25, 1970

Dear Dr. Kubie:

I have been promising myself nearly every day to write you a letter to tell you how much Betty and I enjoyed your visit. I was, however, distressed to note the amount of pain you showed by your walk. I hope that is greatly lessened.

I would like to say that the privilege of knowing you has been one of the highlights of my life.

Incidentally, I have not heard from Father René since last Christmas and I wonder if you have any news about a Minnesota boy.

Betty is still unpacking things and reorganizing the house. She sends her very best to you, as do I.

Sincerely yours,
Milton H. Erickson, M.D.

Hendrick

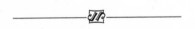

In 1934, Ives Hendrick, M.D., responded to a letter from Erickson, in which Erickson asked Hendrick to review a preprint of Erickson's paper, "A Study of an Experimental Neurosis, Hypnotically Induced in a Case of Ejaculatio Precox," which was eventually published in the British Journal of Medical Psychology (Erickson, 1935). Hendrick was an internationally renowned academic psychoanalyst who occupied a prestigious chair at Harvard and whose views were somewhat *unorthodox, but well within the boundaries of the contemporary psychoanalytic practice of his day.*

Hendrick wrote:

> August 6, 1934
>
> Dear Dr. Erickson:
>
> Thank you very much for the opportunity to study your paper. I profited very much from the stimulus. . . .
>
> I hope very much you will call my attention to any significant oversights which my criticisms reveal and let me know in what ways my view of the work differs from yours. My criticism is oriented mainly by my experience as an analyst, and I have not strained myself to see it from the angles of other departments of psychiatry. I presume this orientation was, however, what you specifically hoped for in sending the paper to me. . . .
>
> Ernst Simmel used to do something like it in the treatment of certain problems with a very excessive sadistic problem at his psychoanalytic sanitorium outside Berlin. His "implanted complex" was a straw man. The patients were induced effectively to attack a dummy and a very effective abreaction obtained (sic). Simmel, by the way, has used hypnosis more than any other analyst of whom I know. . . .

This reply to Erickson's request consisted of three pages, followed by nine and a half pages of critical remarks, all handwritten, and with numerous corrections.

At this point, it should help the reader to have an overview of Erickson's paper.

In 1934, Erickson collaborated with Paul E. Huston and David Shakow on a paper entitled "A Study of Hypnotically Induced Complexes by Means of the Luria Technique," which appeared in the Journal of General Psychology *(Erickson, Huston, & Shakow, 1934).*

In the paper, the authors describe an experimental technique invented by Luria, a Russian neuropsychologist, in which one would hypnotize a patient and then describe a scene in which the patient committed a reproachable act inconsistent with his or her personal ethics. Subsequently, the subject would be given a word-association test that included a number of words related to the "implanted" memory. The subject also would be given a motor task and the response latency would be measured for words related to the memory versus neutral words. Reportedly, the affect from the memory interfered with motor performance as evinced by a longer latency in response to the key words.

*In their 1934 paper, Huston, Shakow, and Erickson reported a modified rep-
lication of Luria's method, focusing on a then-24-year-old man, who evidently
was the subject of Erickson's later paper, "A Study of an Experimental Neurosis
Hypnotically Induced in a Case of* Ejaculatio Praocox" *(Erickson, 1935). In that
paper, Erickson used a seemingly homeopathic principle of "likes curing likes."
He had discovered that the subject was troubled by premature ejaculation. Under
the guise of conducting another experiment on an implanted memory, he surreptitiously implanted an imagined scenario in the subject that paralleled his
premature-ejaculation problem. Erickson hypothesized that "recovery from one
illness (or conflict) frequently results in the establishment of a new physiological
equilibrium (or redistribution of "libido"), thereby permitting a favorable resolution of a second concurrent, and perhaps totally unrelated, illness (or conflict)
(Erickson & Rossi, 1980c).*

*In the pseudo-memory implanted by Erickson, the patient shamed himself by
placing his lighted cigarette ("symbolizing" a penis) into an ashtray ("symbolizing" a vagina), thereby breaking it due to differential heating. The ashtray had
been made by a young girl for her father, and was broken in her presence. Although she reassured the young man that no real damage had been done, he left
the (imagined) situation mortified by his bad conduct.*

*In the paper, Erickson described how the man's behavior subsequent to the
trance was influenced by the implanted conflict. He maintained that even though
the patient had no conscious recognition of the relationship of the implanted story
to his problem, he was cured of his sexual difficulty.*

*In describing the case, Erickson reported, "In consequence of this procedure,
there appears to result an identification of the induced conflict with his original
neurosis in a fusing of their affective reactions. After the patient had been forced
to relive, and react, and gain insight into the suggested conflict, it was discovered
that he had made a clinical recovery from his original neurosis, and that he was
still able to function normally a year later" (p. 335).*

Curiously, nine years later, Erickson (1944) published a paper in the Journal
of General Psychology *in which he described word for word the method that he
employed to formulate the complex story for the induction of the experimental
neurosis.*

Following are samples of Hendrick's critical remarks from his 1934 letter.

1. I feel that generally your use of "complex," although quite in
keeping with Jung's original meaning, has definite implications which
are out-of-date and distort the discussion of the material. I refer to

your using it to denote a group of associated *ideas* (*Vorstellungen*), with the implication that this group of ideas, as such, is effective. The most profitable discussion would involve throughout the recognition that in referring to "complex" (or "constellation," or whatever you wish), it is not the idea, but the emotion, which is dynamic. I myself believe that Freud's reference to "instinct-representatives" in his paper on "Instincts" is a vital psychological concept solving many of the monistic-dualistic problems, but strangely overlooked; this means that whereas consciousness is a sort of filtered unconscious fantasy or ideation, conscious or unconscious is a mental *representative* of *biologic* forces.

(I expect to spend the next couple of years studying things further from this angle.) The reason I regret your using "complex" in the narrower sense is that it leads to certain undesirable implications. For example, the references to the "artificial neurosis," the "implantation of the complex," the "incorporation of the complex," etc. These remarks are perfectly justified so long as one has in mind these ideas only, but lead to a certain confusion when one considers the psychodynamics. I see no justification myself for considering that a new, artificial neurosis was induced. What I do see is conclusive evidence that the ideas imparted to him were immediately utilized as new representations of the old conflict; and secondly, that the story, together with other factors in the hypnotic situation, affected this conflict in such a way as to make it a conspicuous determinant of his behavior and ideation for a certain period of time. Briefly, the discussion here and there is too much oriented by the overemphasis of the *idea* (by implication rather than intention), to the neglect of the emotional forces it represented. . . .

Hendrick then provided a psychoanalytic perspective on the psychodynamics of both Erickson's procedure and its effect on the patient. He argued:

I, like you, find the greatest interest of all in appraising the possibilities of this experimental technique. There is no question, it is ingenious, and worth extensive investigation. Tentatively, when contrasted with psychoanalysis, I feel that the possibilities of analysis as an experimental technique are not fully appraised, and one illusion of any hypnotic technique's advantages overlooked. . . .

Hendrick closed his letter by summarizing:

The values of your contribution can be put more succinctly.

1. The data are of unusual interest, and seldom so exactly reported.

2. The possibilities of applying the method as a therapeutic agent in other cases, as a refinement of Breuer's cathartic method, are suggestive.

3. The discussion throughout is stimulating, combining a reluctance to depart too far from imperial data without being killed by a lack of that investigative quality essential to productive work, even in science. (Don't you think 95 percent of "research" today has all the earmarks of an unrecognized religion, ritualistic devotion to a "Thou shalt not" ideal?)

4. Personally, I am most indebted for the stimulation of thinking which I feel has very much clarified my visions of hypnotic methodology at its best.

Editor's Note: The handwritten letter and notes from Hendrick are available at the Archives of the Milton H. Erickson Foundation.

In the following correspondence, Erickson and Hendrick dialogued about one of Erickson's cases, which is presented here for the first time. The case is remarkable for its innovative approach. It is interesting, moreover, to see the reply of Hendrick, a liberal although doctrinaire analyst. This is a stimulating and spirited exchange between two practitioners whose approaches diverged widely.

To: Ives Hendrick
June 28, 1937

Dear Ives:

You may remember at Pittsburgh when we were taking dinner with Ackerly that I made a remark about the therapeutic use of anger and told briefly about my occasional practice of making a patient so angry at me that it would compel him to keep returning to me in a frantic endeavor to prove me wrong in everything and that by manipulating the anger carefully it was possible to make him give up his neurosis. Here in summary is a case I am winding up.

Last November, a 24-year-old Italian flutist came to me demanding hypnotic therapy for a swollen, chapped, lower lip which had resisted all medical treatment for six years and which rendered him unable to play in an orchestra, although he did succeed in practicing fairly regularly despite the cracking and the bleeding. He was working as a busboy at $9.00 a week, in mortal fear of being discharged, spending most of his time lamenting the fact that he was a genius deprived of the opportunity of contributing what he should to music. He declared that he would take only the position of first flutist in the Detroit Symphony Orchestra, and if that were not given him, he would continue as a busboy. Further information disclosed that he had repeatedly arranged to take an audition for appointment to the orchestra but had avoided it in an utterly irresponsible fashion, despite the fact that his teacher was prepared to make any number of sacrifices to secure an appointment for him and actually was in a position to secure such an appointment.

I spent the first two sessions with him leading him out, finally concluding that he would treat me as he had all previous therapists. Following this, I spent a great deal of time building up a situation in which he was induced to boast endlessly to me about his ability to view things objectively and to react to them intelligently. As soon as this had been done, I took him to task, doubting each boastful comment he had made and leading him on to a more extensive commitment of himself until he was most thoroughly tied up, doing this in a very quiet dispassionate fashion so that he would not mistrust me. I then sent him home to think over the question of whether or not he wished me to talk honestly and freely with him.

In the next session, I led him on again, getting him to confirm his statement that I could talk honestly and freely. After he was very thoroughly committed and had promised to take everything I said under careful consideration, I reviewed his past conduct with therapists, reminded him of one of his first statements, which was his expectation that I would fail, following which I turned loose on him with every bit of contempt and condemnatory discussion of himself, his behavior, ancestry and everything I could think of until he raged back and forth in the office, literally trembling, while I kept interrupting his remarks and construing them in a derogatory fashion for him until he was ready to commit murder. Following this, I gave a carefully worded denunciation of him, having the effect of daring him to come back for another interview and he wound up with the statement that if it killed him, he'd show me where to get off at. Throughout December, January, and February he had just one purpose in mind, namely, that of proving me "the most ignorant, conceited, unsympathetic, narrow-minded, cold-blooded, would-be doctor." On my part I retaliated by accusing him of cowardice, willingness to be a busboy, lacking intelligence enough to accept fifth chair instead of first chair in the orchestra and would periodically go into long metaphysical discussions concerning his neurosis, leading him to criticize my philosophy, understanding of his entire situation, and pointing out to me how his lip condition should be viewed as an organic condition instead of my superficial judgment that it was purely a neurosis. In the latter part of April in an outburst of temper he quit me, and swore that he would never see me again. In a very smart alec fashion, I took up my appointment calendar, turned over a few pages and wrote something which aroused his curiosity. A few days later he telephoned me asking for an appointment and desiring to know what I had written on the calendar. In the most irritating manner possible over the telephone I gave him the appointment and when he arrived I showed him what I had written in the calendar, namely, my guess as to how many days it would be before he would call me up for an appointment. This of course led to further bitterness and denunciation on his part, which he wound up with a very decided compliment for understanding him well enough to realize that he had not quit despite his very emphatic remark. As soon as he had given me this compliment I unlocked a desk drawer and took out another sheet of paper on which I had outlined previously the expected course of this interview, including his complimentary remarks. This threw him into a terrific rage but instead of rushing back and forth in the office and trembling while he waved his arms, he sat rather quietly in his chair trying to talk in a tremulous fashion but felt himself too utterly helpless to give expression to any of his anger.

I then began asking a few casual questions about music. How one read it, told him that I was tone deaf and let him take a teacher's role toward me. Having succeeded in proving my ignorance in this fashion I then demonstrated to him that I was color blind also and wound this up by reminding him of his demands for hypnotic therapy and told him that if he would ask me politely and courteously, I would consider it. He went through a terrific emotional struggle trying to humiliate himself sufficiently while I took an aggravating role with him and it would up with his statement that I was wrong in everything, that I was even more ignorant than he thought and that if there was anything he could do to show me up as a charlatan and perhaps make me realize that I was a charlatan, he would do it. I then began hypnotic therapy on him, ridiculing every response he made to hypnotic suggestions until he was in a frantic state to do more than my suggestions implied. Following this, on the average of every third session he would lose his temper with me completely but showed marked changes in his attitude toward himself, quitting his job as a busboy, securing employment with a W.P.A. orchestra and getting $22.00 a week instead of $9.00.

During May I outlined my views on his lip condition in great detail in the most unsympathetic fashion possible, denouncing it as a coward's alibi, challenging him to prove its organic nature, informing him that I could give no therapy and would not give any therapy for it since it was obviously a weak man's escape from the demands of reality and that he obviously was unwilling and lacking in the qualities necessary to face reality. The rages began again but carried with them a set purpose of proving me entirely wrong in every one of my misconceptions of his character. He secretly arranged an audition and then told me about it. I contemptuously advised him that even if he passed the audition he would do something nonsensical to invalidate it. He reacted in a very peculiar fashion, namely, that of completely forgetting about his audition, making no preparation for it and suddenly remembering at a quarter of eleven on the day that his audition began at 11 o'clock. He dressed, shaved, and took a taxi to the place of appointment, arriving on time, and was given an extremely difficult audition but passed it. He called me up immediately to tell me that he didn't need any help from me, never had and never would, and that the only bit of appreciation he had for me was in consideration of the fact that I had wasted my time with him. I started to laugh over the phone and hung up on him. About two days later he came out to tell me that he had been appointed first flutist for the summer season at the salary of $75.00 a week but that when offered the position he had refused it and had then recalled my statement about his doing something nonsensical and felt extremely enraged that I had guessed he would, retracted his refusal, and signed the contract. He then demanded that I do some direct therapy on his lips since he would have to make good during the season. I asked

him to sit quietly in his chair for about 15 minutes and observe his conduct. He sat there, quietly looking at his hands and feet, gazing around
the office, and after about 20 minutes he wanted to know what idiotic
idea I had. I reminded him of the many times, months ago, I had ridiculed
him for pinching his lips, licking them and twisting them with his fingers,
and how he had declared that it was a conscious habit of massaging his
lips and I pointed out that the last 20 minutes when he had had nothing
to do he had not made a solitary movement in that regard and that he
should draw his conclusions about the justice of the interpretation of the
previous behavior. After thinking it over and getting rather angry, he told
me that the entire issue, so far as he and I were concerned, did not lay in
any therapy condition at all, that his lip condition was simply an out-
growth of an unfortunate home situation and an unfortunate personal
situation and he outlined these things with remarkable clarity, including
the usefulness of his lip neurosis. He grudgingly admitted that there had
been a marked improvement in his lips and that with the reasonable
amount of care that any flutist should exercise his lips, would not constitute a handicap for him. I then indicted him for unwillingness to admit
improved behavior and lip improvement followed by contemptuous and
obviously and conciliatory reassurance to the effect that his lip condition
was useful and he could keep it and would.

Since then we have had reasonably calm, peaceful therapeutic sessions
in which he has reviewed intelligently the entire situation for himself, summarized very adequately the therapeutic effects of his outbursts of rage,
and has shown much amusement over his unwilling meeting of his problems, first as an endeavor to confute me and then as unrecognized efforts
to accept the aid that I was really giving him.

At the present time the situation is really an ideal one. There has been
a complete change in him. He seems to have matured immensely in the
emotional sphere and he is now looking forward to the summer season
which begins today with all the eager pleasure that one could desire. His
attitude toward me is one of profound respect and gratitude and he is
planning in the most serious and consistent fashion on his summer's work
since a vacancy that he knew about last December will put him in line for
a permanent position as first flutist.

His reaction to the intense fits of rage that I induced seems to be entirely
one of amused understanding. Particularly when I place him in a trance
does this come forth and occasionally in the waking state he will make

unfavorable remarks and signify that he wishes to go into a trance. Immediately afterwards in the trance state he will then come out with a more correct statement suggesting to me that I had probably made such an interpretation despite the unfavorable character of his waking remark, but that would make him feel better to tell the real truth in the trance state since he was not yet ready to tell it in the waking state.

Of course I realize that the case is not yet settled since he has the next six weeks in which to blow up but my guess is that he will make good since the general background of his thinking indicates that he now has the proper emotional attitude toward his profession.

I realize that this is a very scanty account but I thought you might be interested in seeing how in a selected case one could deliberately induce anger for the purpose of inducing the patient to remain in the therapeutic situation so that he could confront the therapist and thus be forced to accept therapy as a necessary procedure in taking the therapist.

In rereading this, I note that I have assumed you would know that my irritating remarks were always in the nature of an interpretation, carefully worded in a general fashion so that when he attacked it to break it down, he himself would discover a probable second or third meaning to it so that all that would be left for him to lay hands on would be an unrecognized feeling that I had hit home. Also, my attitude was, as consistently as I could make it, one of cold dispassionate objectivity in which I had no personal emotional participation except for an occasional simple amused laughter. He has summarized my behavior by declaring that my conduct is "sardonic like Pirandello, who looks at the world and its puppets, is amused, sympathizes intellectually just enough to make the puppet play its role, and gives the puppet its chance to know and do what it can if it wants to."

Sincerely yours,
Milton H. Erickson

From: Ives Hendrick
August 21, 1937

Dear Milton:

. . . I venture a few thoughts in the way of discussion. The most active component of his presenting neurosis was the revenge on the teacher, repeated with his therapists. The motive was his fellatio fantasy. At the same time as he revenged himself on the teacher for not gratifying sufficiently his wish for fellatio, or denied it: it isn't that I want to suck, it's that I am the greatest of flutists. The dynamics of the therapy seem to be not only an adequate verbalization of this need for protest and revenge, provoked by your insults and permitted by your passivity otherwise. It was also the gradual development of his wish and capacity to accept his passive homosexuality, and learning that he had more to gain from this (money, position, success, your respect and self-respect) than from his fight against it. The good result seems clearly the nice manipulation of both passives. There cannot be much doubt, I think, that hypnosis (gratifying the fellatio fantasy) alone could not have been so successful; assuming success through hypnotic suggestion in ending his mutilation of his lips and his acceptance of a position, the motive of doing these things because they were ordered would have, I should think, taken the pep out of his musical performance and made it a rather flabby business. Nor could the evocation of his rages have succeeded by itself; without the homosexual gratification, they would have resulted only in intensified inferiority feelings and more incapacitating neurosis.

I think of you as the American Aichorn. Though you treat different types of cases, you both have a gift for utilizing your own personalities to a much greater extent than most of us can for the purpose of a really dynamic therapy (in contrast to the "therapeutic personalities" which are beneficial because they protect and encourage or shoulder responsibilities). The two most tangible features of the special talents of both yourself and Aichorn seem to me to be the capacity to play the omnipotent role for your patients, and to trick them into reacting the way you predict they will. In other men, their values as psychotherapists end where these qualities begin. Their omnipotent tricks and ruses are their limitations, not their assets. That is especially true of analysts. Your methods resemble analysis in that both rely upon the repetition of the infantile conflict in the therapeutic situation, and the conscious management of this as the central feature of the therapeutic method. But analysts allow the conflict to emerge as the transference develops, whereas you activate it. Whereas the analyst's chief subjective role is the identification with the patient's experience, yours is to activate it like a sounding board, through duplicating the role of his unconscious object. One gain of your method in such a case is acceleration. The shortcoming is that it cannot be formulated and taught. And perhaps it is not so well adapted as analysis to working through conflicts involving roles you are not uniquely equipped to play or those other aspects of your patient's personality which do not come so clearly into the therapeutic situation for this reason. Also, I think, it is likely to block off the eventual discovering of vital unconscious motives which you had not recognized. . . .

Sincerely,

Ives Hendrick

Editor's Note: Only the relevant sections of Hendrick's letter of August 21, 1937, are included above. The entire letter is on file at the Erickson Archives.

Hendrick's August 21, 1937, letter to Erickson was handwritten and Erickson had his secretary retype it. In the first paragraph, Hendrick used his analytic lens to comment on the dynamics of both the patient and the therapy.

In the second paragraph, he assumed a more personal tone and commented on Erickson's style. He implied that Erickson's methods were idiosyncratic and difficult to teach. However, let us examine Erickson's method and extract principles that are classically Ericksonian in nature.

The case of the flutist demonstrates five cardinal features of Erickson's treatment.

1. An understanding that designing therapy happens in the patient's life and is not limited to the consulting room.
2. Utilization.
3. Tailoring.
4. Utilizing patient resources.
5. Making therapy experiential.

It seems that one of the principles that Erickson used early in the treatment was to assess the position that the patient took. Obviously, the flutist took a position of frustrating both himself and others, a neurotic pattern. Neurotic be-

havior is characterized by the repetitive use of "solutions" that are destined to fail. The flutist then behaved in ways that were illogical and self-defeating.

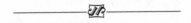

Once the therapist understands the patient's posture, the therapist can anticipate subsequent patient reactions. Knowing that the patient had frustrated previous practitioners, Erickson surmised that he would continue that pattern and neurotically try to frustrate him.

It is as if Erickson "beat the patient to the punch." He provided treatment by frustrating the patient. Because the patient responded in an oppositional fashion, the effect of Erickson's use of frustration was to commit the patient to the treatment. He argued against Erickson. Erickson paradoxically utilized this to position the patient into taking a more constructive stance.

Erickson did not provide traditional treatment. Rather, he would establish a symbolic emotional drama in which the patient discovered within himself or herself the fact that sufficient resources were present to change his or her behavior. Erickson did not direct the flutist to change his behavior. He knew that this patient would defeat such congruent measures. Instead, Erickson utilized the patient's frustrating behavior by parodying it. The patient responded by arguing against Erickson's frustrating behavior, and thus, paradoxically, eased himself into a more effective stance. Through most of the treatment, Erickson did not offer the patient a remedy. He provided no solutions. He withheld hypnosis. Consequently, the patient could not "defeat" Erickson, an action that would lead the patient to self-defeat.

Erickson assumed that the patient would change only by virtue of experiential learning. Once the patient relived aspects of his neurotic conflict, he was able to take more salutary measures.

In order to effect the therapy, Erickson took a position of anticipating the patient's responses. It is an if X, then X, pattern. Erickson seemed to be thinking, "If the patient behaves in a self-frustrating way, then he will frustrate others." If the patient behaves irrationally in one context, he will behave irrationally in others. Hence Erickson made accurate predictions. Merely pointing out the patient's pattern would not lead to change. The patient must have an experiential recognition of his own patterns in order to modify his own patterns in order to modify his own behavior.

In summary, it is interesting to see how clinicians can apply Erickson's method.

Initially, they can orient themselves to the position that the patient takes. They can attempt to discern the position and distill it to its lowest common denominator. Once the therapist understands a patient's position, he or she can predict how the patient will respond. Then the therapist can create a drama in which the patient can suddenly recognize previously dormant abilities.

Although Erickson was 36 years old at the time that he was writing to Hendrick, he presented himself as a mature and seasoned practitioner. His interventions were bold, his attitude was certain. It is hard to imagine that this case was conducted in a time when psychoanalysis was the sole method of treating neuroses. One wonders how Erickson could separate himself from the psychoanalytic establishment to devise such a unique approach to treatment. The maturity that Erickson showed in his approach was impressive.

From: Ives Hendrick
January 18, 1940

Dear Milton:

What can you tell me about: 1. auto-hypnotism; 2. its relationship to catatonia?

I have just had a rather novel clinical experience. Two weeks ago the father of this patient, an elderly, jovial, naval doctor, consulted me about his daughter. The history seemed that of a typical hysteria with a girl generally healthy and sociable, whose love affairs always had ended in disaster, who had had several operations ending in hysterectomy, and who had consulted many psychiatrists and been twice for brief periods in mental hospitals in an apparent hypomanic state. She is 38. For the past two years she had been refusing most social opportunities. Previously she had been very much in love but had not wanted to marry because the man was a Catholic. For the past two years she has been more and more seclusive, staying in her room in the hotel apartment with her mother and father and rejecting most social opportunities and being very obstinate to people who have encouraged her to get going. She has had several doctors visit her but refused to see them again and hates psychiatrists. I felt there was no point in my going to see her and that she would not come to see me, so I told her father I would write her a letter. I wrote the letter and she came.

I have seen her daily. I began immediately on an analytic technique, asking for associations. She had already had some experience with a quack analyst. The most notable feature has been the contrast between her behavior on the couch and before and after interviews. Off the sofa she has a normal, agreeable, social manner, enjoying the personal relationship with me. Most of the time on the sofa she lies in a fixed position, her legs together and straight out, her ankles hyperextended, and mute. She answers questions but does not continue with anything spontaneous. My impression has been that she was a severe hysteric who finally was so frustrated sexually that she was reverting to an obstinate, defiant attitude toward her mother and hence the world. Although it has been suggestive of a minor catatonia, the posture is now and then interrupted by normal motions. Now and then she asks me questions, which I answer simply, and there is pleasure and emotional responsiveness on her part to such things. There have been a few moments of real analytic "give and take" but they are always quickly terminated and the posture resumed. One of these has been a memory of how much she loved a dog as a child and put the dog in a baby carriage and played that the dog had been bad to Mama. At another time she feels the room is quivering and her associations are to a day on which she experienced an earthquake when a love affair with a fiancé at 20 was coming to an end.

Today she comes in with her normal agreeable manner, lies down on the couch and says, "I don't know why but I think of Dr. Deutsch and mesmerism. I don't know why I should think of it but Dr. Deutsch asked me if I believed in mesmerism. Do you?" She had previously mentioned one single visit by Dr. Deutsch, saying she had not understood a word he said, but an emotional reaction to him was apparent to me. We exchanged a few remarks about mesmerism in which she said she heard it could be actually done. She asked me if I had ever seen any person mesmerized and I said, "Yes, several times." She asked me if it was harmful and I said, "No, not when done properly though I do not think it is a good parlor sport." She then resumed her posture and I spent about ten minutes in very productive inquiry into my own resistance to practicing hypnosis. I felt this was what the girl wanted and I had better not negate it but see what happened. After fifteen minutes' silence I said to her the word "mesmerism." She looked around, spoke in an objective way, but at this instant she folded her hands with the fingers upward on her abdomen. This gesture means: "I want to be mesmerized," for she had held her hands here habitually in this posture until three days ago.

Three days ago I had asked her if the way she held her hands suggested anything to her, and she had not responded verbally but had put them behind her head and subsequently had put them behind her neck, on her chest, and various positions normal for a person lying down when holding their hands together. Incidentally, one of the late events of this unproductive two weeks has been her seduction of me to say that she could go to the funeral of a lifelong friend. She is too sick to be mourning him but she wanted very much to go because her mother told her she was not well enough. After this gestural affirmation she was quiet for a while and said, "Why did you think of that?" [saying "Mesmerism"] and I replied, "Because you want to be mesmerized." After a while she then told me she had very strange sensations. She felt paralyzed, her legs were cold. (Yesterday she had remarked that if she could leave this cold weather and get into a warm place, she thought she would be all right.) She discussed her sensations, felt that she was "floating away," and had felt this "floating away" before in my office. Above the hips she did not feel the paralysis. I terminated the hour with a mild suggestion. I asked her if she usually went home directly from here and suggested that today she go to Schrafft's on her way. She asked what for and I said "to get a soda or a hot chocolate." When she got up from the sofa, she said she still felt a little strange, and I said it would be gone in a minute.

Here then is a case which is clearly hysterical and, except while on the sofa, behaves in a fully conscious and normal way. The mental experience which she has while lying in the posture and its sudden interruption with the thought "no thoughts come to me" seems to me after today to be clearly a self-imposed dissociation in which she alternates between a mild hypnotic trance which she has developed without suggestion from me and a waking state. As to how much of this is latent schizophrenia, I have no opinion as yet. But I feel that in order to successfully establish a genital relationship for the analysis of the hysteria I have got to gratify her need for the pregenital hypnotic transference.

I should be extremely interested in any comment you make on such a situation: when the hypnotist is not available the patient tends to hypnotize herself.

Sincerely yours,
Ives Hendrick, M.D.

To: Ives Hendrick
January 20, 1940

Dear Ives:

(1) *Auto-hypnotism*: This is usually practiced after the experience of being hypnotized, although occasionally some people succeed in self-hypnosis after watching a demonstration very intently. These subjects are generally unusually capable as hypnotic subjects, but when they develop a practice of self-hypnosis, the tendency is almost invariably to employ it for definite and fully conscious purposes. That is, they *map* out in their minds some specific task they wish to accomplish through the employment of self-hypnosis and, hence, the self-induced trance is limited to that predetermined goal.

Occasionally, the self-induced trance is employed as a defense measure to escape reality, but it almost always proves unsatisfactory as such. The general outcome is the replacement of the self-induced trance by physiological sleep, and sometime later, if they continue prefacing the physiological sleep with the self-induced trance, they develop some other and more satisfactory defense measure, which meets the personality, particularly ego, needs.

Sometimes the capacity for self-induced trances appears spontaneously, especially in some mediums, etc., who are not fakers. This type of trance is also of a markedly limited character. That is, it is dependent very much upon consciously determined circumstances and it is very largely a tool of the consciousness. Occasionally, it may become useful as a defense mechanism, but again there is a tendency for physiological sleep to replace the self-induced trance, and it is dropped in favor of better and more adequate defense measures that meet the personality needs.

(2) *Relation to Catatonia*: Briefly, so far as I can tell, there is no real relationship between self-induced trances and catatonia.

A recovered catatonia in excellent remission, trained to be a good hypnotic subject, impresses upon one most effectively the profound difference between catatonia and the trance state in the same person. If that recovered catatonic, now trained as a hypnotic subject, is made to relive a previous catatonic state in the hypnotic trance, the hypnotic elements drop out of the picture as soon as he begins reliving the cat-atonic state and rapport is lost, and he ceases to be amenable to sug-gestion until he makes his own spontaneous recovery from this new induced catatonic state. If, however, one succeeds in maintaining hyp-notic rapport with the subject, it is impossible to get him to relive the catatonic period except in an obviously false way.

Also, it is not possible by hypnotic suggestion to limit directly the duration of the induced catatonic state except by such a measure as suggesting carefully that the reliving of the catatonic period be limited to the tail-end of a period of catatonic stupor. However, the induced catatonia is generally of relatively short duration and recovery is spon-taneous. In other words, you cannot instruct the subject to relive a selected catatonic period; you can only suggest a general period of time in which he is to relive his catatonic experiences and hope that the subject will be able to strike that range of time in his response.

As for auto-hypnosis in the case of persons who have suffered from catatonia—well, I have never seen anything of this sort. My own gen-eral experience with catatonics and with hypnosis causes me to doubt if they would even bother with it since their other patterns of behavior are so much more effective.

(3) *Other Dissociated States*: In this connection, I have in mind those brief, transient, but highly intense dissociations that one sees so fre-quently in extremely intense emotional states, particularly in children, highly sensitive girls, and even middle-aged women. The example that comes to mind is the badly frightened child whose patterns of conscious behavior may be coordinated and purposeful but whose attention is so bound up, fascinated, fixed, and limited that there seems to be no ca-pacity to become aware of anything outside the immediate fright situ-ation. Thus, the highly terrified child may fend off a playful puppy, crying in a most frightened fashion while doing so, and yet be unable to run away, unable to hear his mother or to respond to his mother, or to become aware of anything except the puppy, and when rescued, shows a decidedly slow recovery of reality relationships.

Or, as another example, the bereaved mother who functions ade-quately but obviously "automatically," "moves in a daze," and who shows a slow recovery of reality relationships, often with a poor mem-ory of that situation later. This poor memory persists even when hypnosis is employed to recover the memory, and those memories recovered usually show a marked incompleteness so far as ideas of reality are concerned.

In relation to these conditions, hypnotic reliving of the trance experience can be directed and controlled with reasonable precision, but the hypnotic findings impress upon you the conviction that, as a result of the traumatic emotional experience, reality has become divested of all its cathexes.

Perhaps the best illustration I can give of that is the amnesia that sometimes follows intoxication. The drinker remembers all events up to a certain hour, has a complete amnesia for succeeding hours, despite the fact that he may have continued to participate in an adequate social fashion, and when he later is given complete info regarding his behavior by reliable and honest observers, believes those accounts, recognizes their unquestionable validity, but still has no sense of the accounts as belonging to him. This general type of dissociative experience occurring in relationship to intensely emotional experience, I have seen repeated as a learned pattern of defense and as a direct measure of divesting reality of its painful attributes. I do not regard it as a hysterical dissociation; it is decidedly different. Nevertheless, it does seem to resemble hysteria. Nor is it catatonic, although it resembles catatonia even more than hysteria. Likewise it resembles that acute, almost fugue-like state, the chief symptom of which is the Ganser syndrome. Yet, I do not think it is even related to catatonia, nor do I regard it as a variation of the Ganser syndrome. In investigating this general type of behavior in people who have developed it as a defensive habit, it seems that the general state that obtains in them is one like the old familiar, and relatively common normal experience of forgetting where one is and going through a process of reorientation.

The best example, and the most familiar one, is the experience of sleeping away from home, awakening in the morning and being unable to account for the total situation, recognizing nothing, remembering nothing, and then watching the walls, the beds, etc., undergo certain imperceptible changes until a sudden rush of realization effects a complete reorientation.

Another example I can offer is a certain experience of my own. Even today for me the sun still sets in the north at my grandmother's home; I have even mapped out the half-mile stretch of road somewhere in which the road loses all east and west attributes and acquires all those of a north and south direction. All intellectual grasp of facts on my part is useless except as a manipulative tool, enabling me to appreciate the fact that other people call west the direction which is north to me.

Careful inquiry into these special emotional dissociative states will disclose that same peculiar divestment of reality of all familiar attributes and yet, despite this loss of familiarity, the person is able to function in a coordinated and purposeful fashion. Each time that I have inquired into this casual, ordinary experience and then into one of these special dissociated emotional states I have been impressed with the marked similarity, despite the difference in genesis.

One other thing that seems to throw light on these special emotional dissociative states is the fact that I have found hypnotically that disoriented states are usually best suggested by first establishing emotional tension. To suggest deafness, blindness, or the reliving of an earlier period of life, or to effect the building up of a strictly hallucinatory, delusional situation, a careful building up of emotional tension is highly desirable. I think that I brought this out particularly in relationship to the suggestion of color blindness in the reprint I sent you some time ago. [Erickson, M. H. (1939). The induction of color blindness by a technique of hypnotic suggestion. *Journal of General Psychology, 29*, 61–89.] Also, in the securing of the reliving of a spontaneous emotional dissociative state, measures promoting general disorientation per se are usually of value. To illustrate this measure, I usually acquaint my subject fully with the exact arrangement of the furniture and then either I rearrange the furniture quietly or I suggest contrary and confusing ideas about the furniture arrangement and in them doubts as to the newness or the oldness of the furniture arrangement, and in this general state of confusion about the actual reality arrangements it is then easier to evoke the previous emotional dissociations.

Another item concerning these special emotional dissociative states concerns my observations that there is a tendency to form memories of a defensive pattern of reaction to stress and there is general alteration in all forms of behavior. The person generally develops certain habitual movements and postures, and employs a definite tone of voice and the range of ideas becomes limited. Also, there is a marked tendency toward infantile or puerile ideation and attitudes. There is a peculiar quality of automaticity, which tends to be fragmented by incursions of ordinary normal behavior in direct response to an immediate reality stimulus. However, this type of defense reaction compels acceptance of reality even though that reality is divested of many of its attributes. Hence, it is definitely altered in character and it does permit a continuance in the consciousness of a total awareness of the traumatic situation engendering it, even though there is only a dim awareness of the behavior responses which develop in the dissociative state. Hence, I have been impressed by the idea that this dissociative state is more or less a means of disregarding and postponing a full and complete contact with the traumatic event so that even though this dissociation does develop, its primary purpose is only to delay temporarily the eventual complete dealing with the precipitating occurrence.

(4) *The Dissociation of the Dual Personality Type*: Undoubtedly you have read Prince's "Dissociation of a Personality," which is decidedly informative, if naive and limited in many of the observations recorded. Then, too, I hope you have had the opportunity of reading the last paper in the *Psychoanalytic Quarterly* by Kubie and myself (Erickson & Kubie, 1939), and I'm going to place emphasis upon these two accounts ... since I have a very strong feeling, after reading the material you sent me, that you may be dealing with the type of dissociation one finds in the dual personality.

In the *Quarterly* paper, if you will check on the account of Miss Damon's behavior when she first showed her intense absorption in catalepsy, I think it may be possible for you to view your patient's behavior in that light. Then, also, in Prince's book you will find various accounts which describe the same sort of behavior as your patient manifested toward you. My whole feeling as I read through your account was that you were dealing with a secondary ego construction which was decidedly limited in character but which was making a very definite effort to get in contact with you, but did not know how. At the present time, I am interested in another instance of dual personality, which went through a long series of endeavors to get in contact with me, but which was mute and did not know how to do so.

Perhaps I am oversensitive on this matter of dual personalities, since I am working on this other case at the present time, and hence am perhaps reading too much into your letter. However, it might be desirable for you to rule out such a possibility. My own tendency in such a situation as you described would be to make careful note of her unusual behavior and separately of her ordinary behavior and thus to build up two completely separate pictures of the two types. Thus, in the case I am studying now, I made a complete study of unusual postures, attitudes, movements, gaits, gestures, etc., and contrasted these with a similar series of the more usual behavior, until I suddenly realized that two separate and totally individual patterns of behavior were involved. Then it became possible for me to establish two different patterns of responsive behavior to my case, until I had built up a definite attitude of expectation for the one or the other type of behavior on my part.

Incidentally, and this is important, this second case of mine is not a hypnotic subject, has never been hypnotized nor have I attempted to use any hypnotic procedure or technique. It was simply a matter of governing my own responsive behavior to fit in with the particular type of behavior being manifested. As a result, I built up that feeling of being understood that Fromm-Reichmann emphasized so much in her article on the transference in schizophrenia.

As for your statement that when the hypnotist is not available, the patient tends to hypnotize herself, I look upon that as only an inadequate and incomplete, but somewhat satisfying, conscious awareness of patterns of dissociation. I have encountered that rationalization in two different dual personalities—one of whom is very similar to the patient you described, even in such details as the love affair at the age of 20, the present age of 38, and the hand folding on the abdomen, although the other descriptive items disclose your patient to be unknown to me.

I hope all of this material may be of some interest to you and I shall appreciate hearing from you on any of these points that may interest you. I realize that I have tried to cover too much territory, but the whole problem is so great that it is literally impossible to discuss it to one's own satisfaction by way of letter.

I really would like to have your patient turn out to be a dual personality since I would like to have that entire problem worked up from the strictly analytic point of view. One case that I know of, who submitted to analysis over a period of many months, failed to make any sort of response to the analyst, although the analyst was very capable. In that instance there was a constant playing off of the analyst, first in one of the personalities, then in the other, so that no progress could be made.

Also, I would like to have you get interested in this problem of what happens when these peculiar disorientation states develop. I think that an investigation of that problem would contribute materially to an understanding of ego relationships. I am mailing this to you hastily and I hope that something I have said may prove pertinent to your problem.

Sincerely yours,
Milton H. Erickson, M.D.

Erickson's description in his January 20 letter of the establishment of "emotional tension" appears to be one of the earliest mentions of the confusion technique in hypnotic induction. He did not discuss the confusion technique per se, but described how emotional tension is a precursor to hypnotically created states of disorientation. Erickson implied that profound hypnotic effects, such as age regression and hallucination, are best created by using emotional arousal. His investigation of the use of arousal seems to be a de novo *contribution to the study of hypnosis, which is customarily seen as entailing relaxation. The confusion technique was not formally detailed by Erickson in the literature until 1964. It was one of his most important contributions to hypnosis and in his later life, Erickson insisted that therapeutic confusion was an essential element of his induction method.*

Here, again, not the difference in style. Hendrick's letters are unpolished; Erickson's are of literary quality. The latter seem to have been written with the same meticulous care as when preparing a manuscript for journal publication.

Hendrick continues the conversation in his next letter, dated March 13. Originally six pages long, only relevant excerpts from that letter are presented here. It is interesting to note the evolution of the form of Hendrick's correspondence. Previously handwritten, his letters became more literary, each typed and well edited.

In the March 13 letter, Hendrick further describes his work with his patient and confirms what Erickson had written about the transformation of autohypnosis into normal sleep. Hendrick's description of his psychoanalytic treatment, the reaction of the patient, and some of the difficulties of the analysis have been omitted. Subsequently, Hendrick returns to the topic of dual personality. He seems to have accepted Erickson's formulation that multiplicity may exist in the patient.

From: Ives Hendrick
March 13, 1940

Dear Milton:

I know that I quite deserve your reproaches. For I was greatly stimulated by your long letter and appreciative of the compliment you paid me by taking so much trouble so promptly; yet I have delayed answering.

My major reaction to your letter was a conviction of being an absolute novice in the field of our discussion. You have a comprehensive grasp of certain aspects of psychopathology of which I have only occasional glimpses. . . .

But the practical point is my indebtedness to one who does employ this method so profitably. Your comments on the transformation of autohypnosis into normal sleep were being illustrated by this patient. During the days following my letter, exactly this happened, the sleep being as rudimentary and of the same degree as her trance had been. . . .

I do not know much about the second personality, which I presume is the preschizophrenic personality that is hidden somewhere behind the more obvious hysteria and chronic depression. Its existence raises questions with which I do not feel completely at home. I am accustomed to thinking of dual personality as typified by states such as hysterical fugues in which a patient's whole conscious life and behavior are for hours or days determined by a second set of fantasies and motivations. I can see that this state of affairs may also characterize other cases in which one cannot so clearly describe the activity of the dissociated personality in chronological terms. But I am not clear as to whether fundamentally, that is, *etiologically* and *dynamically*, the "second personality" is not identical with a "complex." If so, a double personality would be only one in which the usually repressed complex at certain times determines the whole conscious activity of the patient—the difference would be one of degree rather than kind.

I have, for example, a case now which is doing surprisingly well although I took her on a basis of doing what little I could with the immediate situation. At first I considered her a typical infantile schizoid whose only real aim in life was to gain a mother's protection, and who hadn't the guts to deal with other problems. During my six months' work with her she has, however, shown typical hysterical transferences in symptoms and fantasies, alternating with obsessional defenses. My original impression is quite valid, but she *also* has a very active, though inhibited, complex of genital wishes. Perhaps you would think of this as two personality systems or even three, and yet we would actually be discussing the same phenomenon. Certainly not only descriptively, but dynamically, her analytic reactions are determined by mother-need, genital anxiety, or obsessional defenses on different days, and are very clearly differentiated. . . .

In the examples in your letter of dissociated states, one thing struck me, and that was that all these samples seemed to be dissociations motivated by realistic anxiety. The little girl who was frightened by the dog is realistically frightened and does not merely suffer from a phobia. I think, therefore, that one should try to distinguish between such dissociations as these and those which are motivated by a neurotic unrealistic anxiety. Discussion of some other problems has recently awakened my speculation about a closely allied idea. I now question whether the amnesia for a dream is entirely explained by ascribing it to repression. This analogy comes to my mind: I have obtained excellent reception of a station on a small radio set, but when I try to get the same program on a powerful radio, I find that so many stations are coming over that it is harder to tune in on that particular station than it was on the small set. I wonder, therefore, if the larger number of perceptual systems which are functioning in the waking state is not as much a factor in the difficulty in recollecting a dream as repression. After all, the aims of repression are pretty well taken care of by the dream disguise.

So much for now. I hope very much that there will be something here that you will feel worth discussing further and I shall be a very good boy and shall not take so long to answer next time.

Sincerely yours,
Ives Hendrick, M.D.

To: Ives Hendrick
October 11, 1940

Dear Ives,

Apparently it is not in the cards for us to become regular correspondents. As I look back over the past months. I note that a goodly mileage of Hell has been paved with good intentions about writing to you. But here goes for another try.

You state, "I am not clear as to whether fundamentally, that is, *etiologically* and *dynamically*, the 'second personality' is not identical with a 'complex.' If so, the dual personality would be only one in which the usually repressed complex at certain times determines the whole conscious activity . . . the difference would be one of degree rather than kind . . . I am accustomed to thinking of a dual personality as typified by states such as hysterical fugues. . . ."

In an attempt to answer this, let me make some dogmatic assertions. As far as my experience goes, a dual personality seems to be literally a construction of two separate and distinct personalities developing not only in degree but also in kind of a total common experiential background. I do not feel that it is just a matter of a complex becoming dissociated with subsequent extensive developments centering about that dissociated experience. Rather, it seems to me that dual personalities actually represent well-organized, coordinated, and integrated use of the same total experience but from two entirely different points of orientation.

As a crude example, Jones attends a poker party, primarily for the social experience. He wouldn't miss it. Even though the poker is only a minor consideration, despite that, he enjoys it fully. Smith, on the other hand, attends the same poker party, enjoys the social aspect fully, but his attendance is based on the fact that poker is his passion in life. It seems to me that this sort of a situation confronts each one of us time after time. That is, where we have a definite choice of reacting in one way to a given situation or in a totally different way to the same situation. My finding with dual personalities is that they react in both ways simultaneously. Usually one of the personalities is active and builds up an experiential background in that way. The other tends to be passive and to orient itself about things of only minor consideration to the other personality. As a consequence, you get two personalities constructed, each of which has its own set and scale of values, based upon totally different usages of the common experiences.

I doubt very much if one can think of dual personalities in terms of fugue states or anything of that sort. While the ordinary personality is usually present, nevertheless, the secondary personality is very definitely in the background, observing, participating, and sharing, but in a fashion unknown to the ordinary personality. I will agree, however, that when the secondary personality is in the foreground, the primary personality is most completely out of the picture, and, so far as I can tell, actually misses completely the experiences of the active second personality. Just how this is possible I cannot conceive, and yet it seems to be so.

I have often tried to think of the dual personality as a general dissociation of various complexes with the building up of an identification system. I doubt, however, if this is true, since the primary personality can have many repressions, and inhibitions, into which the secondary personality can have adequate insight, and understanding, and yet actually be free of it, so far as the function of the secondary personality is concerned. In other words, *B* can recognize that *A* has a phobia, can understand its nature and origin and sympathize with *A* in relationship to that phobia, but at the same time be free of the symptom. On the other hand, *A* can possess insight and understandings and attitudes and likings which are without value or meaning so far as *B* is concerned.

Every time I have tried to think of the dual personalities I know as being single personalities with two sets and forms of behavior, I find myself in the same situation that one would be in trying to view twins as a single person. No matter where you look, the dual personalities seem to differ greatly in kind rather than just in degree of reaction and behavior. . . .

I am very much impressed by the analogy that you draw in relation to dreams and amnesia for a dream. The excellent reception of a station on a small radio set, when you could not get the same program on a larger radio because of the many stations coming over the larger radio, is parallel to my experience with hypnosis. By limiting and circumscribing mental activity of all forms, it is possible to get very adequate and complete material which it would be impossible to secure if there were in existence other associations as would be the case in the waking state.

I wish you would take this idea of yours and elaborate on it much more. I think it would serve to correct many of the mistaken ideas now in existence about the nature of repression. . . .

Sincerely yours,
Milton H. Erickson

In a letter dated October 18, 1940, Hendrick continues the discussion of multiplicity from his psychoanalytic perspective. He does not seem to accept Erickson's formulation. Rather, he prefers his concept of complexes to explain dual personality and questions Erickson's formulation of dissociation. Because there was no response from Erickson, this letter is not included here.

This, the last of the correspondence from Hendrick that could be found, was a letter of December 9, 1943, to Lewis S. Hill, M.D., another noted psychoanalyst. In January 1944, Erickson and Hill published a paper in the Psychoanalytic Quarterly entitled, "Unconscious Mental Activity in Hypnosis—Psychoanalytic Implications." In that paper, Erickson offered two similar cases of women who were in a quandary concerning their intended spouses, Erickson merely applied hypnosis and effectively "got out of the patient's way" while the patient decided her destiny. His approach was minimalist.

Hill's discussion was conciliatory. He indicated, "The study of unconscious mental activity by other techniques provides benefits of checking psychoanalytic data, theories, and techniques. If it is found that the therapeutic results of psychoanalysis seem to be duplicated by different and much less time-consuming techniques, psychoanalysts should be quick to investigate these possibilities in the hope that they may be verified."

Hendrick wrote to Hill and seemed more defensive about psychoanalysis than Hill was. Hendrick makes two points to Hill about Erickson's cases. Because the second point is the more interesting, it is included here. The complete letter is available in the Archives of the Milton H. Erickson Foundation.

To: Lewis Hill
From: Ives Hendrick
December 9, 1943

Dear Lewis:

We were all very sorry you couldn't be here with Erickson. His formal presentation at the Society was supplemented by one at the Psychopathic, and a good deal of informal discussion on various occasions was engaged in by some of us. We felt his visit had been a most invigorating one for our somewhat jaded faculties.

As usual, his portion of the paper gave us a different slant on the use of hypnosis than his previous ones, and your discussion of the material brought home its significance for psychoanalysis. Together they raise essentially two problems: (1) the need to understand as clearly as possible the mechanism of his therapy; (2) the comparison—or challenge—of his few hours' work with these two cases with the therapeutic results of psychoanalysis. . . .

Simply stated, the paper is implicitly a challenge: *Why spend two years if Erickson can show us similar results in a few hours?*

I think there need be no disputing the fact that the results are good, not only from the standpoint of solving the immediate dilemma, but from that of ultimate marital adjustment. The second goal particularly would be a principal one in justifying the ordeal of a long analysis. These are results which every experienced analyst would force himself to be satisfied with in a goodly number of difficult cases, and better than he achieves in his disappointing cases.

So it is not so much a comparison of results which might lead one to differ with Erickson's implied conclusion as it is the data on which he bases the conclusion. He states his case as though it were simply: solve the dilemma, the girls marry and make a decent adjustment. But his data do not give me any conviction that the analyst would appraise these girls' problems and personality, and hence the therapeutic problem, as Erickson has. It was suggested at the Boston meeting that several such cases be interviewed by several analysts—say, Kubie, you, and myself. It seems likely that analysts would not see the problem as whether to marry or not tomorrow, but as a typically severe ambivalence conflict of an intellectually dominant woman, apparent in the double object-relationship between selecting the man regarded as notably inferior, and denying oneself fulfillment by selection of an overvalued man. The analyst would consider the therapeutic problem the solution of this conflict and the development of the ability to sexually accept a respected man. He would fail to achieve this in certain cases, but it would be his goal and criterion.

As suggested above, I do not think that these results can be attributed to hypnotic sessions alone. We all know that personality maturation is dependent upon the solution of situations involving emotional problems, and that in many lives maturation is only possible after living through tragic experiences—rejection by a lover, disastrous first marriages, accidental deaths, etc. Many years ago in my book I emphasized that the dynamics of analytic therapy were comparable to these ordeals. As I have suggested above, these girls went through such an experience. Erickson's results depend in these cases, not only on the use of hypnosis, but on the long-standing transference conflicts . . .

Thanks again for the privilege of reading your paper, and looking forward to seeing you at the Executive meeting in New York, I am

Sincerely yours,
Ives Hendrick

IV

IMPORTANT NAMES IN HYPNOSIS:

Leslie LeCron and André Weitzenhoffer

LeCron

On January 15, 1945, Milton Erickson received a letter from Leslie LeCron, which begin:

> May I introduce myself as a lay practitioner of hypnotherapy and hypnoanalysis. Together with an associate, Dr. Jean Bordeaux (Ph.D.), I am about to complete the writing of a book on hypnotism and hypnotherapy, which we hope to have published. . . .

LeCron went on to request that Erickson write an introduction, explaining, "There is no real textbook on hypnotism or hypnotherapy other than Hull's summation of experimental work." The working title of the book would be Hypnotism, the Neglected Science. *It later was published as* Hypnotism Today *(LeCron & Bordeaux, 1947).*

In his letter, LeCron encouraged Erickson to criticize the manuscript freely. He admitted that, in general, psychotherapy should not be practiced by laypeople, but he hedged this statement by asserting that people such as himself should be permitted to conduct therapy because of the shortage of psychiatrists.

LeCron also indicated that he was setting up a clinic in the Los Angeles area, as a West Coast version of the Menninger Clinic, with an ex-army psychiatrist, J. O. Cromwell, M.D. He invited Erickson to join them, and expressed the hope that Erickson could arrange a teaching position on the staff of the Medical School that was about to be established at the University of California, Los Angeles. In concluding, LeCron asked Erickson to provide the name of a Chicago obstetrician who was mentioned in an article about hypnotic methods that appeared in American Magazine.

In Erickson's reply of January 19, 1946, he said that he was flattered by LeCron's request, and that he might consent to write an introduction after he had reviewed the manuscript. Erickson agreed with LeCron about the role of psychologists (LeCron had mentioned in his letter that he held a bachelor's degree in psychology). Erickson also furnished the name of the obstetrician mentioned in the article—William S. Kroger, M.D.

The next correspondence in the Erickson files was the following handwritten letter.

March 16, 1946

Dear Mr. LeCron:

Hastily: I just received the ms., immediately looked at the index and found listed with eight references a well-known charlatan who is definitely engaged in an illegal practice of medicine, describes himself as a psychologist, yet has no degree in psychology, and according to a classmate of his, was flunked out of college.

I personally have treated patients he has "treated" and through this and the personal investigation of a friend who posed as a patient, know him to be a fraud, though highly convincing to the lay public and even to psychologists and medically trained people. I can assure you, however, that he is a charlatan highly successful in securing favorable publicity.

Additionally, this man's publications, which you quote from, and even describe as pioneer work, were ghost-written for him and based on other people's work, often mere revisions or plagiarized material. Or [they were] mere armchair speculation described as actual controlled experimental work when there were no experiments of any kind, just dreamed-up experiments and dreamed-up results reported as facts.

Your purpose is to write a sound reliable authoritative book and I think you are honest and I think you are desirous of contributing to the hypnotic literature.

Therefore, I must ask you what you want me to do in reading your ms. about such matters as the above because additional scrutiny of the index discloses other questionable inclusions and the omission of highly desirable inclusions.

I sincerely hope that the labor this manuscript represents signifies a desire to make a contribution to the literature and not just a wish to publish another book, as was the case in relation to a book and author from whom you quote extensively and who wrote me personally that he was glad to get the book off his hands, that most of it was false, but that it was a book.

If you want to publish a good book, I'll be glad to read your ms. critically. Please let me know your wishes at once.

Sincerely,
Milton H. Erickson

In a letter dated March 18, 1946, LeCron responded to Erickson, stating, "Your letter was just received and I appreciate the spirit of your criticism." He said that he knew to whom Erickson was referring (i.e., the "charlatan") and that, although he did not definitely know the character and style of the "expert," he did suspect that Erickson's characterization was true. Promising to delete all references to that person in the manuscript, he reiterated his desire for Erickson's candid critique and maintained that his interest was in producing a noteworthy book with accurate information and citations. "I would be glad," he wrote, "to send you all rewritten pages so that you can be sure nothing is said which would be contrary to your desires, although there may be some legitimate and honest difference in opinions."

Moreover, he said:

Your criticisms and comments would certainly be a great help, and if you feel we are close enough to a good book to warrant the time on your part, perhaps you will be justified as aiding in contributing to the literature. We sincerely feel that you are a foremost authority and that your ideas closely approximate our own so that any definite criticism of a section would indicate that it should be revised.

In a letter of March 26, 1946, Erickson commented, "My wife, who is extremely critical of my work, is most favorably impressed by your book. I have not yet read enough of it to formulate a definite opinion, but so far, I am favorably impressed."

To: Leslie LeCron
March 30, 1946

Dear Mr. LeCron:

Mrs. Erickson and I have both gone through the first hundred pages of your book. We are very much impressed by its quality and the method of presentation. In brief, if the rest of your book lives up to the first hundred pages, it will be by far the best book published to date on hypnosis.

However, in accord with your letter, we are assuming that you want full criticism of everything. So without regard for your personal feelings, these criticisms for the first sixty-two pages are offered, with more to follow in the very near future.

Please accept them in the spirit in which they are offered, namely, one of a desire to be helpful to you.

Sincerely yours,
Milton H. Erickson, M.D.

Erickson provided a detailed critique of LeCron's manuscript, including suggestions regarding style, grammar, and content. However, in the following transcript of pages 2–4 of Erickson's 65-page letter, references to routine grammatical and punctuation errors have been deleted.

PAGE 4

Why are you excluding the neuroses of the civilian population that do not derive from wartime living?

There are such neuroses, and they outnumber war-related neuroses.

PAGE 11

Second paragraph   You state that in 1943 the Menninger Clinic became interested in hypnotism. Actually in either 1939 or 1940, the Menninger Clinic invited me to give a series of lectures and an equal number of demonstrations on hypnosis over a period of a week. That was the first development of interest in hypnosis at Menninger's. Also, if you will consult *American Psychiatry, 1844–1944*, Columbia University Press, you will find mentioned there the development of hypnosis at the Worcester State Hospital and subsequently at Eloise, considered sufficiently important to be mentioned in *100 Years of American Psychiatry*.

Last line   You really don't mean "proficiency." Rather you mean a comprehensive understanding of the methodologies of hypnosis.

PAGE 12

Second line   If you can find that reference of Freud's, by all means include it. This is one of the most valuable references that you can use. If you can't substantiate it, revise the sentence. However, I hope greatly that you can find it.

You use the word "medic." Isn't this really slang? I noticed that you have used it repeatedly, and I wish you wouldn't. It will antagonize too many of your readers.

Second paragraph   You don't mean curative agent; you mean therapeutic agent. The word "cure" has a definite meaning to the layman and a very definite meaning to your critics. Don't arouse their ire.

Middle paragraph   Regarding the case history of miraculous cures, I would tend to discredit this because actually medical knowledge was limited and ordinary remissions in certain neurological diseases, such as multiple sclerosis, were regarded as hypnotic cures. Today our better knowledge prevents such error, at least in relationship to multiple sclerosis.

PAGE 13

Middle paragraph   I can actually name a lot of physicians who have published more significant articles than have psychologists. Credit should be given to both psychologists and physicians.

    Regarding the last sentence, I disagree because I think the psychiatric publications were instrumental in arousing general interest, but, of course, this is my opinion.

Last paragraph   Hull ought to be credited, but only with an effective demonstration of the desirability of the application of experimental methods to hypnosis. Otherwise, his book is primarily a loss. As I said before, Winn merely tried to cash in on fame by rehashing the work of others.

    I also hold a B.A. and M.A., am a full member of the American Psychiatric Association, and I have published extensively in psychiatric and psychological journals. The total volume of my original reprints far exceeds that of any other original research worker.

PAGE 14

Bottom of page   You describe Hull's workers as chiefly graduate students. Indeed they were later, but a lot of that work was done by undergraduates, many of them naive, inexperienced, and actually untrained. I know, because I was associated with practically every one of his workers. I criticized Hull's work very harshly while it was in manuscript form because it is unreliable and not critically oriented, and because of its failure to appreciate the human personality as a definite factor in experimental work. That is the reason Hull makes one inaccurate reference to me and does not give me credit for any of the experiments I actually suggested and developed for that book.

What is this reference to W.? To the best of my knowledge you are referring to the paper that W. published and which he described to me personally in essentially these remarks: "I controlled my experiments so that they would contradict Hull's. That was my object." W. even proposed that he and I carry on work apparently similar but so done that we would get divergent results so that we could then start a polemic in the journals. You might better understand this if you knew W., who is a terribly pitiful neurotic who needs to dispute everybody and yet inspires tremendous loyalty.

PAGE 15
Last paragraph

Dr. R. is a crackpot. His findings in many proved instances result from minimal cues, lack of controls, and distorted mathematics. Additionally, you may be rather appalled to learn that Dr. R. has published as "scientific" the delusional productions, and I do mean delusional, of two of my patients. He is credulous beyond words, even though he means well. I think this entire paragraph ought to be rewritten carefully and reference made rather to the proved instances of Dr. R.'s work based on minimal cues and similar comprehensible things.

Bottom of page

You have William S. His name is (Erickson provides a correction) and please delete him. If you want to make reference to autohypnosis, base it on the work of the acknowledged quack Coue, or make reference to some of the anthropological studies of autohypnosis on the Balinese, particularly those of Bateson and Mead. Hull was extremely misled in sponsoring S. and has been apologizing ever since, and S. only paraphrased Coue's writings.

The Bateson and Mead [1942] book *Balinese Character* published by the New York Academy of Sciences can give you some information on autohypnosis. Jane Belo's studies in the literature may also give you some information. Belo, Bateson, and Mead spent a great deal of time in Bali. I have discussed their works with them and have seen their motion pictures of Balinese autohypnosis.

PAGE 16

Second paragraph   Dr. F.'s book is not excellent. It is terribly misleading, although it does make a number of good statements.

Last paragraph   W. and B. set out to prove their point. Both had make-believe, pretense, and "as if" experimental conditions. W. proved crime by conspiring with a subject to rob himself. What manner of crime is it when one helps you to rob oneself? B.'s experiments were based largely on "Let's pretend" situations.

Erickson's critique was completed in stages. The final stage was mailed to LeCron on May 23, 1946. The samples below are commentaries from the final segment and include the page numbers of the LeCron text. Note the remarkable diligence Erickson brought to his editing.

PAGE 43   You say ordinarily no more than ten or fifteen minutes are needed [for hypnotic induction]. I think a much more cautious statement is warranted. With three trained subjects, despite repeated efforts, you couldn't get a trance in ten or fifteen minutes on page 38. Actually, the time required is a function of the purpose of the trance and of the personality structure itself. Too often people get the idea that hypnosis is a matter of magical utterance and a verbal formula, a ritual of movement and the lapse of a specific period of time. Personally I don't know how much time is required. But I have plenty of time to spend when I want to do work of profound significance.

PAGE 46

You may be interested to know that I like to suggest that they are beginning to realize that they may become sleepy. And then slowly, by the omission of this and that word, I bring it down from a remote future possibility to a present reality, to an accepted fact, while I move on to the suggestion that they may become sleepier and sleepier and finally that they are sleeping and have been sleeping for some time.

Are you sure that the best possible proof is anesthesia? I have had good actors successfully simulate analgesia and anesthesia except for clinical considerations of which they were unaware. The best test I have encountered for hypnosis is a combination of catalepsy and motor responses to hand pressure. Catalepsy, to be genuine, includes all muscle groups. The faker overemphasizes or underemphasizes certain muscle groups, and his cooperation with directed movements is always in terms of his comprehension or understanding, and not in accord with the actual tactile stimuli.

PAGE 66

I agree that subjects can be hypnotized unwittingly to them. But then you have the problem of continuing them in a trance state, which is possible only with their consent. As you merely give them posthypnotic suggestions through the guise of giving posthypnotic suggestions to others, you are likely to come to personal grief. Whenever somebody in my audience goes to sleep unwittingly, I take special care to protect myself and to protect him from the consequences of emotional reactions against the experience.

PAGE 91   "Down the hypnotic toboggan slide he goes," is a threat to the reader and a mockery of hypnosis.

Also, in the first paragraph, I feel that the "bull-headed" are good subjects if you utilize their bull-headedness. So can attitudes of anxiety or highly critical analytical attitudes be utilized. They require more ability on the part of the hypnotist. Also, over-active cooperation can always be guided.

My secretary has just mentioned to me one important consideration—the difference between my technique and that of other hypnotists: namely, I orient myself entirely around what the subject himself does. I make intense utilization of whatever he offers me, and I feel that what I do is extremely unimportant.

PAGE 115   You're the first one not a student of mine to realize the value of the future tense, the present tense, and the need for the lapse of time.

PAGE 131   As for Dr. R., some of his best statistical papers are based on the delusional findings of a paranoid praecox patient whom I had been caring for for years. Yet Dr. R. has accepted this strictly delusional material as if it were actual scientific data.

PAGE 133   Concerning the genuineness of hallucinations, I have had more than one college student hallucinate A in chair No. 1 when actually A was sitting in chair No. 2, and then see both chairs as occupied by A. My highly trained college subjects have many times demonstrated their capacity to differentiate between a hallucination and the real object by watching both and suggesting to themselves that A move his arm or his leg. Naturally the hallucinatory figure would respond to the mental suggestion that the subject merely thought.

PAGES 163 AND
165

I think you ought to stress that autosuggestion is too often employed by a sick person who knows he should receive treatment and attempts to give himself treatment when he doesn't even know what his ills are. Therefore, in such cases autosuggestion is a blind, hopeless, and stupid procedure. Autosuggestion, intelligently directed, is definitely of value.

Certainly you are going to get in trouble with that last paragraph. Inferiority, anxiety, and depression cannot be overcome by autosuggestion, nor is such self-treatment properly to be called auto-psychotherapy. It is primarily a means of repressing and suppressing. What you actually mean is that a person can intensify his self-confidence and his willingness to become self-confident.

PAGE 177

The conditioned reflex theory has to be thrown out. [Robert] White's idea of meaningful, goal-directed striving in which the general goal is to behave like a hypnotized person makes this definition ridiculous, because how can you or I, regardless of our experience, communicate to a small child the mental process by which to recover a forgotten memory. Therefore, we cannot define to the subject how to behave like a hypnotized person. Nor is his regnant motive submission to the hypnotist's demands. For example, a naive college student, wishing to investigate forgotten memories, posed for me this problem: He knew that his mother had never punished him, at least he had no recollection of it. He also knew it was her proud boast that she had never laid a hand on any of her children. I had him do some crystal gazing and he saw a small child in the high chair spilling a glass of milk and being slapped by his mother. At first he did not recognize himself or his mother. Then he did not believe it because it was not possible. The mother's subsequent violent antipathy toward me convinced him that she had once punished him. Certainly I did not define for the subject what he must do or how it must be done, etc., in order to act like a hypnotized person. Certainly involuntary processes were involved.

PAGE 199   Please avoid all the harsh criticism that you invite by favorable mentions of telepathy. Hypnosis is having a sufficiently difficult time and your book is much too good to be blasted because of telepathy. Instead of the mention of telepathy; why not put in the statement that the unconscious can at times be unbelievably adroit and sensitive in picking up small cues, subliminal stimuli, minor changes in facial expression, breathing, etc. For example, I once gave a two-hour seminar in psychiatry to some residents. One of them had brought his fiancee, who I met for the first time. At the conclusion of the two-hour lecture, she offered to tell my fortune. The items of information that she had about me were incredible. She was very much offended, too, when I went back over the lecture and the conversation and discussion, and demonstrated to her how carefully she had added up, with good clinical sense and judgment, facial expressions, intonations, emphases, motor responses, etc., which disclosed my own personal attitudes on a great variety of topics. She has since demonstrated her capacity to me of listening to a lecture and pointing out the vocal intonations that betray facts.

PAGE 240*

Bottom of page   Freud's interpretations cannot be disproved. You can only prove that there are also other meanings.

Psychoanalysts do not lose all perspective, and they do not overlook sexual dreams.

*Remember that Freud was alive at this time.

PAGE 263
Top of page

When a patient has had a neurosis for ten, fifteen, or twenty years, and it has been the governing influence in his life, who are you or who am I to say that 100 hours of re-education is too long a time. That's scarcely more than four days, as contrasted to ten or fifteen or twenty years of education by the neurosis.

PAGES 271–272

Please stop kicking psychoanalysis around. You are writing a book on hypnosis, not a critical evaluation of psychoanalysis.

PAGE 280

I don't think that you are treating [Lewis] Wolberg quite fairly because he was really dealing with a hebephrenic schizophrenic, and I am wholly in sympathy with his procedure. I realize that there are oversights, but remember that he was doing pioneer work. Also, I disagree with Wolberg in many regards, but I think you need to emphasize the things with which you do agree, instead of burdening your reader with the knowledge of those things with which you disagree. To paraphrase LeCron—emphasize the positive and eliminate the negative.

PAGE 283

Still kicking poor old psychoanalysis around, I see. I simply don't understand what you mean by the assertion, "It seems most unlikely to regard the causative factors or emotions as possessed of any actual dynamic force or energy which produces the neurotic symptoms." You are really asking for trouble from everybody who knows anything about personality disorders. Aren't you putting a peculiar and limited construction upon the concepts of dynamic force? Why not accept the significance generally accorded to that concept instead of creating a new one?

PAGE 295
Middle paragraph

Auto-suggestion is not so helpful. Human nature demands help. Self-suggestion can at the most lead only to a greater readiness to accept help, but it is not help in itself.

There is no royal road to knowledge, to adjustment, to health, to strength, to education. Nevertheless, what you say seems to advocate hypnosis as a short cut to Utopia.

PAGE 347
First paragraph

Your statement is, "Emotion and suggestion operate in exactly the same manner to charge the brain." This is an excellent example of an unscientific statement, gratefully received by all critics.

Erickson ended the commentary with the following sentence: "This completes the first going-through of your book. We have not attempted to go over the revision as yet; that will come later."

LeCron responded to the first stage of Erickson's critique with a letter of April 2, 1946, stating, "We certainly had no intention of asking anything like this, which will require so much of your time. Your kindness is much appreciated and we will be greatly indebted to you if you feel like doing this work. . . ."

In his letter of April 14, 1946, LeCron wrote:

The criticisms are exactly what is needed to make the manuscript really worthwhile, and your points are certainly searching and apt. Your comments are illuminating and constructive and the text will be greatly improved as a result . . . pull no punches as you continue the criticism, for it is just what is needed!

Erickson responded with the following letters of May 1 and May 10, 1946.

To: Leslie LeCron
May 1, 1946

Dear Mr. LeCron:

I am sending you some reprints and I would like to reply to your letter of the twenty-sixth.

First of all, I think your book is excellent. I think it is very definitely going to be a significant contribution, far superior to any of the books that have been written. As for our own personal disagreements, just bear in mind that this is your book. My only interest is the best possible presentation of hypnosis.

In the last paragraph of your letter, you ask if Mesmerism is not more nearly synonymous with animal magnetism. My response is this: Mesmer was in error in what he believed. So is the patient in error in his religious beliefs. However, the processes by which certain psychological results are obtained remain the same. Therefore, even though Mesmer thought he was using animal magnetism, he was in many instances using hypnosis and therefore I don't care what he believed. I am more concerned about what he did.

Concerning the rewriting on Wells, Rowland, Brenman, and Erickson on antisocial behavior, I have not read the pages yet. The emphasis I was concerned about is that Wells with one case of mistaken procedure, Rowland on four cases with recognizable errors and self-expressed doubts, and Brenman with a technique definitely worded as "let's pretend such and such and so and so," are all cited as if they were on an equal basis with a definite experimental study involving a total of fifty subjects.

I shall be in Texas for the next few days. In the meantime, Mrs. Erickson is continuing her criticisms and if there are any more reprints that you want, please let my secretary know.

Sincerely yours,
Milton H. Erickson, M.D.

Editor's Note: For additional information on the controversy, see Chapter V on antisocial acts.

To: Leslie LeCron
May 10, 1946

Dear Mr. LeCron:

I have just returned from Texas where I was the guest speaker for the Texas Psychiatric Association. I had a nice time and interested the whole group in hypnosis as well as psychotherapy. Now I am planning to rest up from that trip by working on your book.

Concerning your letter, the project sounds decidedly good. I am primarily interested in teaching, research, and psychotherapy. I have hitharts resisted all temptations to go into private practice because of the interference with teaching and research. However, an adequate setup would certainly interest me. My present situation is one of full-time, and I am forced to turn down an ever-increasing number of would-be private patients who have heard about me.

But I think I had better get to work on your book now.

Sincerely yours,
Milton H. Erickson, M.D.

In a letter dated May 23, 1946, Erickson told LeCron.

> We have completed going through your book. I have just finished dictating the last of the criticisms. I have not gone through any of the revised material yet. I think your book is still in the first stage of writing. I still think it can be an outstanding book, but you are going to have to put into it much more care and labor and effort. You will have to disregard your desire to take a poke at some of the things that you don't believe in. . . .

In a June 5 letter, Erickson mentioned that he had given LeCron's name to the publishers Grune & Stratton. He stated, "I definitely want your book to be the outstanding lay publication, and actually even more than a lay publication."

The book ultimately was published by Grune & Stratton. Throughout the interchange, Erickson often sent LeCron reprints of his own work to clarify points.

In his three-page letter of May 7, LeCron indicated, "It is very gratifying to have your approval and good opinion of the manuscript. Your assistance and Mrs. Erickson's is improving it tremendously, and I really believe it will be a worthwhile contribution. . . ." LeCron proposed talking to a physician who was affiliated with the Medical School at UCLA to see if there was a possibility that Erickson might be appointed chief psychiatrist. Neither the school nor the hospital had yet been established at the time. As it turned out, this was a dead end and seemingly a carrot that LeCron held out to Erickson.

On July 17, 1946, LeCron wrote:

> I would much prefer to have undertaken this book with another year of experience behind me in psychotherapy, but this is the opportune time for such a book. I lay no claims to being an expert, and my knowledge is none too great. I have only been in this work long enough to have had about 150 cases and still have much to learn . . .
>
> Bordeaux has much more experience and I depended on him more than I should have. For his experience was more in the 1920s and early 1930s. Until a couple of years ago, he had been engaged in business for a number of years, and his modern experience is much like my own. . . .

LeCron continued:

> Whether or not you undertake the foreword, you've been so kind that we'd like to include this dedication: "To Dr. and Mrs. Milton H. Erickson and Dr. Adolf Meyer, in grateful and deep appreciation for their kindly help and encouragement, which made the writing of this book possible."

LeCron pointed out that Bordeaux had studied under Meyer for two years, which was why he later wanted to include him in the foreword.

On July 19, Erickson replied: "The dedication as you have worded it is entirely satisfactory to both of us. Finally, I think it will be the first real book published on the subject."

In correspondence of September 29, 1946, LeCron. stated, "Praise from you is praise indeed, and I am really 'tickled to death.' Your kindness in undertaking all this work you've done is something I will not forget. . . ."

On November 8, 1946, James Holsaert of Grune & Stratton advised LeCron:

We have just realized with a start that you dedicated the book to, and the foreword is written by, the same man. While we realize the sincerity of your intention in dedicating the book to Dr. Erickson, we feel very definitely that it will look to the reader like a rather blatant exchange of favors. Obviously, Dr. Erickson's foreword will be valued in several respects. We would suggest, therefore, that you take out the dedication.

LeCron agreed, in his response of November 11, 1946, to change the dedication, and proposed the following: "Dedicated to Dr. Milton Erickson and his wife, Elizabeth, for their kindly help and manuscript criticism, which aided greatly in the preparation of this book." It was decided to omit Meyer since he had not read the manuscript.

In his reply to LeCron on November 18, Erickson wrote: "[Mrs. Erickson and I] are both disappointed, but Holsaert is right, and there would be no excuse at all for giving an opponent of hypnosis the slightest opportunity of damning your book, and the really important thing is your book, and not our personal satisfaction. . . ."

On January 7, 1947, Erickson informed LeCron that he had sent him the foreword and hoped that it was satisfactory.

In the preceding and subsequent correspondence, LeCron wrote to Erickson about various cases and about his experiments in hypnosis. For example, a May 17, 1947, letter contained a report of LeCron's testing of hypnotic subject with the assistance of an ophthalmologist. The subject was told to open her eyes and look at a flashlight near her right eye. Her pupil contracted when the light was turned on. Then she was told that the same test would be performed on the other eye, that she would see the light as before, and that the pupil would contract. An unlit flashlight was placed in front of her eye and the pupil contracted. LeCron said he believed that this proved the reality of hypnotic hallucinations.

On March 18, LeCron described a case of spontaneous regression. Erickson replied:

I've been laid up for the past six weeks with serum sickness, aggravated by benzedryl toxicity, and I've not yet fully recovered. Hence, the delay in my reply to your letter of March 18.

Concerning this spontaneous age regression without suggestion to the age of five, I've had that happen on a number of occasions. It usually signifies an excellent prognosis and a tremendous need for making unconscious memories conscious. . . .

In a letter of July 17, LeCron again proffered the possibility of Erickson's working with him in a private clinic. It seems there were delays in the establishment of the psychiatric hospital at UCLA. LeCron added:

> I wonder if you would give me your personal and confidential opinion as to Dr. C. Do you think she might be induced to enter? I know nothing about her except that she seems to be a leader in the field, and that we'll need a woman. As we want to feature brief psychotherapy, perhaps her ideas are too Freudian and orthodox. . . .

On July 23, Erickson sent his two-sentence reply:

Dear LeCron:

Do not consider Dr. C. under any circumstances. I shall write you details later.

Sincerely yours,
Milton H. Erickson

In a January 29, 1949, communication, LeCron discussed his plans to edit a compendium, entitled Experimental Hypnosis. *The book would consist of papers by 20 authorities explaining the nature of hypnosis and indicating successful areas of clinical application. It was published essentially as planned in 1952. LeCron consulted with Erickson regarding contributors and incorporated some of his recommendations in the final roster.*

In a letter dated April 27, 1949, LeCron indicated that he was trying to arrange a lecture for Erickson in California. In addition, the letter discussed his contact with Aldous Huxley:

> He wants me to work with him on a dual personality story, which he believes should be first done as a play or novel, probably the first. He says he can arrange production, and then it could be sold for much more as a screenplay. We are now trying to work out a suitable plot incorporating some of the situations and material learned from you. I

would want your approval of anything we use before publication of any kind. Of course, this is to be of fictional nature, and we want to bring in as much comedy as possible, though treating it entirely seriously. Of course, some of the episodes and situations can be developed in a very amusing way. Huxley knows nothing of the actual facts. He is eager to meet you and Mrs. Erickson, and I think you will find him very likable personally, as well as interesting. He has some bronchial difficulty, and I am quite convinced that it, and also his visual trouble, is psychogenic. I wish you could do some analytic work on him, though I have not mentioned it to him. He would be an interesting case, but beyond my abilities, I'm afraid.

In conclusion, LeCron added a personal note:

My wife joins in "best regards" to you and Mrs. Erickson. We certainly enjoyed meeting you, and all your kindness. We are looking forward to having you stay with us when you can come over this way. Just as soon as I find a better residence, I will urge a visit.

Then, on May 18, LeCron wrote:

I know how interested you are in institutional work, but my own idea is that for the benefit of family, etc., you should be in private practice at this time of your life, returning to the more desired field later with a good financial condition. And private practice will permit you to arrange your time for your other interest of research. The more I learn of psychotherapy and of hypnotism, the more convinced I become that the latter is the eventual solution for the former, and much more research and knowledge are needed. You are our best researcher, and your talents are needed there.

In a letter dated June 21, 1949, LeCron wrote Erickson regarding plans for the Ericksons to visit California over the July 4 holiday and spend some time with the LeCrons and the Huxleys.

Huxley is very tall and slender, about 54, a bit shy and very reserved until he feels a little acquainted, when he can relax and open up. His wife, Maria, is a Belgian, and much less reserved. They're most attractive people and we like them personally very much. They have displayed a lot of enthusiasm over meeting both of you, and are looking forward to it. . . .

By the way, Huxley is very well informed on hypnotism and tells me he is writing an essay of some kind about De Puysegur. He will talk to you on that subject, I am sure. I have taught him autohypnosis but have never obtained more than a medium stage with him.

A steady stream of letters continued to flow from LeCron to Erickson through 1949, many of them about LeCron's interest in the project with Huxley. Some contained LeCron's cases and research; others requested information from Erickson.

On April 24, 1950, LeCron wrote to Erickson explaining that he wanted to produce an article about why hypnotists are hard to hypnotize. He had sent the following mimeographed questionnaire to a number of experts.

I would like to obtain from you some statistical data for use in connection with some research. I would greatly appreciate your answering the following questions (I hope to tabulate the replies of about 50 "authorities"). This involves a consideration of why most workers with hypnosis are not themselves good hypnotic subjects, which I am sure is the case. The questions:

1. Are you a good hypnotic subject? Rate yourself as poor, fair, good, very good.
2. If not a good subject, can you analyze and state the reasons for this in your own case?
3. In your opinion, what do you believe are the main reasons why hypnotists are seldom good subjects?
4. May I quote you on any of your comments?

Thanking you for any information or comments, Leslie LeCron

Erickson responded with his letter of April 26.

The LeCron/Huxley collaboration on the screenplay never materialized, although they did remain friends. LeCron conducted hypnosis with Huxley's wife when she

was dying in the hospital. Throughout the years, Huxley referred a number of people to Erickson.

By 1953, there was correspondence about teaching programs in which LeCron and Erickson collaborated. A number of other experts were mentioned and there were discussions regarding whom to invite to present at various seminars.

On March 18, 1954, LeCron described his work with Mrs. G., indicating that he had induced a "36-hour deep trance" with her, apparently with good results. LeCron felt that he had uncovered a "dual personality." It seemed that one personality told him to "mind his own business" and criticized him thoroughly, explaining that she did not dislike LeCron but wanted to have nothing to do with him.

LeCron wrote to Erickson, asking his advice. He recalled that Morton Prince used hypnosis, but, "How did he squeeze Sally out without her consent?" He described the alter as an "evil malignant personality."

Erickson responded in a letter dated March 28, 1954.

To: Leslie M. LeCron
April 26, 1950

Dear LeCron:

The answer to your note [regarding the questionnaire] is going to be given informally. I'll just dictate the ideas that come to me as I read the questions:

(1) Are you a good hypnotic subject? The answer is no. I am probably the world's poorest hypnotic subject.

(2) My reason for being a poor hypnotic subject, I think, derives from the intensity of my interest in hypnotic processes—with the result that consciously I keep full tabs on everything without allowing my unconscious to take over. I know that in working with subjects like me, my primary problem is always to give the conscious mind some elaborate interest that so intrigues the conscious mind that I can deal directly with their unconscious. Additionally, everybody who has tried to hypnotize me has been a student of of mine. I have succeeded in doing automatic writing, hand levitation, and crystal gazing—but was so consciously alert that it was a laborious problem on my part to keep conscious elements out of my activity.

(3) You ask why I believe that hypnotists are seldom good subjects. I do not believe that is the case. I think hypnotists can be excellent subjects. The problem is this: most good hypnotists become interested in doing hypnosis rather than in experiencing it. Then it becomes a matter of the direction of interest and not a question of capability. In working with medical students, I found that medical students who who first became excellent hypnotists could be trained to be highly capable subjects, as soon as you redirected their interests. I also found that hypnotic subjects could be trained to become excellent hypnotists, if care was taken to redirect their actual interest. Of course there are always certain people who become interested in one direction and never can get interested in another direction. I have also found that competent hypnotists who had been doing a great deal of hypnosis could be trained to become excellent subjects if they could be outclassed in psychological manipulation—and that very often these excellent hypnotists would then become as interested in experiencing hypnosis as they previously had been in doing hypnosis. One other thing about making good subjects out of good hypnotists that I frequently encounter is the feeling of uncertainty and insecurity that many good hypnotists have about their actual capacity to induce hypnotic phenomena. I have worked out a technique wherein I employ a retrospective displacement of experiences and a displacement into the future, in order to correct their feelings of insecurity.

(4) You can quote me on these points, and if you want further information, I will try to give it to you.

Yours truly,
Milton H. Erickson, M.D.

To: Leslie M. LeCron
March 28, 1954

Dear Les:

I got home from San Francisco all right and spent quite a bit of time in the hospital getting intravenous and a few things like that. I started work again on the fifteenth, but am taking daily rests, quitting early and nonsense like that. I drink broth between meals to keep up my blood protein, which has a habit of going underground, or at least dropping out of sight.

You can see, therefore, that I do not regret the inability to get the May 20 date. You are quite right. Summer is not a good time, and if we do lecture, it would be better to arrange the lecture for September or even later.

Concerning Mrs. G., I would like to believe that there is a dual personality there, but your description indicates very strongly the dissociated state of a hysterical fugue. In bawling you out, in telling you to mind your own business and yet stating that there was no dislike of you, the behavior is quite characteristic of hysterical dissociated states. The only way to deal with them that I know of is essentially a matter of passivity and acceptance, with now and then encouragement offered to the effect that they discuss you and anything else.

I am not sure that Prince used hypnosis to squeeze Sally out. I think Sally merely got a little bit more subtle.

In such dissociated facets of the personality, there is a tremendous need to express hostility and aggression and, if given the opportunity, such an individual will sit quietly and the dissociated facet can become beautifully vituperative, with tremendous relief resulting. In fact, every effort should be made to arrange such aggression at a verbal level and I have also used the measure of letting them squeeze my hand, taking good care that I place my hand so that they could not really hurt it, but could think that they were crushing it. This will obviate their throwing things and other forms of violence.

I am sorry to be so slow in writing you, but I think you can understand why now.

Sincerely,
Milton H. Erickson, M.D.

In the follow-up letter of May 29, 1954, LeCron expressed the opinion that nothing important had been written regarding dual personalities since Morton Prince.

He inquired about Erickson's interest in collaborating on a book on the subject. Nothing resulted, however.

Although we do not have a record of many replies from Erickson, there was frequent correspondence from LeCron to Erickson in 1954 with news of LeCron's activities and of the Huxleys. There was also considerable correspondence between LeCron and Erickson in 1955, but again, the file consists primarily of letters from LeCron to Erickson.

The main subject of the 1955 correspondence was the collaboration on a seminar featuring Erickson, LeCron, and Ted Aston (a New York dentist who worked with Erickson and LeCron in these early years). The historical importance of the seminars is that they were among the earliest hypnosis workshops held in the United States to train professionals from medicine, dentistry, and psychology. Erickson was the acknowledged maestro of the group; LeCron spearheaded the organizational and promotional efforts.

At the same time, a group in New York led by Milton Kline was teaching hypnosis. Kline was one of the founders of the Society of Clinical and Experimental Hypnosis (SCEH) and the first editor of its journal. There was some tension between SCEH and the seminars group. The Erickson seminars, which eventually included two other professionals, Seymour Hershman, M.D., and Irving Secter, D.D.S., came to be known as the "Seminars in Hypnosis Foundation." Erickson, Aston, Hershman, and Secter subsequently were instrumental in establishing the American Society of Clinical Hypnosis and its educational wing, the Educational and Research Foundation.

The 1955 correspondence contained frequent references to Erickson's health problems, most of which seemed to be related to allergies. LeCron also had allergy problems, although more minor in nature.

In 1956, correspondence between LeCron and Erickson continued against an important background that should be noted. In 1955, the British Medical Association had recognized hypnosis as a legitimate treatment modality in medicine and dentistry. A similar policy position was stated by the American Medical Association (AMA) in 1958 (Crasilneck & Hall, 1985). The AMA endorsed hypnosis as offering much of value and advocated that clinical applications be taught in all medical schools.

LeCron presented a paper in May 1956, before the American Psychiatric Association, in which he described the state of hypnosis. He estimated that some 2,500 dentists in the United States used the technique. He pointed out, however, that little training was available for psychologists and psychiatrists, and he described the seminar series in which he and Erickson were involved, from the group's inception in 1954. He listed the instructors as himself; Erickson; William Kroger, an obstetrician and gynecologist; Hershman, a general practitioner; and Secter and Aston. Both Secter and Hershman were from Chicago.

LeCron described the seminar program as consisting of an intensive course with primary and advanced levels. It included lectures, demonstrations, discussions, roundtable luncheons, and evening practice sessions. Conducted over a three-day weekend, Friday and Saturday were devoted to the theoretical aspects of hypnosis, including information on hypnotizability tests, trance stages, self-hypnosis, misconceptions about hypnosis, and the history of hypnosis. On Sunday, the group was divided into medical and dental sections. Induction practice in the evening was supervised by instructors. The hypnotherapy section covered such topics as hypnotic phenomena, suggestions, uncovering techniques, induced conflicts, and the use of hypnosis in various medical specialities.

LeCron mentioned that the seminar group was seeking institutional or associational sponsorship, but that was not easily found. At the time, he pointed out, 1,200 people had attended the seminars, coming from almost every state in the United States.

At some point in 1956, dissension arose between Erickson and LeCron. On October 2, 1956, Erickson wrote to Bernard B. Raginsky, M.D., a Montreal physician who was a leader and then president of the SCEH, regarding his concern that a charlatan had addressed the society's chapter in Los Angeles, which was headed by LeCron. Erickson also wrote to Milton Kline, then editor of the Journal of Clinical and Experimental Hypnosis, *indicating that he thought that LeCron should be dropped from the Board of Advisory Editors.*

In a September 21, 1956, letter to Raginsky, Erickson had remarked that LeCron had been a member of the Seminars on Hypnosis teaching faculty, but that Erickson and other faculty members felt that he did not maintain a high degree of professionalism. LeCron evidently had used his relative as a practitioner although that person had no clinical experience or training. Additionally, Erickson said he was disappointed because he believed LeCron affiliated with nonprofessional people, and concluded that he should not be continued as an SCEH member. He also recommended that the Los Angeles branch of SCEH have its membership thoroughly scrutinized.

Erickson was tenacious in confronting practitioners whom he thought were unethical and he spared no effort in tracking down perceived discrepancies. With regard to LeCron, he wrote to the registrar of the University of Colorado at Boulder asking the specifics of LeCron's degree, which he believed was an A.B. degree conferred around 1920. It seems LeCron advertised himself as having a degree in psychology. On November 20, 1958, Erickson received a letter from the registrar confirming that LeCron had received a bachelor's degree in history in 1919.

A brochure found in the LeCron–Erickson file announced medical and dental hypnosis symposia in October, November, and December 1958 in Phoenix, Las Vegas, and Miami Beach respectively. Instructors included Leslie LeCron and M. Eric Wright, Ph.D., M.D. Erickson was not on the faculty of any of these meetings. All of the instructors were identified as SCEH members. It seems that by 1958 Erickson no longer collaborated with LeCron.

Even though Erickson confronted LeCron vigorously, in both 1961 and 1964, between the two discussing professional issues concerning hypnosis.

The last correspondence in the Erickson–LeCron file was dated 1964.

Weitzenhoffer

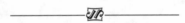

André Weitzenhoffer was one of the most influential researchers in the field of hypnosis. In 1959, he and Ernest Hilgard published the Stanford Hypnotic Susceptibility Scale, Forms A and B, which to this day remains the most widely used measure of hypnotizability in experimental hypnosis. Weitzenhoffer published General Techniques of Hypnotism in 1957. He was one of the members of the editorial board of The American Journal of Clinical Hypnosis during Erickson's tenure as editor-in-chief.

In his capacity as Journal editor, Erickson wrote to André Weitzenhoffer on October 2, 1959, with regard to Weitzenhoffer's paper, which was subsequently published as "Unconscious or Co-conscious? Reflections Upon Certain Recent Trends in Medical Hypnosis" (Weitzenhoffer, 1960). In this article, Weitzenhoffer decried what he viewed as a nonspecific, overly inclusive use of the term "unconscious" by medical hypnotists. He went on to stratify various functions and characteristics of consciousness and to contend that much of what these hypnotic practitioners considered manifestations of unconscious activity actually involved conscious participation.

Weitzenhoffer hypothesized that a secondary personality, or a "co-conscious system," operates when responses are elicited through finger- or pendulum-

*movement techniques. He questioned the widely held assumption that the uncon-
scious mind produces responses to suggestions, and urged better (that is, more
specific) questioning practices in order to obtain therapeutic data from hypnotized
subjects. In conclusion, he recommended clarification of the noted ambiguities in
references to and practices utilizing the unconscious. He espoused studies to de-
lineate specific therapeutic factors in hypnosis similar to those used in the medical
sciences.*

To: André Weitzenhoffer
October 2, 1959

Dear André:

I have read your paper with much interest and find myself in extensive
agreement. It will go in the April 1960 issue. However, I note that you
reify id, ego, superego, and Unconscious in much the same fashion as the
medical and dental hypnotists reify the "unconscious."

I know I use the term "unconscious" in a very loose way, because I am
dealing with patients and students—how else to convey my meaning, yet
I do not believe I actually deceive myself—at least, not too much, I hope.

I feel you use "secondary personality" when you mean personality facets—for example, the aspect in the home, the aspect socially, the aspect
in the bar, the aspect in a forbidding situation, etc. Each can be a rather
complete and yet totally different thing.

One thing you overlooked in the paper is multiplicity of communication. For example, I have had a patient in the waking state give as much
historical fact as could be remembered. In the trance state, I obtained
more. With Yes–No hand motions, secured more. Then found that the
following could take place, since I give my patients freedom to answer yes
or no with head, hand, or finger movements:

Q: Is there more history?
A: (Hand) No. (Head) Yes.
Q: So you have told it all:
A: (Hand) Yes. (Head) No.
Q: Do you need to repeat?
A: (Hand) No. (Head) Yes.

Q: Perhaps you ought to repeat the history, because in listening I may not have understood accurately.

A: (No response.) (No response.)

Then, upon simple, not loaded, instruction, my patient begins to relate in the trance the same historical sequence and I watch hands, head, and fingers.

Item 1:   (Hand, head, finger)
          One, two, or all make "yes" signal.
Item 2:   Hand moves yes; finger or head, or both, move "no."
          (This item checked for reexamination.)
Item 3:   Related easily as before. Head, hand, finger—one, two, or all make a no movement.
          (Item checked for further inquiry.)

Item 1:   Later found verifiable and true.
Item 2:   Later found to have repressed additional elements not yet available, but regarded as complete, marked by the "feeling that there should be more but there isn't."
Item 3:   Later found to be a belief, mistaken and not founded in fact, but accepted as absolutely factual.

In that last comment, the use of the word "accurately" could be a cue word, but it is a correct word in its application to me. Also, I have employed the measure of saying, "Perhaps you ought to repeat that material so that this time I can write it down."

Inquiry indirectly much later discloses that my patient is unaware of how I have "stumbled" onto "completely forgotten (repressed) facts." For example, one patient readily listed by name, date, duration, and place a series of affairs. Fortunately, I had explained such head, finger, and hand movements to her. She related accounts of seven affairs in the waking state, and confirmed that account in the trance state. In giving the original account, she said, "My first affair was—," but I noticed that her hand did a "no" sign.

She introduced each account of the succeeding affair by saying, "The next man" or "the next affair" or the "next involvement." All went well until she reached the fourth account, during which her finger maintained a "no" position. At the sixth, another finger "no."

In the trance, she related the same account, but gave me the "no" signal, much as you see students who agree or disagree with you, nodding or shaking their heads without being aware of it.

I recorded the accounts and later read them to her in the waking and trance states. Invariably as she listened attentively I noted either with her head, hand, or finger the "no" signals. This rereading was not exactly that simple, since I read parts of the accounts at random, apparently to insure that the information was correct as to the spelling of names, the identity of the month or the street address, always saying, "And now the next one was on XYZ Street, was it not?" She would agree verbally, but on those three instances, there was the consistent negative sign.

Further in therapy, while she was discussing her economic problems, I handed her a slip of paper bearing this communication.

$$\longleftarrow 2 \longrightarrow 3 \longrightarrow ? \longrightarrow 4 \longrightarrow$$

She looked at it in bewilderment and asked me if it was supposed to mean anything. I told her that one could give a meaning to it. She looked puzzled, continued with her discussion, but in the last few minutes of the hour had a startled reaction, told me that in some way that she could not account for, she had omitted relating the affair she had had at age 23. This she told with her hand in "yes" position. She established no connection between the slip of paper in the first part of the hour and this rush of memory in the last few minutes.

At another time, while she was discussing her child, I handed her a sheet of paper in the center of which I had written in small characters, $7 + 2 = 9$. She misinterpreted this to be some oblique reference to the child's school work, launched into a discussion of that, misspoke the teacher's name, reacted with profound astonishment, and told me of another "forgotten" affair. Her hand during the narration maintained the "yes" position.

Still later, when she happened to raise the question of my views on Sunday school for children, I replied, "The problem that concerns me is the first three words in the Bible." She looked at me blankly, then with utter terror, and then launched into an extremely disorderly emotional account of her first sexual experience, which she had aggressively solicited from an "old man" and to which she had subsequently violently reacted and then completely repressed. As she related her account, hand, finger, and head signs for "yes" were repeatedly given.

At a subsequent hour she went through her sexual history slowly, laboriously giving the ten accounts, now and then making a slight error in her narrative, but correcting it shortly.

Now this isn't the only such patient. I've had it happen many times and in varying ways. This particular patient still does not know that I deliberately stimulated her memories. She made remarkably rapid progress after the recovery of that initial incident.

Sometimes I have disclosed to patients the meaning of my cryptic stimuli and have had them recognize it immediately. Sometimes I have had them spontaneously discover the connection with their productions. I have had patients as long as five years later spontaneously recall and identify some clue I had given them.

Well, I've enjoyed these little discoveries, and I hope they aren't too much of a headache for you.

Sincerely yours,
Milton H. Erickson

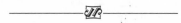

Erickson's October 2, 1959, letter certainly had an impact. In his 1960 article (p. 180), Weitzenhoffer included this footnote:

In view of some comments with regard to reification which were made in respect to my use of the expression "the unconscious" by one of the editors of this Journal following my submission of this paper for publication, a note seems in order here to offset any further misunderstandings. When talking for myself I use the expression "the unconscious" as a convenient abbreviation denoting a certain totality or system of unconscious processes having certain characteristics, and I neither think of this totality as having a spatio-temporal locus or being an entity in any other sense of being an object of discourse. On the other hand, when I am talking about these unconscious processes as some other writer writes about them, I am no longer presenting my own concept but his, and if this includes a reification, this should obviously not be ascribed to me. These remarks, I would like to add, apply equally well to my use of such terms as "ego," "id," etc., in this paper. In any case, I must emphasize the fact that the question of reification is not the problem being considered and is not even relevant here, for I am only concerned with deciding which ones of a number of possible systems of unconscious processes are being subsumed under the expression "the unconscious" by current medical hypnotists.

From: André Weitzenhoffer
June 10, 1960

Dear Milton:

As you know I have been conducting research on time distortion on a USPH grant. The main purpose of this work has been to see if I could find a more objective way of studying time distortions than has been used in the past. If this could be done, it might lead to two things: help to establish the "reality" of time distortion in a different sense than has been done previously, and give us new tools for studying the nature of the perception of time as well as of time distortion. Besides using tests similar to those used by [Linn] Cooper, I have introduced other kinds of tests built around time-dependent phenomena such as flicker fusion and apparent movement. Thus far the results have all been negative in the sense that while we have been able to get good subjective evidence that our subjects were experiencing time distortion, their performance on the tests has not been any different. This is even true in the case of the memorizing of nonsense syllables.

Now I was very much impressed by your demonstration of time distortion with Mrs. M. last fall in S.F. I do not think I will feel satisfied with my research until I have made certain that the negative results are not caused by my own personal equation. As a matter of fact, I am a little disappointed because I really believed that I would observe certain effects of time distortion on the tests I used. Now, when I applied for my grant I made provisions for the possibility of bringing you in as a consultant. I have until September 1 to carry out this work. Are there any possibilities that you could come here for a few days to work with me on this problem and see if with you inducing time distortions we can get the effects I feel ought to take place? I would pay your expenses, and of course any publication coming out of the part in which you collaborated would bear your name as co-author. The other alternative would be my coming down to Phoenix or some other suitable place (for you). The problem here is mainly that of equipment. The instruments I am using at present are fairly bulky and not the easiest to carry on a plane. I hope, however, to shortly have a miniaturized version of one of the more important and larger pieces of apparatus and in this case, I would have no further problem. If more feasible, we could work out perhaps several short visits on your part, rather than one longer one. July would be the best time in many ways for our getting together, however, the important thing is to get together with you and I will work things out at my end to make most effective use of what you could give to the project.

As ever,
André

To: André Weitzenhoffer
July 11, 1960

Dear André:

As I know from long experience, the best experimental subjects are those who are highly motivated to achieve some particular goal of personal value to them. In college students you run across those dedicated to contributing to science, to achieving new understandings, to undergoing new experiences.

I have found that patients are often excellent experimental subjects since they have much to gain. For example, certain cancer patients have such unlimited motivation that they can do the most amazing things.

In time distortion, Cooper ran into a tremendous problem finding subjects with proper motivation. He soon found out that he could not offer pay because then the results were questionable and definitely suspect in many instances. He had to comb through the student body to get subjects that were of the "responsive" type—such as Mrs. M.

I do not see any way of coming to San Francisco until late this year. I'll be in Florida and Venezuela in August.

I am going to see if any of my subjects will be in San Francisco and can help you.

Hastily,
Milton H. Erickson

With regard to the Erickson/Weitzenhoffer 1960 correspondence, it should be noted that during the first half of the twentieth century, most scholars believed that all of the phenomena of hypnosis had been documented and investigated in the preceding century. However, in 1948, Linn Cooper (a Washington, D.C., physician) wrote a groundbreaking paper on the phenomenon of time distortion.

Erickson collaborated with Cooper on the book Time Distortion in Hypnosis *(Cooper & Erickson, 1954). This work detailed Cooper's experimental investigation of time distortion and Erickson's clinical applications of the phenomenon. The book constituted a significant contribution to clinical and experimental hypnosis. "The only detailed study of a single specific hypnotic technique—aside from that of symptom disappearance by direct verbal suggestion—with which I personally am familiar" (Rosen, 1959, ix). A second edition of* Time Distortion in Hypnosis *was released in 1959 with the addition of a section on time condensation.*

In his June 10 inquiry to Erickson, Weitzenhoffer demonstrated his thoroughness as an investigator. Erickson, in his reply of July 11, reiterated how important he considered the hypnotic subjects' motivation. Remember that in the early part of his career, Erickson was primarily a researcher.

Erickson wrote two papers about the case of Anne, "Hypnotically Oriented Psychotherapy in Organic Brain Damage" (Erickson, 1963) and "Hypnotically Oriented Psychotherapy in Organic Brain Disease—An Addendum" (Erickson, 1964c). He described a novel technique in which he used frustration to help a patient overcome the limitations resulting from a cerebrovascular accident. Erickson asked Weitzenhoffer to critique the manuscript that became the first paper. In an undated eight-page, handwritten letter, he described some of the innovative techniques that he used to provoke Anne into marshaling personal resources. A second handwritten letter is a precursor to a seminal paper Erickson was writing on the caifusion technique (Erickson, 1964a).

To: André Weitzenhoffer
[Circa 1963]

Dear André:

I'm including two papers which I would like to have you read and freely offer criticisms of them.

Most important is: Have I made the brain case clear enough? I hesitate to include the details of the therapeutic hour because it would be so meaningless to the reader. For example, with Anne alone in the room, I would talk casually about her children. She was horribly homesick for them, and just as soon as I saw tears in her eyes, I would speak casually of her most recent gain in weight, jestingly accuse her of developing a pot belly. At her effort to smile at my very feeble stupid joke, I would remind her of her first pregnancy, how good it would feel to remember the first nursing of her right breast, go on to tell a stupid joke, assure her that I would respect her privacy in my history taking, and hence I would not ask about the first time her husband played with her breasts, left and right, narrate a shaggy dog story, making it very prolonged until her vexation became most apparent, tell a brief very funny joke, and then another brief funny joke right up to the final punch line, leaving the story in midair just at the moment she was hanging on my words for the denouement, then tell her to guess the ending and dismiss her. In other words, I used the therapeutic hour to create a confused welter of mixed emotions of all kinds, mixed ideas of the present, of the future, reminiscences, past events of strong emotional quality—her husband gladly told me their own secret language of lovemaking—which I fitted into the casual discussion unexpectedly just the day her husband would be arriving in Phoenix that evening. Her confusion and bewilderment, rage, anger, fury, intense embarrassment, the haunting of her mind, until the next session, about the punch line of the joke I had withheld, the haunting of her mind by my intrusion into a single simple casual statement of a very special lovemaking word she and her husband used without my seeming not to know what the word meant and certainly it didn't belong in that context—in other words, she was kept in a constant almost obsessional "guessing" state of thinking.

The careful use of that meaningless (seemingly so) use of their private love language, a word at a time, while I was describing different kinds of palm trees or something like that and she was anticipating her husband's arrival that evening led to the first intercourse in many months, with her the aggressor. He had restrained himself because he had learned how much it pained her. At the next session, she excitedly, with extreme embarrassment [said], "I . . . I . . . I . . . . fucked Vic. . . . . . . sorry [about] word . . . hurt little . . . but I liked it." (Much later she explained that she had used the vulgar word because no other word could be said—that was the first word of that meaning she had learned—that all of the special love language had come forth in her and was uttered with ease.) Then she left the room saying, "He . . . tell." Her husband then came in frightfully embarrassed and said, "Anne wants me to tell you about last night. I'm embarrassed and don't know what to think, but to me, I, well, I think it means she is making tremendous strides in recovery. She was all excited when I came in, she trembled and staggered and I was alarmed. I thought she was having another stroke, I put my arms around her, partly to kiss her on the left cheek, and she dragged me over to the bed and swarmed all over me, almost tore my clothes off me, she only had a dress on and she let that fall off and I think every word we ever used, that I told you about before, she used and she really raped me. Then she did the same thing this morning and she had climaxes, several of them. It was like our most passionate lovemaking when we were first married. Then on the way here she said, 'You—me—last night, this morning, you tell doctor.' That's the most she has talked since her brain hemorrhage. Now I'll give you more details if you want them. I'll do anything to help her, but knowing how painful intercourse has been for her, I was afraid, but the way she was, I was just helpless. It sounds funny, a man my size (6 feet 2) being raped, but that's it."

I told him that apparently I was succeeding in my plans of teaching her to talk and getting her brain to function in a new way, that Anne was beginning to understand and wanted me to know through his ease of speech that I was effecting changes in her. He added, "It sure scared hell out of me when I saw her trembling and shaking and then when she dropped her dress and started on my clothes, well I just lost control."

Another example, Anne showed me a whole lot of pictures of her children at various ages. Well, with an aphasic alexic woman you wanted to teach how to talk, it didn't seem right or sensible to make the appropriate proper comments that one would to a normal person. I looked at each picture silently, and when finished, I went the very limit in disparaging insulting comments on each picture, disdainfully handed them back. She was glaring at me in the most towering speechless rage imaginable with murder in her eyes. It was truly a horrible sight. Then I smiled sweetly and with a merry chuckle said, "They really are sweet kids, aren't they?"

André, you could almost have physically photographed the emotional and mental flip-flop that she did, and she said, "They are, they really are" easily and fluently. Then with utter astonishment, she spent 10 minutes trying to say in self-bewilderment, "I . . . . talk."

But I see no way of putting the above into print because our readers haven't got the clinical understandings requisite to recognize that I built up in her the same kind of speechless fury that would occur in a normal person, then transformed the situation into a normal one by my smile, chuckle, and normal remark, and thereby evoked a normal response from her.

I assure you that these sessions were a peculiar play upon every possible pattern of stimulus–response situation I could dream up. . . .

Milton H. Erickson

To: André Weitzenhoffer
[Circa 1963]

Dear André:

I wrote this hastily last night. It can be properly filled out. Stored away, I have many old manuscripts, starting with such ideas as, "If your left hand were your right hand, then your right hand wouldn't be your right hand. Instead your right hand would be your left hand, and your right-hand, left-hand pants pocket would be your right-hand left-hand pants pocket; and your left-hand pants pocket would be your right-hand pants pocket. But that would put it on your other leg." (I trust, merely trust, that you followed me without difficulty.)

You can start a confusion technique with literally anything; for example, that chair (1) is *there* (1) and that chair (2) (pointing to another) is *there* (2). And where is *there*, and if that chair (1) isn't there (2), and that chair (2) isn't there (1), tilting the head slightly to direct the subject's gaze, but we might talk about yesterday instead of today, but last year has so many yesterdays.

It's really simple. Keep time, particularly present, recent, and remote past, in mind as you say obviously factual things, but without leaving your subject time to catch his breath or to interrupt, or to reach any clear understanding. Then when you offer a clear understandable idea, he grabs it and holds on for dear life, even if he has to regress to do it.

In any event, on the yellow sheet is a crude rushed paper I wrote last night after I got ready for bed.

Should it be worked up? Should I do it? I wish you would collaborate because my rapidity of shifting ideas on papers like this tends to ruin them, and I feel that I need your clarity of thought.

Sincerely,

Milton

P.S. Betty can't stand to read this material. She has the reaction of being so irritated by it that she escapes into a trance—so do others—and some laboriously follow along and go into a trance. And when people get too irritated, I shift into another technique, which they gladly accept.

P.S. by Betty. Milton is wrong when he says I escape into a trance! Some subjects may react that way, but the technique irritates me so that I refuse to cooperate in any way. I leave the room if possible.

To: André Weitzenhoffer
April 8, 1963

Dear André:

I think it is time I put into the literature an explanation of the "Confusion Technique," which everybody talks about but I believe with little real understanding, so I am writing it up in rough form as I originally worked on it though I have now abbreviated it to what seems to be nearly a handshake.

Always in the past I have been accused of leaving most of the meat out of my papers and presenting too little material.

Will you look over the enclosed and see if it is reasonably comprehensible?

Put your comments in freely because I'll try to meet them adequately without changing the actual content. What I am afraid of is that I have either oversimplified or not explained adequately. All I really know is how to do it quickly and easily.

I'm ashamed to ask you to do this favor for me considering how hard you work but I know of nobody else with your clarity of understanding. So please forgive me.

And if you are willing to make it a collaborative paper, I shall be highly honored. In fact, I urge you to do so.

Sincerely,

Milton H. Erickson, M.D.

The manuscript that Erickson sent Weitzenhoffer for review was eventually published as "The Confusion Technique in Hypnosis" in the The American Journal of Clinical Hypnosis *(AJCH) with Erickson (1964a) as the sole author. Twelve years earlier, Erickson had included a section on the confusion technique in the chapter "Deep Hypnosis and Its Induction" in* Experimental Hypnosis, *edited by Leslie LeCron (Erickson, 1952). The confusion technique was one of Erickson's most innovative and important contributions to hypnosis. These verbal and nonverbal methods created disorientation, disrupting habitual sets and paving the way for enhanced responsiveness.*

A 1958 article by Erickson (1958a), "Naturalistic Techniques of Hypnosis," described a demonstration he conducted in which confusion was used. The 1964 article (Erickson, 1964a), reflecting Erickson's own advancements, was much more inclusive than the earlier pieces. It covered a host of topics related to the technique and its application.

At the time of his reply, Weitzenhoffer, in conjunction with a psychiatric colleague, Bernie Gorton, M.D., was compiling a book about Erickson's work. In a section of his April 8 letter, which is not included in this book, Weitzenhoffer discussed previous experiences with publishers and options for the book. The volume was neither completed nor published. Jay Haley took over the project and, in 1967, compiled a collection of Erickson's papers in Advanced Techniques of Hypnosis and Therapies *(Haley, 1967). Still, Erickson's letter to Weitzenhoffer is testimony to the esteem in which he held his colleague. It was high praise, indeed, for Erickson to tell Weitzenhoffer, "I know of nobody else with your clarity of understanding."*

The Weitzenhoffer file contains a number of exchanges in which Weitzenhof-

fer offers continuing critiques of drafts of Erickson's papers, including that on the confusion method and papers on the therapy of patients with organic problems.

From: André Weitzenhoffer
April 17, 1963

Dear Milton,
    . . . Re: "Confusion Technique." That is a wonderful idea and after looking over your first draft, I think you did a darn good job. I'll be glad to try and improve on it, if I can. As for my being a coauthor, I doubt that what little I could contribute would justify this. In any case it is I who would be proud to do the paper jointly with you. Well we don't have to decide about this until the paper gets in final shape. One thing, I would like to include it in your book. One section I have worked up has to do with techniques, and in order to do this, I have had to turn to some of the taped material to supplement the available papers. This material is now being typed up in ms. form. When I get it back, I probably will send it and the first section to you for comments before I proceed further along similar lines. After you read this material you may want to add or to write an extra paper to take up certain things which you may feel need taking up. . . .

As ever,
André

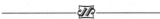

In the following letter, Erickson discusses with Weitzenhoffer his view that a mutual colleague, an expert in hypnosis, often overlooked details to his detriment. That section has been omitted. Erickson segued into two clinical anecdotes in which he demonstrated the extent of his ability to utilize minimal cues for a patient's benefit. The anecdotes are included here as prime examples of Erickson's aptitude for utilization of even the most subtle of naturally occurring elements.

To: André Weitzenhoffer
June 20, 1963

Dear André:

. . . Subjects in a good trance can pick up minimal cues. Did you ever watch a 6-month-old baby read the mother's face accurately? Most subjects do not recognize minimal cues but respond to them.

I have played the trick with a subject of bringing him out of the trance and returning him to the trance by the minimal cue of a slight unrecognizable change in the rhythm of my breathing. Ray Birdwhistell* is the only chap I know who can check up on me quite well. The subject always thinks it is their own spontaneous act and hence they can accept and respond adequately.

I just got a long distance call from Texas tonight from a doctor who had referred a patient to me for psychological impotence. He was a good hypnotic subject. I got all the history out of him that I needed using one respiratory rhythm and reached the conclusion that he really loved her but that performing the sex act with such a delightful person terrified him.

Then I got a very searching account of his wife's emotional behavior when she felt libidinous, had him almost relive it for me—"vivify" would be the better word—then as I noted his vivification I memorized what seemed to be his wife's respiratory rhythm as he explained her passionate feelings. I had to exert extreme care in the questioning to avoid the implication or appearance of undue and morbid curiosity.

With this as a general background, every therapeutic thing I said was with his wife's respiratory rhythm as I judged it to be.

That was two years ago, and the doctor who referred him to me wanted my opinion on another case he had just sent up to Phoenix, so I got an up-to-date report on the previous case. I had spent just about 6 hours with the man who had not been able to get an erection for 3 years. Now, he has one unaccountably available whenever his wife feels so inclined. She was asking the Texas doctor a few days ago what on earth I did to her husband. She knows that it is entirely a response to her feelings which he "divines" because he never has an erection unless she is in the mood and the marriage is now most happy.

---

*Birdwhistell was an anthropologist and a renowned expert on nonverbal behavior.

. . . In colloborating with Kubie and Hill and Buckner they made me write and rewrite until they could understand everything.

Usually I incubate my papers a year ot two or even longer, to be sure I get them completely informative.

Sincerely,
Milton H. Erickson, M.D.

In an earlier section of his June 20 letter, Erickson criticized a research colleague. He contended that inadequate attention to detail might have confounded research that his colleague had conducted. Erickson was well known for his seemingly uncanny ability to detect subtleties and nuances in people. The passage included here is an example of the manner in which Erickson ingeniously utilized "minimal cues," small but important facets of a patient's experience.

To: André Weitzenhoffer
July 5, 1963

Dear André:

Thanks for the suggestions on the aphasia paper. It made me see some awfully big holes. I'm going over it and trying to clarify it.

You see, a couple of days ago, Betty asked me a simple question to which I replied, I thought, with comprehensible simplicity. She, Robert aged 18, and Roxie aged 13 really hooted at my complete stupidity. I knew I was right; they agreed wholeheartedly that I was incredibly wrong.

Later, Betty sat me down and said, "That is the outrageous exasperating thing you are always doing." She reminded me of the question and my answer, and then went on to explain, "I'm reasonably intelligent but it has taken me 18 hours of hard thinking to find out that your answer was right. It's that habit of yours of jumping from Point A to Point H, leaving out all the informative steps of B, C, D, E, F, and G, and expecting your listener to make the same enormous jump that you did."

"Now let's take the question as Point A. That leads to the thought B, and clearly and understandably, from B you go to C and the picture gets clearer. And so on for D, E, F, and G. Then your listener understands and is in full agreement. I've explained to Robert and Roxie and they know you're right. But you are always doing that."

Your comments really jarred me into some intelligent thinking. I am having it retyped and sent to you. Now maybe I have put in too much!

Let me give you a clinical example. This college-bred person needing therapy flatly refused the concept of hypnosis or of an unconscious mind.

I replied, "It will be rather easy to convince you of an unconscious mind. Now if I say 'table' what word comes to your mind?" The answer was "chair." "All right, (blue)." "Sky" was the reply.

Then I said, "Now I am going to say three numbers that are related to each other *in only one way*. I will name them and instantly I want you to name three numbers between 20 and 100, say them instantly, that are related in exactly the same way." I named 1, 2, 17. Almost instantly, my patient said, "23, 47, 91."

My patient worked on that problem 2 weeks and said, "Well, I got it worked out finally. I tried everything I knew, and nothing made sense even though you had told me I was right in saying those numbers. Well, last night, I went out to Newtons Prime Rib (a restaurant) for dinner, and as I looked at my slice of meat, I knew without thinking, 'They're prime numbers.' "

My next remark was, "How much of the serving of prime rib did you leave?" My patient was startled and said, "I left about half of it. How did you know?"

How?

Step A—College bred

Step B—The numbers problem

Step C—Hungry, restaurant

Step D—Newtons serves large helpings

Step E—"Looked at meat"—a *problem* of eating all of that large serving

Step F—*Prime* rib problem

Step G—Problem = Problem, and both were prime.

How can you get to college without learning prime numbers, and so you eliminate the question of odd and even by throwing in 2.

The patient concluded that somewhere out of the unconscious mind came the answer, since all conscious mind work had failed.

So keep this weakness of my mind well in mind when you go over my papers.

Betty read this and said, "With my thinking I would come up with 21, 22, and 37." Immediately I recognized that out of that laborious listing of steps I had omitted the really most important one of all. *Betty does simple straight-line thinking.* My patient was *schizoid* and I knew that the answer would unexpectedly come to mind.

I won't ask Heaven to help me, but I do ask you.

Sincerely,

Milton H. Erickson, M.D.

———————⟨ℳ⟩———————

In this fascinating letter, Erickson provided Weitzenhoffer with a map of how he thought, how he conceptualized the clinical task. It was clear that this patient was not going to accept didactic persuasion regarding the existence of an unconscious mind. Erickson, therefore, created a context in which the patient would "experience" his unconscious. He worked on the level of guiding associations, striving to understand the web of associations within his patients that "drove" cognitive and behavioral limitations. Describing psychotherapy as the reassociation of internal life, he elicited constructive associations so that effective behavior could be "spontaneously" generated to the credit of the patient.

Erickson respected Weitzenhoffer greatly, and sent him a number of papers, including "Hypnotically Oriented Psychotherapy in Organic Brain Damage," subsequently published in the American Journal of Clinical Hypnosis *(Erickson, 1963).*

An exchange of letters between Erickson and Weitzenhoffer in January and February 1965 began with an inquiry from Erickson regarding Weitzenhoffer's status in the American Society of Clinical Hypnosis (ASCH). His membership had lapsed, Weitzenhoffer explained, as a result of his increasing disenchantment with the functioning of the organization. He said that he was also disillusioned with the Society for Clinical and Experimental Hypnosis (SCEH). Erickson did not respond to Weitzenhoffer's concern. Instead, he maintained that ASCH was not feuding with SCEH, but that it was the reverse that was true.

In Weitzenhoffer's reply of February 1, he lamented the snub he perceived in the failure of both ASCH and SCEH to elevate him to officer status despite his contributions to the field. Erickson responded by explaining the manner in which early officers of ASCH were chosen. He was frank about the extent to which he engineered appointments and elections, subtly and gently implying that Weitzenhoffer was too sensitive for these positions. The men he chose as officers, he said, were much "thicker-skinned," better able to withstand the personal attacks that marked those controversial times. Erickson did seek recognition for Weitzenhoffer by placing him in a responsible position at the American Journal of Clinical Hypnosis. *To the editor's knowledge, Weitzenhoffer to this day has never held elected office in either society.*

To: André Weitzenhoffer
January 13, 1965

Dear André:

The question of your personal feelings about the Societies will not in any way affect my personal regard for you. That is a matter apart from the Societies.

However, for your information, not since the latter part of 1958, or perhaps it was actually the beginning of 1959, has ASCH in any way ever feuded with SCEH. I know that over and over again SCEH has published falsely that we have taken issue with them. We haven't. That has been a rigid policy. It is true that Milton V. Kline has falsely misrepresented his degree and that I pointed that out in a book review* but I would have done so if I were reviewing a book by you and found that you deliberately falsified your degrees. I feel strongly that an author should not deliberately deceive his reader. But this was not an attack on SCEH. In brief, the "political struggle" has been one-sided, with ASCH nonparticipatory. We have screened news notes which were legitimate for publication, and have not used them for fear that they might be interpreted as attacks on SCEH.

[Erickson then recounts his perspectives on some of the notables in the SCEH and financial and political difficulties with that society.]

As for you, I hope you stay in ASCH. I like your name on the editorial masthead.

---

*In the review of a book edited by Kline, the first editor of the *International Journal of Clinical and Experimental Hypnosis* (official organ of the SCEH), Erickson noted that Kline had misrepresented his degree as Ph.D. when in fact it was Ed.D. The review appeared in the *American Journal of Clinical Hypnosis* (1965, 7, 94).

May I hear from you before your unconscious consigns this letter to limbo?

Sincerely,
Milton H. Erickson, M.D.

———————— 🎵 ————————

The following letter from Betty Erickson to Weitzenhoffer and his reply refer to a book of Erickson's collected papers that was being compiled by Weitzenhoffer. The project actually had been initiated in 1957 by Bernie Gorton, M.D., who died in 1959. Subsequently, the project was taken over by Weitzenhoffer, and then by Jay Haley, who published a selection of the papers as Advanced Techniques of Hypnosis and Therapy *(Haley, 1967). Erickson's complete papers were published posthumously in 1980, edited by Ernest L. Rossi, Ph.D. (Ericksen & Rossi, 1980a–d).*

To: André Weitzenhoffer
From: Betty Erickson
January 27, 1965

Dear André:

Sitting on my table of unfinished work, as it has for many, many months, is the manuscript copy of the edited material for Milton's book, which you sent to Milton. He did want me to read it critically for my comments, suggestions, etc. I plunged in a couple of times, but I'm sorry. I might as well face the facts; I just haven't got time. One issue of the Journal—which I help to edit, proof, mark up, etc.—is no sooner done than the next is upon us. I'm also responsible for considerable correspondence, in connection with both the Journal and Milton's practice. I hoped to have extra time when we turned over the International Relations committee to Yanovski, but, as usual, "Work expands to fill the time available" (Parkinson).

I'm sorry to have been a bottleneck. However, I think it's high time I was bypassed. Now the question is, how much current material of Milton's current output has to be consolidated into the book?

I think I should give you the bad, or good, news (according to how you look at it) that Milton has a large number of roughly written, semipolished, and almost-finished articles in various spots in his office. Furthermore, he has more planned in his head.

In other words, a complete collection of Erickson's works can ONLY be published posthumously.

I think that we should stop right *now*, if not sooner, and publish the stuff, as to date. What do you think? If so, what is to be done next to get the show on the road?

I'm going to ask Milton to scribble off a note to be added to this letter, which is being written on scratch paper and will be transcribed after he leaves tomorrow for a week in Regina, Saskatchewan.

Cordially,
Betty Erickson

To: André Weitzenhoffer
February 3, 1965

Dear André:

With only an assertion that I regret profoundly the genuine distress occasioned you, please read my explanation of what has happened.

At the time of the founding of ASCH, I realized at once it could be done only if we had psychology emphasized. Therefore, as *my* choice I proposed Frank Pattie because he was the only one really known to the organizing group. I knew you, but none of the dentists did nor did most of the physicians. You were an excellent book but not a person, if you understand what I mean. I put forth arguments for Pattie as founding president. Pattie pointed out that, though I lacked a Ph.D., I could emphasize psychology as completely as he could, that I could also emphasize medicine, psychiatry, a professorial background in both psychiatry and psychology, and that in the organizing group there was no other such person. Hence I was made the founding president despite personal ambitions of others. There were no dissenting votes.

Before definitively organizing the society, I emphasized that it should be set up in such a fashion that both medicine and dentistry would have a motivation for continuance of interest. This could come if we did not too quickly satisfy personal ambitions. Accordingly, the presidency was first set at two years with the full knowledge that as soon as possible it would probably be reduced to one year, thus to make possible more personal satisfactions. Also, we agreed unanimously that if I were the first president, a psychologist should follow. Pattie had the advantage of having been considered a possible first president. So that settled that. Medicine and psychiatry well emphasized with psychology in the background, now it was time to put psychology into the foreground.

We also debated the problem of the third and fourth presidencies— these would have to come from medicine and dentistry, but whom? [Erickson names a physician] became extremely opportunistic, as did two other medical men. All three were known to me as competent builder-uppers who invariably wrecked their achievements once fully accomplished.

That's when the life of ASCH came to precarious straits. How should these three men be handled? They wanted the presidency so badly, and they would use it to destroy the Society.

I personally recognized that Herb Mann, by his strength and diplomacy, would be most effective in handling these three overly ambitious destructive men. So Herb was elected president. It had been suggested I take a second term. I knew that Herb would be more competent than I in this situation (as indeed he so proved) and Herb was readily agreed upon. Also, the importance of selecting a general practitioner, with the overemphasis so many persons and organizations have placed on hypnosis as being only in the domain of psychiatry, is obvious. The dentists felt that a general practitioner should precede them. Then the question of the fourth president came. That had to be a dentist if the dentists were to feel they had any real importance in the Society—[Irving] Secter and [Larry] Staples were both in full view and certain other ambitious driving but destructive dentists had to be obscured. It was a difficult decision, but the life of ASCH had to be considered. The price of the presidency had to be the satisfying of demanding ambitious men by sprinkling them in minor offices among unselfish officers. Thus the truly effective offices remained in good hands (although some of these were close to the edge) and unintentional destructiveness was curtailed.

Then came the question of the next president. Who should follow Secter? The Executive Council agreed that it should be one with membership in both societies and psychology should play a part. The Nominating Committee, though not bound, heeded this advice. You and Erik Wright [Ph.D., M.D.] were considered. Attendance at meetings annually and participation in the program were raised as an issue and bitterly fought for by one who had to be eliminated as an officer. This matter of the elimination from effective office of a serious threat to the life of ASCH was achieved by accepting his contention, while recognizing that you had rendered a most important service to ASCH that probably could never be appreciatively acknowledged to you, even though you had not been seen in person at recent gatherings.

The above was written after I had read only the first four lines of your letter. I have now read the entire letter.

Your use of the word "expedient" distresses me. Yet we did resort to measures for expediency. [Erickson names a physician] nearly bankrupted the Society, was utterly and ruthlessly intent on being president, and a great deal of juggling had to be done to maintain the presidency along the lines originally conceived as being most helpful to the three professions. One other man, by dint of much traveling and personal solicitation for nomination for president or as a write-in candidate, made an intensive effort to influence the nominating committee, and the strength of that personal solicitation was phenomenal, as was the strength and integrity of the Nominating Chairman, who resisted all pressure and never lost his patience, tolerance, temper, dignity, or even his sense of humor. A second serious effort was made to compel the nominating committee to nominate two undesirable men who got together and supported each other. This eventually led to the formation of a nominating committee which will always consist of the three most recent living ex-presidents and two appointees by the current president. We think now that there will be little attempt at steam-rolling by politicians, all of whom in their completely selfish ambitions are abhorrent to me.

Efforts have been made repeatedly by [Erickson names a physician] to get me ousted as Editor and replaced by him. He had wonderful ideas about sensational pictures with articles for both the lay reader and the scientific reader, illustrations for the lay reader, etc.

He actually got [Erickson names two members of ASCH] to support him, and they had a hard time discovering their error. One still hates to admit it and tries to smooth over everything by pretending nothing has happened. The other tends to spread the blame because he seems to feel that there *must* be faults on both sides. [Erickson names the physician] succeeded in persuading the Executive Council to have the Journal published in Chicago where he could influence the printer. It caused us a loss of over $2,000 in overcharges and false charges, which by contract we had to pay. [Erickson relates a number of additional manipulations by the named physician.]

. . . You were well out of this mess. You are a scientist, a dedicated man, and you would be at a total loss if [the physician] turned on you as he has on me.

As a psychiatrist, I am exceedingly familiar with every kind of intrigue. I don't like them, but I know when and where and from whom they develop. So far I've borne the brunt of dirty politics, and so far the original aims of ASCH, as formulated before any actual organization occurred, have been preserved. Furthermore, I have found that under the surface in every institution, organization, group, foundation, learned society, and so on, there is invariably one or several more or less well-concealed feuds and bitter strife.

There are a significant number of us who are concerned about your recognition. Personally, I would like to see you given the full recognition that you deserve, and so do others.

You haven't been forgotten; this is a young medical–dental–psychological society with the ridiculous professional jealousies that exist everywhere—sometimes at a statewide level as, you may recall, that bitter quarrel between medical men in Michigan and their treatment of the Ph.D. in psychology as less than an M.A. in social work.

Briefly, we are, in spite of difficulties, building up slowly a group of scientifically oriented men who will want simple honest recognition for those deserving, without the control of the petty selfish politicians who are found everywhere.

I greatly want your name on the Masthead and your help with the Abstracts Dept., and elsewhere. You deserve that recognition more than any other one and it would hurt to lose you.

I hope this letter reaches you before you conclude your own thinking.

Sincerely yours,
Milton H. Erickson, M.D.

From: André Weitzenhoffer
To: Betty Erickson
April 12, 1965

Dear Betty,

Please excuse this delay in regard to replying to your letter regarding Milton's ms. I really thought I had replied to it. I rather agree that we should publish that which is available insofar as Milton's writings are concerned. In fact, when I sent you the ms. I sent you what I considered to be the total material which would be published, except for a short introduction to the experimental work I planned to write. As you will recall, my request was that Milton go over the material and add such notes as he might wish to make, correct, or append to the various statements I had made in my various introductions. If it is Milton's wish that the material be published as is without his having gone over it, then we can go ahead and find a publisher. Personally I think it would be desirable for him to at least read it. He might even write some sort of preface or introduction for it. Well, let me know just what is to be done. I do need to know so that I can plan accordingly.

As ever,
André

To: André Weitzenhoffer
October 25, 1968

Dear André:

I was very pleased to receive in the morning mail the paper which you sent, "Hypnosis and Eye Movements. I: Preliminary Report on a Possible Slow Eye Movement Correlate of Hypnosis," and especially glad to learn that you are resuming your work in hypnosis. We have missed your valuable and thought-provoking contributions, and I hope this is only the beginning of a number of future studies.

At the close of the Tenth Volume, which was April of the current year, I resigned as Editor, although the Society insisted on giving me the title of Editor Emeritus. My successor as Editor is William E. Edmonston, Jr., Ph.D., of the Department of Psychology, Colgate University, Hamilton,

New York. Dr. Edmonston is a most able young man and he was my personal choice as successor. I am sure the Journal will continue its successful course under his guidance, hence, I am sending your paper on to him with my recommendation for publication.

It has indeed been a long time since I exchanged correspondence with you and I hope we shall now resume a more frequent exchange. At the present time, I am continuing with my private practice on a limited basis and also doing some teaching, but increasing physical disability has necessitated my discontinuing travel. I had hoped to make an exception of the Annual Meeting of the American Society of Clinical Hypnosis, which took place in Chicago last week. However, I fractured my hip in May and whereas progress has been quite satisfactory, the prospect of the long round trip to Chicago necessitated my giving up the planned trip. I do hope that I shall be able to attend next year's meeting in San Francisco.

The teaching to which I refer is a course in medical hypnosis which I have been presenting under the auspices of the Evening College Division of our local Phoenix College. It is a non-credit course, but the enrollment is restricted to physicians, dentists, psychologists, and Ph.D. candidates in psychology when individually approved. This is the third semester in which I have presented the course and I hadn't realized that there was this much demand for such a comprehensive graduate study. Present enrollment is about 25 and we have an excellent attendance. Most of the enrollees are from the Phoenix area but I have had enrollees in this and the previous courses from Tucson, Chandler, Yuma, Flagstaff, and other communities which necessitated a long trip weekly for the students . . .

Sincerely yours,
Milton H. Erickson, M.D.

V

ON HYPNOSIS AND ANTISOCIAL ACTS:

George Estabrooks, Loyd Rowland,
John Larson, Jacob Conn,
Wesley Wells, Philip Ament

The following several letters relate to an avid debate about the possible antisocial uses of hypnosis. George Estabrooks and Loyd Rowland, both renowned academic psychologists, believed that hypnosis could be used as an aid in promoting blind obedience to immoral suggestions. Wesley Wells (1941), a professor at Syracuse University, wrote about its use to induce criminal behavior. Erickson and his wife, Elizabeth, refuted those arguments, and expressed the opinion that hypnosis was more likely an impediment to the induction of corruption than an impetus. The controversy was even brought to the attention of J. Edgar Hoover and the FBI.

The debate about the use of hypnosis to induce subjects to perform objectionable acts has a long history. As early as 1927, Schilder and Kauders, in their book Hypnosis, *reviewed the misuse of hypnosis, and according to Erickson (1939), argued that antisocial acts are not induced because the hypnotic subject is aware of the status of the experimenter.*

The correspondence that follows concerns an initial salvo that appeared in an article in which Rowland (1939) described how he induced hypnotized subjects to reach for a live rattlesnake and to throw acid at the experimenters, who were protected by invisible glass. Rowland asserted that the subjects did not know about the protective glass. Subsequently, Estabrooks (1943) published a book, also entitled Hypnotism, *that summarized his theories on the use of hypnosis in crime and warfare.*

Late in 1939, Erickson (1939a) presented his opposing views in "An Experimental Investigation of the Possible Antisocial Use of Hypnosis," which appeared in Psychiatry. In that article, he described a series of experiments conducted with approximately 50 trained hypnotic subjects and his efforts to induce them to commit sociopathic, unconventional, harmful, and even criminal acts. The 35 accounts by Erickson covered a variety of such attempts, including trying to involve subjects in physically or mentally injuring themselves, violating their moral codes, and committing offenses against the property of others. Erickson concluded: "The findings disclose consistently the failure of all experimental measures to induce hypnotic subjects, in response to hypnotic suggestion, to perform acts of an objectionable character, even though many of the suggested acts were acceptable to them under circumstances of waking consciousness" (see Erickson & Rossi, 1980a, p. 529).

Elizabeth Erickson (1962, 1966) published two articles on the topic. In the first, "Observations Concerning Alterations in Hypnosis Concerning Visual Perceptions," she argued that hypnotic subjects may be more sensitive to environmental clues than waking subjects, and that Rowland's hypnotized subjects might have better noticed than did waking controls how they were afforded protection. They may even have perceived the "invisible" glass better than the controls did.

This correspondence is an example of the scholarly interchange among the protagonists. It was a pointed but friendly discussion that extended over many years. The last known correspondence between Rowland and Erickson was in 1962. They had met in 1946 in Michigan, and perhaps again in 1959 when Erickson spoke in Louisiana, where Rowland lived. The letters sent between 1946 and 1962 were brief and few and far between, and mainly referred to exchanging reprints and visiting. Although their interest in the question of hypnosis and antisocial acts continued, Rowland did not seem to publish further on the matter.

A sidelight regarding the ethics of Erickson and Rowland: In 1946, Erickson wrote to Roland to express his concern about a proposed compendium to be edited by Salvatore Russo. The collection was to include reprints of papers by Erickson and Rowland, as well as an article by a lay practitioner of hypnosis. Rowland agreed, and voiced his objection in a letter to Russo. (That letter is not included here.) This is another example of Erickson's activism on behalf of the professional and ethical use of clinical hypnosis.

Estabrooks

From: G. H. Estabrooks
March 16, 1939

Dear Erickson:
   Thanks tremendously for your reprint on color blindness. Frankly I wouldn't have believed it. However, I wouldn't have believed Rowland's last article in the *Journal of Social and Abnormal Psychology*, unless I had faith in his experimental technique. By the way, what do you think of that last article?

Cordially yours,
G. H. Estabrooks

Editor's Note: Obviously, Erickson answered this letter although there is no record in his files. The dialogue continues with Estabrooks' next letter.

From: G. H. Estabrooks
April 10, 1939

Dear Dr. Erickson:
   I still think that article by Rowland has its points. You disagree with me and Hull disagrees with me, which puts me very much in the minority of one, but for my particular problem this sort of experiment may be pretty important.
   For example, I agree with you when you say that the subjects behaved as they would only because of their faith in him, the situations involved being so violent that they realized he could not have allowed them to come to harm.
   Yet it seems to me this is very important to one aspect of my own problem. For example, let us suppose that I take my subject who has faith in me and persuade him to snap a pistol at you at three o'clock tomorrow afternoon. Instead of dummy cartridges, I load the pistol with live cartridges. I am inclined to think you would be in very grave danger.

Then, if you will admit that I can prevent him from ever being hypnotized by anyone else—which I think is possible—and remove from him all knowledge of ever having been hypnotized—of which I am by no means certain—it seems that from my own particular point of view I have pretty much achieved my end.

To be sure, my subject has not committed a crime in one sense of the word. He has been maneuvered into a criminal situation because of his excessive trust in myself, but from another point of view—that of the jury—he has committed a crime and I don't see exactly how you are going to bring the guilt home to me, but maybe I am wrong.

I have argued this point at great lengths with Dr. Cutten, who, as you may recall, wrote *The Psychology of Alcoholism* and was perhaps the leading American authority in 1896. I think I am gradually converting him to my point of view. Now, all I have to do is convert Hull and yourself, and I will be satisfied that I have done a good day's work.

Cordially yours,
G. H. Estabrooks

To: G. H. Estabrooks
April 21, 1939

Dear Dr. Estabrooks:

Let us continue our argument, not for the purpose of converting me to your point of view, but quite the opposite.

Concerning the fictive crime with a real revolver in which you have replaced the dummy cartridges with live cartridges, you unquestionably could get him to snap the trigger, but I can assure you that the proposition has been placed before a dozen subjects, all of whom have explained that, "Yes, certainly the pistol would be fired, but you don't have to point it at the person. If you do aim, you could aim carefully past him, but the probability is that you would point it either straight up or straight down, if you agreed to fire it at all." Practically all of my subjects have volunteered the information that they would not fool around with a pistol under any circumstances. Since that is only a fictive crime, I have not bothered carrying out such an experiment, because it would be literally impossible to convince my subjects that I had any intention of having them fire a gun at anybody.

Another consideration is the fact that if you were to replace dummy cartridges with live ones, how on earth would you govern your behavior to the subject so that he would not become aware of your emotional tension? Even in minor things, subjects are so extremely aware of the hypnotist's tension that suggestions will be refused time after time only because there seems to be some sort of unfavorable tension about the hypnotist. I wouldn't want to hand a loaded revolver to a subject because I doubt if I could control my emotions sufficiently to keep him unaware of what I was doing.

As to preventing a person from being hypnotized by anybody else, I would limit that to restricted situations entirely. The best measure would be to offend them so that they would never again get into the hypnotic situation, but even so, they would require sufficient conscious understanding and recollection of the offensive situation to act upon it, so that for the purposes of concealing crime, it would not serve.

I feel entirely confident that any effort to prevent a hypnotic subject from ever again going into a hypnotic trance for anybody else could be refuted very easily. I have done that sort of thing experimentally and have found that it is very easy to circumvent any such measure.

To remove from a hypnotic subject any memory of anything is literally impossible. You can inhibit his recollection of things, but the experience, being an actual fact, will be recorded and any adequate technique will enable its discovery. But, if the material concerns something of great emotional significance, your attempt to inhibit it and suppress it would only add to its emotional character and it would be revealed much more quickly. In my own work I found that attempts to bring about an amnesia for having been hypnotized and an amnesia for things suggested were most unsatisfactory, unless I limited it to a special length of time. Your subject is very prone to remembering spontaneously any unpleasant things that occur and that tendency becomes more pronounced if you attempt to throttle him in any fashion.

I feel very strongly that you can get a person to do in the trance state at most only what he is willing to do in the waking state, but usually not even that much in the matter of offensive behavior. I look upon hypnosis as only a questionable and rather useless technical auxiliary. Its role is one of ornamentation only. I think, however, that you will agree with me sooner or later. Shall we set as a possible date for conversion the reading of my present paper?

Surely now, with this last paragraph, I ought to get a good argument out of you.

Sincerely yours,
Milton H. Erickson, M.D.

From: G. H. Estabrooks
May 5, 1939

Dear Erickson:

Please pardon my delay in answering yours of April 21 but, as a matter of fact, I have been devilishly busy. Have been appointed Head of the Psychology Department and Acting Director of the School of Biological Sciences, which adds the headaches of zoology and botany to an already aching head.

Frankly I think you are one of those unregenerate heathen, probably a rock-rid [sic] Republican, who is in close proximity to Henry Ford and is rendered immune to light. Just as frankly I have a sneaking suspicion you are right, but I'll be darned how I can see how either of us can prove his point.

My own experiments have been pretty much exploratory and while pretty conclusive within a limited field, I must confess that the number of subjects has been altogether too small on which to base any sweeping assertions. I do feel I could get my fictitious crime committed. I think Rowland bears me out in this. To be sure, the crime would only be committed because of the absolute faith which the subject had in the operator.

But, then, what is the next move? Can I remove from him all knowledge of ever having been hypnotized? My own experiments would seem to indicate that I could, but I must admit that I have taken the greatest care not to submit these subjects to any emotional strain and, of course, emotional strain would very certainly be involved in the type of situation you suggest.

Then, again, would it be possible to render him immune to hypnotization [sic] by a second party? Once again it seems true and once again I don't know what would happen in an actual life situation with the electric chair in the offing.

And I don't see how we can prove it, unless Mr. Roosevelt very thoughtfully gets us into a large-sized war in the near future. I note one press correspondent remarked, by the way, that Roosevelt would make a good wartime president. Perhaps the writing on the wall.

In war one has pretty much a free hand with no silly defense attorneys around asking questions and no prosecuting attorneys looking for the real culprit.

You know, this reaction of different human beings to the same problem is really interesting. You state, for instance, that you doubt if anyone could kill a man without a tremendous emotional upset. I was an officer with the First Canadian Division in the World War and can truthfully assure you that I would have much more reluctance in running down a kitten on the road than in killing another human being if it were in the line of duty. Just a matter of background. On the other hand, many of the experiments which you report would leave me with the jitters for a week to come. I simply haven't the nerve to put them through. Too much sympathy for the subject or something of that description. Now, if you can reconcile those two conflicting attitudes toward the same human being, you are a better man than I am.

Do please send me a copy of that paper in question. Being as I am a hard-shelled Baptist with the stiff-neckedness associated with the clan, I doubt if old Mesmer himself could convert me, but I do think we can do a great service to psychology if we can get this thing out in the open and have it discussed as an academic problem.

Incidentally, do you mind my sending a copy of your letter to Mr. [J. Edgar] Hoover and to the War Department? I have been giving them a considerable barrage of wild assertions which frankly I don't think they take too seriously. I think it would do them good to have in their files the statements of other folks like yourself who distinctly disagree with my point of view. After all, the thing will either work or it won't and what we want is the truth of the matter.

Cordially yours
G. H. Estabrooks

From: G. H. Estabrooks
May 22, 1939

Dear Erickson:

I am returning your manuscript. The work is easily the most significant that has been done in this field. In my opinion you should write it up much as it is without committing yourself too far as to the significance of facts. In other words, I would get a good strong anchor out to leeward. I have a very strong suspicion that many of these results are really contingent on the personality of the operator.

For example, yours contrast very definitely with those of Rowland. Another example occurs to me; namely, the results on the ergograph obtained by Nicholson and by Williams, I think I have the two right. The sharp contrast obtained by these two investigators, it seems to me, can probably best be explained on the basis of motivation. Sidis, I recall, makes this observation in one of his books, pointing out that with the same subject he could obtain very different degrees of acquiescence merely by changing his tone of voice.

Of course, as I have repeatedly pointed out to my superior, Dr. Cutten, the technique you use is above all things the technique I would avoid in the particular type of criminal suggestion in which you happen to be most interested. Where you run into direct conflict with the will of the subject I would always suspect that results would be more or less like your own. For that reason I was much surprised by Rowland's experiments. Frankly I would have expected his subjects either to have awakened immediately or to have behaved more like your own. But facts are facts. I will be much interested to see his further work.

My entire contention is that if proper rapport is established, then at least a certain number of subjects can literally be fooled into committing a crime. Provided the subject is quite convinced that you mean no harm and that you are using him merely to demonstrate a point, then my own inadequate experimental work would seem to indicate that he would put fake poison into my coffee, would forge a check which he knew I was going to tear up immediately, or would snap a revolver loaded with dummy ammunition at an individual. It seems to me that the success of such experiments as those I have just mentioned depends entirely on the attitude of the subject toward the operator. Frankly I have never tried the sort of thing you suggest because of a certain tenderness of mind on my own part. I do everything possible to avoid coming into conflict with the will of the subject but to persuade him that he is taking part in a very interesting little experiment which has no particular significance and which he is doing more or less as a favor to myself.

Can you suggest any way in which it would be possible to check further on this matter of rendering the subject immune to hypnotism by another operator or having any knowledge of ever having been hypnotized? It seems to me that those two points are rather crucial.

Take, for example, Rowland's work. The subject quite evidently was willing to throw sulfuric acid in his face. If he had thrown the glass as well, I only hope the invisible glass would have protected the operator. Granted this for the sake of argument, although you may not grant this much, would Rowland now have been able to commit the perfect crime by the cover-up methods I have suggested?

I certainly hesitate to take issue on a point like this with yourself. It is the type of experiment which I am particularly unqualified to carry out. I am not hard-boiled enough. I don't think we can really answer the question until we are allowed to operate under war conditions wherein nobody asks questions, but perhaps we could approximate an answer.

Once again allow me to congratulate you on the work. Had I attempted this I would certainly be in the Utica State Hospital myself at this particular moment. On the other hand, I wouldn't commit myself too far when I write up results. Keep a line of retreat open—just in case.

With your permission I am sending a copy of this letter to Mr. [J. Edgar] Hoover, since I am anxious that he have all sides of the question filed in his office.

Cordially yours
G. H. Estabrooks

Rowland

From: Loyd W. Rowland
November 14, 1939

Dear Dr. Erickson:

Let me thank you for the reprints you sent and for the liberal space you gave my experiment in your August 1939 article in the *Journal of the*

Biology and Pathology of Interpersonal Relations (Erickson, 1939a). My apologies for not answering sooner. I don't have the boon of stenographic help and have to wait for a holiday or something to break up my schedule of fifteen classes a week.

Some striking differences appear in the behavior of your subjects and mine. Your subjects seem to talk freely and to argue with you while in the trance. Mine are lethargic and never talk spontaneously. Their answers are limited to "yes" and "no" as much as possible, and we make a genuine effort to keep the subject and experimenter in a completely agreeing relationship. I have a hunch that talk, expecially of the defensive or argumentative sort, is associated with a high degree of consciousness, which seems somehow incompatible with hypnosis. Could it be possible that your subjects, in a deep trance at the beginning, move into a lighter sleep during verbal parrying of the sort you describe? For example, have you tried them out on hallucinations while they are activly defending themselves? Have you unwittingly felt the need of taking a little time at the close of an experimental period to put a subject back into a deeper sleep before waking him up? We have never had a subject show resentment during the trance or afterward. I wonder if you tend to tease the subjects in any way.

Another thing, I was convinced by my work reported in the *Journal of Experimental Psychology* that repeated emotional stimuli with the same subject—especially if the same stimuli are offered—leads to a very important lessening of the response. They simply don't take seriously the stimulus offered a second or third time, in spite of a similarity of outward behavior. In the running description of your accounts, I got the impression that some of your subjects might be "worn out" by repeated exposure to stimuli of an exciting character.

Still another difference might account for the disparity of our results. Your records indicate a rather large percentage of hospital cases. I assume yours is a mental hospital, and I wonder just how far we can go in using as subjects people whose years are already running backwards. I guess it depends on the kind of patients in the hospital. This summer I visited the U.S. narcotic hospital at Ft. Worth and one of the psychiatrists—I have forgotten his name right now—told me that his experience with the use of hypnosis in connection with drug addiction confirmed my thesis that persons in deep hypnosis can be made to do unreasonably dangerous things.

You seem to give some credence to the explanations that the subjects give for their behavior. I would tend to discount them 100 percent, except in so far as they reveal attitudes. You know how it is, we use the "explanations" of hypnotized persons, traditionally, as examples of rationalization.

It seems to me that these "lesser sins" which you have used may actually be the occasion for more inhibitions than the *greater sins* with which I worked. The lesser sins have been in the realm of experience of the subjects, whereas grasping a rattlesnake or throwing acid onto the face of another may actually have less meaning.

In general, for experimental work in hypnosis, I favor (1) subjects who are well adjusted, (2) subjects who have not been hypnotized too many times but who go into a deep sleep at once, (3) the hypnotized person in a completely submissive role—no arguments and little talk—and (4) the use of deceptive stimuli only once. I should be as interested in knowing the complete hypnotic history of my subjects as I should be in knowing the life history of Kohler's apes! In other words, I shouldn't want any deceit prior to my attempt at inducing the subject to wrong himself or others.

Whatever the explanation of the disparity, this one thing I know: you will never see this side of Dante's seventh circle a more horrible sight than that of one of my subjects reaching for that mighty diamondback rattlesnake right up to and touching the invisible glass a few short inches from the head of the snake with lashing tongue, inflated head pouches, rattles vibrating until they were blurred. It is a thought I don't dwell on very long.

One thing is certain: a lot more work has to be done before we settle our problem, you and I. Let me hear from you when you have the time to write and feel like it. If you have not sent a reprint of your last paper to Professor G. H. Estabrooks at Colgate, I am sure he would appreciate one.

Best wishes,
Loyd W. Rowland

To: Loyd W. Rowland
November 24, 1939

Dear Dr. Rowland:
Thank you very much for your letter of comment. I will attempt to reply to the points you have raised, so that we may reach a better under-

standing, since we are both so much interested in contributing to this subject.

Concerning my subjects, they ranged from psychotic to normal, children to middle-aged adults, and feebleminded to superior and better intelligence. However, the greater part of my subjects have been normal, well-adjusted college students.

Concerning the differences in behavior of our subjects, particularly in regard to the "high degree of consciousness" of my subjects and the "lethargy" of yours, I think this is only a matter of the amount of responsiveness that is permitted to the subject. I find it quite easy to render them lethargic, inhibited, and restricted in their behavior, but I have come to regard that state as decidedly limited as an aid in discovering what the hypnotic subject is, as a person, and how far his behavior can be influenced. Hence, my tendency is to induce a trance, at first lethargic in character, and then to continue with the trance induction by further insistent, repetitious general instruction to the effect that they are to continue to sleep with ever-increasing soundness until they feel and know that they can make, while still asleep and without awakening, a full and complete response to any and every instruction given them. After this instruction has been given adequately, I then set a pattern for spontaneous activity on their part by instructing them to give me, when they are ready to make complete response, some word or sign to show their readiness (usually they choose to turn their head toward me or to lift their hand or to make some little expectant gesture in a lethargic manner). Then, after further emphasis upon continued deep sleep, I elaborate that pattern of spontaneous activity by bringing them slowly into contact with reality, since invariably they lose all contact with their reality situation. This I do, for example, by suggesting an awareness of several chairs and instructing them to choose a new seat. Often this is exceedingly difficult for them to do, but once their lethargy has been overcome and they have made their own choice of the new seat, the foundation has been laid for an ever-increasing range of spontaneous activity, which is carried out in the hypnotic state.

Since, in this connection, you have asked whether or not I have tried subjects out on hallucinations while they were actively defending themselves, I will cite the following example. I was aware that the subject I was using for a group demonstration had had a very bitter quarrel with a third party who had told me of the quarrel, although my subject was not aware that I knew about the affair. During the course of the demonstration, I decided to demonstrate hallucinatory behavior on the part of the subject, and instructed him accordingly to hear footsteps outside the room and a knock on the door, and I told him that I intended to admit that person and that he was to hear and see and respond to that person. I then went through the act of admitting the suggested comer, greeted him by the name of the person with whom my subject had quarreled, and placed a chair for him in the same fashion as I would had he really been there. My subject showed marked resentment at the inclusion of this hallucinatory visitor, but nothing overt occurred until I untactfully led the general conversation around in such a fashion as to ask the visitor to tell about his most recent exciting contact with the subject. This caused my subject to start very visibly and to assume a watchful attitude. My knowledge of the episode enabled me to make the appropriate general comments as I went through the behavior of listening to the telling of that episode. My subject listened in a resentful manner, directing his gaze first toward me and then toward the imaginary visitor, and, when the highly disputed crux of the quarrel was apparently reached, my subject intruded into the conversation, and disputed the remarks which he hallucinated the visitor as making, and proceeded to renew his quarrel. Finally, he demanded that I dismiss the visitor from the group. When I attempted to dismiss the visitor by merely suggesting that he was gone, my subject refused to accept those suggestions and forced me to dismiss him by conducting him to the door as one would a real person. Upon my return to the room, I found that I had my own peace to make with the subject.

The outcome of this situation is equally interesting. A few days later, during a casual visit with my subject in the waking state, he gave me an account of the original quarrel and obviously had no realization that I knew anything about it previously. Incidentally, this subject is a highly successful and capable physician engaged in general practice.

Nor is the above account an only illustration, since I have secured similar results on many occasions. In addition I have also secured positive and negative hallucinations in ordinary experimental situations and in situations where the subject was actually defensive in his behavior toward me. On more than one occasion, the hallucinations that I have secured were susceptible to adequate testing measures, since one always needs to be on his guard in such matters. In my articles on hypnotic deafness (*Journal of General Psychology*, vol. 19, July 1938, pp. 127–150, and pp. 151–167) [Erickson, 1938], and hypnotic color blindness [Erickson, 1939b], *Journal of General*

Psychology, vol. 20, January 1939, pp. 61–89), I give some illustrative examples, and if you are interested in reading these reports, I shall be glad to send them to you. Also, will you please send me a copy of your article published in the *Journal of Experimental Psychology* in 1936 on repeated emotional stimuli, since I would like very much to read it?

You also ask if I have felt the need of taking a little time at the close of an experimental period to put the subjects back into a deeper sleep before awakening them. Usually my procedure is to allow the subjects to rest quietly and to prepare themselves to awaken, since awakening them out of that deep sleep in which they were so active constitutes a rather serious shock to them. It seems that this peculiar state of activity in the hypnotic sleep results in so complete a psychological and physiological orientation that an awakening to the ordinary reality state constitutes a definite strain upon them and causes a feeling of distress, discomfort, and often severe headaches. By letting them rest and thus to awaken in a gradual fashion, these unfortunate reactions are avoided. The rest period is only for the purpose of decreasing the trance.

You mention the possibility of "wearing out" the subjects by repeated exposures to stimuli of an exciting character. I agree with you fully that a subject exposed to the same stimulus repeatedly may become acclimated, but with an adequate technique of suggestion such a possibility should never occur.

As for giving credence to the explanations that subjects give for their behavior, I did so with full awareness that they might be rationalizations, but even so those explanations are exceedingly informative regarding attitudes and the attitude of the personality is an essential consideration.

In brief, I do not look upon hypnosis as a miracle worker and I doubt very much if it can be used effectively, under the time and situation limitations of a trance, to overthrow the attitudes and habits and practices that have been built up in the subject through a lifetime of experience. In psychotherapeutic work, where the patient is often so desirous of correcting some minor little habit or practice, the difficulties encountered in achieving socially acceptable behavior even with cooperation are enough to make one doubt the feasibility of a character and habit alteration of an undesirable kind.

Sincerely yours,
Milton H. Erickson, M.D.

From: Loyd W. Rowland
December 14, 1939

Dear Dr. Erickson:

Thank you for your long letter of November 24. I do not know that there is anything in particular that I have to say by way of reply, since you have done a good job of explaining things from your standpoint and I think I understand exactly what you mean.

I missed your articles in the *Journal of General Psychology* of July 1938 and January of 1939. I can look them up but would like to have reprints if they are available. I am sending you a reprint of the article to which I referred in a previous letter.

Please let me hear from you, especially when you are cooking up some research that seems exciting.

Best wishes,
Loyd W. Rowland

From: Loyd W. Rowland
November 6, 1945

Dear Dr. Erickson:

It has been a good many years since we have been in touch. Apparently you took my name off your mailing list because I cannot imagine you have stopped writing suddenly. In 1938 you were turning out stuff at a pretty terrific rate. Your Jerome Beatty article in the *American* has just been called to my attention and I enjoyed a complete reading of it. Incidentally, I have never had any luck hypnotizing my wife. I don't know what that means in terms of dominance or some such. At any rate, I gave it a try once and she looked over in my direction as much as to say, "Come, come now; let's don't really be serious about this thing."

I was interested in the quotation. "Pistols for two, coffee for one," which some psychologist wrote you after you had reviewed his book. This could be no other person than Estabrooks.

I am surprised that you are only 43 years old. That is my age too. Somehow when we were writing back and forth away back in 1938 I had pictured you as a blond Norseman of uncertain age.

The quotation that you encountered, "no changes, no alterations in personality in 500 subjects," is a little bit surprising to me. I encountered one three years ago that was a complete surprise and came so near to upsetting the college that I determined not to use hypnosis any more in that particular school while I was teaching.

You will be interested to know that perhaps the spot in the nation where most hypnosis is used is in Tulsa, Oklahoma, by Dr. L. S. McLeod, Professor of Psychology and Dean of the Graduate School of Tulsa University. So far as I know, he has never publicly summarized the extent of his work, but there have been times when he has used hypnotic therapy as much as four hours a day for month after month.

When are you coming around to the notion that hypnotized persons can be made to harm themselves or others? I think my experiment on the point is conclusive, and I wish you would duplicate it.

Sincerely,
Loyd W. Rowland

To: Loyd W. Rowland
November 16, 1945

Dear Dr. Rowland:

I was somewhat amazed to receive a letter from you, but I am delighted that you wrote. I am still doing hypnotic work, but not as extensively as previously. Wartime increase of duties and the tremendous increase in teaching duties have occupied my time almost exclusively. I hope soon to do additional work.

You are quite correct about that pistols for two and coffee for one. It was Estabrooks. I understand he has now published a detective story.

The incident you describe of a disturbing experience with a hypnotic subject was in all probability a subject with a well-concealed neurosis or personality disturbance, who merely utilized the hypnosis as an excuse for making the difficulty manifest. And I don't think you ought to blame hypnosis for it. In psychiatry one finds a large number of instances where any little thing can be utilized by the personality as a means of uncovering hitherto well-concealed difficulties.

I am glad you discovered that I am not blend, Norse, and of uncertain age. I am far from being blond, and my age is definite.

Here's hoping that some time we meet at a psychological meeting.

Sincerely yours,
Milton H. Erickson, M.D.

From: Loyd W. Rowland
November 19, 1945

Dear Dr. Erickson:

Thanks for your note. I did not make myself clear with reference to the disturbing experience which I had with a hypnotic subject. I quite well realized that a concealed neurosis had been uncovered, but I could not take the personal risk of wild behavior exhibited by such a student in the presence of a hundred others. As it turned out, I am sure that the crying, explanations, etc., made up a very splendid catharsis for the student but there was considerable personal risk as far as I was concerned. A psychiatrist has quite a bit more control than a psychologist because he is licensed. I believe that Hull has taken out $25,000 insurance against a chance that suit might be brought against him some time.

Sincere best wishes,
Loyd W. Rowland

To: Loyd W. Rowland
February 6, 1946

Dear Dr. Rowland:

I received a letter from Mr. Salvatore Russo, requesting permission to publish in an anthology one of my articles. In looking over the list of contributors, I find listed one who holds neither a degree in psychology nor a degree in medicine, and who has been reported by reputable men as a charlatan. Also, my own experience with some of his patients confirms the judgment that he is a charlatan. Additionally, all of his works have been unfavorably criticized by competent persons.

I think it is entirely possible for an anthology to be organized without the inclusion of that particular author's works. Therefore, I have refused Mr. Russo permission and I think it is incumbent upon all of us to make every effort to insure that the layman's knowledge of hypnosis derives only from the best sources.

I don't think honest, open criticism of experimental results should exclude anybody, but I do think that when there is a grave question of the nature of the work and the character of the man who does it, and when there is evidence that he lacks qualifications, we ought not to favor his acceptance.

I think R. S. and his radio show [on hypnosis] is doing hypnosis enough damage without favoring the publicizing of another unqualified man. I shall appreciate your comments.

Sincerely yours,
Milton H. Erickson, M.D.

Editor's Note: Rowland responded by writing Russo, withholding permission to republish his work if the offending author were included.

Larson

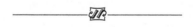

On April 29, 1940, John A. Larson, M.D., Assistant Director in the Recorder's Court Clinic of the City of Detroit, confidentially wrote to Erickson about his forensic work investigating criminals. He queried Erickson about the effectiveness of hypnosis in determining the guilt or innocence of accused parties. Larson indicated an interest in publishing a monograph on police psychiatry.

Larson was a person whom Erickson respected, and when Erickson left Detroit, he moved to Arizona to work at the State Hospital in Phoenix where Larson was the superintendent.

To: John A. Larson
September 30, 1940

Dear Dr. Larson:

Perhaps the following brief outline will constitute an attempt at answering your questions.

The answer to your question concerning the efficacy of hypnosis as a measure of determining the guilt or innocence of a suspect depends upon the directness or the indirectness of the use of hypnosis. The more direct is its use, the less is its value. Conversely, the more indirect is its use, the greater is its value and its general effectiveness. But at the same time, this indirection serves to decrease the immediate, direct, and satisfactory possibility of proving the findings legally.

To illustrate: A has killed B, but convincingly claims to be innocent. A is hypnotized and questioned directly and (as I have found experimentally when lied to by subjects in a trance) is even more convincing in his claims of innocent. By indirect measures one can apparently accept A's claim of innocence and induce A to agree in an objective fashion that the real murderer of B, who most certainly is not A, would inevitably have a tendency to suffer conscience pangs, might reasonably experience nightmares and, above all, that the real murderer would have to struggle seriously to protect himself against those tendencies. Further indirect suggestion would be to the effect that the real murderer would have to do everything possible to avoid knowing that he dreamed, to avoid remembering his dreams, and would be most convincing, when questioned about the possibility of his dreams, in his denial of any dreams. Suggestion might even be made that the real murderer might meet that problem by having a wealth of perfectly innocent dreams, but that whatever he did do, it would need to be of the same character as would be an innocent person's behavior.

And thus, one can give the suspect a wealth of suggestions in the form of an indirect general objective discourse, arouse in him a need for behavior and a morbid fear against certain forms of behavior with, at the same time, adequate possibilities for compensating in all of his behavior. The mere fact that the suspect was guilty would compel him to accept and to act upon these suggestions and in every avoidance response he would betray his need to avoid something. At the same time, in his efforts at avoidance, he would betray himself increasingly.

There is, however, a possible way of using it in an indirect–direct fashion. I have found that it is possible with hypnotic subjects to secure from them information they were totally unwilling to give me by the measure of disorienting them and then reorienting them to an earlier period in life, which preceded the time about which I wished information. Then, by suggesting a dream or a fantasy, or by open wishful talking about the future, it has been possible for me to secure from them a speculative account about the future, which included a part or all of the information that I wanted, mingled with much other material.

For example, a patient of mine flatly refused to give me some pertinent information about a certain asocial act she had committed. I felt it highly important that she give me that information, and the more she misinformed me about the matter, the more important it became to have a direct admission on her part. Accordingly, I first built up in her the feeling that such an antisocial act would be a most offensive, disagreeable, and unfortunate and important matter. When this conviction was thoroughly implanted, I hypnotized her and again implanted the same general ideas about it. At the same time I impressed upon the hypnotic subject the fact that she never would tell me or admit such a thing, and that she would lie to me most successfully if it were necessary to lie about that item. When I had succeeded in convincing her that there was no possibility of her betraying the information to me, I dropped the matter apparently, and became emotionally concerned about a remote and actually indifferent childhood experience, and, with much fatiguing effort, tried to extract that information from my patient. Finally, I resorted to the suggestion that reorientation to the childhood experience might secure that new information, and, upon acceptance of that suggestion, I reoriented my subject and then was in a position to give to my subject in that "regressed period" many suggestions for a miserable, unhappy, unpleasant, and disagreeable dream about the future. The dream was that, when my patient had reached adult life, unfortunate circumstances of an unknown character would conspire to bring about some miserable, unhappy and guilty performance, and that this dream about the remote and distant future would be so troublesome that my subject would tell it to me in order to gain reassurance, and to enlist my help against such a possibility.

By such a measure I have secured an adequate description with much additional detail of otherwise suppressed and repressed material. However, the possibility of losing your hypnotic subject is exceedingly great. One needs, after having so secured the information, to secure it by other measures, which one can do by utilizing minute details to lead up to associations on the part of the subject which will become increasingly informative, so that the patient has the possibility of realizing that out of these general associations there came a peculiar relationship of significances that eventually led to the revelation of the withheld matter.

Concerning the ethical significances, the question is most involved. In the matter of the treatment of neurotic patients, or psychotic patients, one is working for the welfare of that patient and is constantly meeting the need to overthrow, by one means or another, the mistaken ideas and attitudes of the patient in order to give him correct understandings. Therefore, one is justified in depriving the patient of the mistaken and wrong things that are his, because he comes to you in the first place for that purpose even though he does not know it. It is primarily a question of working for the welfare of the individual as that individual understands his welfare.

In the matter of the criminal, the ethics are quite different. One is working directly against the criminal and the only justification one has is adherence to the principle that the truth is paramount and constitutes adequate justification for the sacrifice of the individual for society. Hence, the ethical problem is a matter of one's loyalty to individuals as a unit or one's loyalty; to society as an impersonal whole. It seems to me that correct ethics must necessarily be some sort of a compromise that depends upon the social implications and the individual implications in the individual case.

As for the legal principle involved, there is very definitely an attack upon individual rights as defined legally. One does make the suspect testify against himself. I may be mistaken in this regard, but I believe that originally fingerprints could not be used by virtue of the fact that they were construed as forcing the individual to testify against himself. Hence, the whole matter becomes a legal question of what does constitute testimony against oneself. In all events, I have no interest in becoming involved in a test case.

Sincerely yours,
Milton H. Erickson

Conn

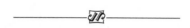

Jacob Conn, M.D., a colleague of Erickson, was past president of both the Society for Clinical and Experimental Hypnosis and the American Board of Medical Hypnosis. At the time of his death, he was an assistant professor emeritus at The Johns Hopkins Medical School.

From: Jacob Conn
May 22, 1970

Dear Milton—

I need your help. I am writing a paper on the dangers of hypnosis. As you know, there are differing opinions on the antisocial uses of hypnosis. John Watkins [a renowned authority on hypnosis] believes that a patient can be induced to perform antisocial acts. Your work indicates otherwise. You have "been accused" of not really trying to induce your subjects to perform antisocial acts. The argument goes as follows: You employed greater imaginative skills in previous psychosomatic experiments but "held back" when you tried to get your subjects to perform antisocial acts. I want your opinion about Watkins' work (as well as of W. R. Wells' work in the production of crime); also, Roland's work in getting subjects to harm themselves.

I agree with you but I would like your opinion with regard to crime and other antisocial effects with the use of hypnosis.

I would very much appreciate your assistance in clarifying this important issue, which has come up in the Charles Manson case: Can murder be accomplished with the help of hypnosis?

I think of you as the best qualified person to answer these questions.

Cordially,
Jerry

On June 18 and 19, Conn thanked Erickson for his letters and further questioned him on the antisocial use of hypnosis. These letters led to Erickson's reply of June 25. Similar to Erickson, Conn was of the opinion that hypnosis did not facilitate antisocial acts. (For further information, see Conn, 1982.)

To: Jacob H. Conn
June 13, 1970

Dear Jerry:

I am sorry I delayed writing to you but the truth is I am rather limited in what I can do.

In reply to your questions, Watkins was not the only one to accuse me of malperformance in my experimentation on hypnosis and antisocial behavior. It is always easy when you do not have the energy or desire to do extensive work to discredit the work of others in one fashion or another. The fact that I wanted to know if in some way I could actually get a hypnotic subject to perform antisocially, and also was willing to employ a great variety of techniques, was easily overlooked. I earnestly wanted my subject to perform antisocial acts. I was intensely motivated in this regard because the Dean of the College of Liberal Arts was dedicated throughout my entire stay at the University of Wisconsin to having me expelled as an undesirable person toying with a dangerous phenomenon. My failure to secure an antisocial act in spite of my desire made me feel that I ought to continue my experiment with complete objectivity. This led to the discovery that "complete objectivity" led to a subject divesting the proposed acts as of insufficient merit to warrant performance. The fact that the question is still being debated shows only a lack of intelligent understanding on the part of those who debate. An antisocial act has to be antisocial. It cannot be just a laboratory performance, Rowland, Wells, and others very carefully limited their investigations to protected laboratory performances.

The best discussion of hypnosis in antisocial behavior you can find is in the book *Hypnosis: Current Problems*, edited by Estabrooks, in the chapter "Anti-social Behavior and Hypnosis" by Martin T. Orne (1962), which has the subtitle "Problems of Control and Validation in Empirical Studies." I have done much more work and so have others in relation to antisocial behavior. I once consulted Knight Dunlap about the advisability of publishing. His academic enthusiasm appalled me. He did not seem to know how society would feel about such publications. Stanley Milgram's experiments that demonstrated that genuine antisocial behavior can be induced (without hypnosis, incidentally) in otherwise "good and normal people" have caused storms of controversy and the appreciative approval of people willing to consider the fundamental nature of human behavior.

So far as hypnosis is concerned, you don't need hypnosis to induce antisocial behavior. In fact, hypnosis is a handicap in inducing antisocial behavior. Anybody doing something antisocial cannot avoid being self-protective. In the hypnotic state there is a limitation in the comprehension of the surrounding world. Anybody doing something antisocial wants to know where he is and who is around and what time of day it is and the possible consequences. Hypnosis used to induce antisocial behavior constricts the awareness of surroundings and this constriction defeats efforts. Masters and Johnson would have been defeated in their study of sexual behavior had they tried to use hypnosis. By this I don't mean that antisocial behavior was involved, but that it was a situation where the person would want to be fully aware and as self-protected as possible.

I can give you a lot of examples where exceedingly positive results were published. For example, consider that book by Dr. Paul Reiter in Denmark, *Anti-Social or Criminal Acts and Hypnosis*. He based his entire book on hearsay evidence. He made no attempt to discover if either of the two criminals involved had been hypnotized or could be hypnotized. He made no attempt to find out if they had hit upon hypnosis only as a claimed alibi and he never once gave publicity to their subsequent denial of all the things upon which he based his entire book.

People get awfully emotional on this matter of responsibility for one's own conduct. How many good Germans admit responsibility for the Nazis, and how many have looked at the nobility of the Puritans in crossing the ocean to find a place for freedom of worship only to drive Roger Williams into the wilderness because he wanted freedom to worship; and how many of these noble people that settled America learned easily that the "only good Indian is a dead Indian," including infants, women, and children? The behavior of the Nazis may be compared to that of the North against the South during the Civil War, where brother fought against brother and father against son and the prison camps of the North and South were similar to the Nazi concentration camps.

I am going to cite an example that should interest you. A man and wife, both psychologists and both competent in the matter of hypnotizing each other and able to do phenomenally good experimental work, were very much in love with each other. They became interested in experimenting upon each other sexually and to their dismay they both found themselves unwilling to be in the hypnotic trance while the other was alert. They consulted me and I suggested various possibilities. With great reluctance each of them served as hypnotic partner in sexual relations with each other. Both resented being in the trance state during sexual relations. Both felt deprived by being in the trance state. Both resented making love to a hypnotic subject even though that subject was a well-loved spouse. With both in a trance state they found they could make love and both found out that they resented being in a trance because sexual relations with each other in the trance state lacked so much. They found no way of employing hypnosis satisfactorily. Nevertheless, it is easy to find girls who will tell you that someone employed hypnosis and kissed them or seduced them by first hypnotizing them. In fact, I have had to warn people doing experimental work that their subjects had sexual designs upon them and were going to pretend to be hypnotized. I have known experimenters who discovered to their dismay that their mistress or their lover was a good hypnotic subject but would not permit sex relations in the trance state but would be readily interested in the waking state. Some day I hope to write extensively on this matter.

I know of one instance where a husband, much in love with his wife, spent a full year in building up a hypnotic seduction of his wife, only to find that it misfired, and I had to comfort both the husband and the wife because even though sex relations had occurred, both were horribly disappointed. Making love in the nude is delightful, but don't do it on a snowbank when it is ten degrees below zero. It is awfully disappointing and the reality of genuine hypnotic trance is far from the reality of the waking state. However, when antisocial acts are committed, well, any old excuse can be used as an alibi as well as hypnosis, and human behavior applauds such things as the explosion of Fulton's first steamboat and denounced the cotton gin and Howe's sewing machine as horrible outrages against the human race.

Nevertheless, it is nice to be alive, to have a spouse, a few friends, and appreciative children, but never really bet on any of these as certainties. It is far easier and much more certain to send a man to the moon.

I hope, Jerry, I have answered your questions.

Sincerely yours,
Milton H. Erickson, M.D.

To: Jacob H. Conn,
June 25, 1970

Dear Jerry:

The endless argument that is offered about whether or not I knew how to do the experiments is always based upon a person's wishes and his willingness to misinterpret laboratory crimes for actual crimes. I am not sure but I think it was Watkins I had the argument with to the effect that if a nurse were placed in a state of hypnotic trance and given suggestions that she go about her duties as if she were wide awake, and that without her knowledge, a poison was placed in the milk in the refrigerator, and that if she were to give the patient in the course of discharge of her duties a glass of that poisoned milk, the result should be called, "The Use of Hypnosis in Producing Antisocial Behavior."

The hypnotic subject has to have a knowledge of what he is going to do. He has to be aware that a crime is to be done or that there is to occur antisocial behavior and that any alteration or prevention, of his knowledge, that there is to be antisocial behavior or criminal behavior and any misconceptions of what his acts are, abrogates any antisocial significance.

If you were to try to alter the hypnotic subject's perceptual awareness in order to bring about a crime, you would have the added problem of altering your own subjective behavior. In other words, to tell a subject that a revolver is loaded with blanks when you know it is loaded with bullet-carrying cartridges would call upon you to alter your behavior very greatly because you would know you could not ask him to point the gun at someone and pull the trigger. There would be alteration in your own subjective behavior. Naturally, Rowland was able to stand behind so-called invisible glass and tell the subject to throw acid on him. He betrayed the fact that he knew he was safe and hypnotic subjects are phenomenally perceptive.

I agree fully, laboratory crimes and any other so-called "antisocial" behavior is possible when the perpetrators are in a completely protected situation and the entire performance is nothing more than make-believe. Such behavior does not require hypnosis; it can be used but is an unnecessary addition, but for real crime or genuine antisocial behavior, there has to be a knowledge of it and an intent. Such knowledge and intent bring forth self-protective behavior.

Sincerely yours,
Milton H. Erickson, M.D.

Wells

The correspondence with Wesley Wells is important for a number of reasons. It is the only correspondence that we found that took Erickson to task. Wells was critical of Erickson's hypnotic technique and his experimental methods for inducing antisocial behavior. A respected academic who championed hypnosis, he believed that Erickson's perspective that antisocial behavior could not be hypnotically induced was bad for the advancement of hypnosis as a science. The exchange further exemplifies the contrasting positions in the controversy about hypnotically induced antisocial behavior.

Wells was a Harvard-trained psychologist who was a professor of psychology at Syracuse University. By 1940, he had written five articles on hypnosis, mostly about hypnotic phenomena and waking hypnosis. His student Margaret Brenman, the recipient of one of Wells' letters reported herein, became even more renowned then her mentor, coauthoring, with Merton Gill, important texts on the psychoanalytic theory of hypnosis.

In his 1941 paper, Wells described a technique of using hypnosis in a single case, creating through direct suggestion an illusion in a highly hypnotizable subject that induced antisocial behavior. It was suggested to the subject that he remove money from "his own coat," a coat that, in fact, belonged to Wells. Amnesia *for the act was subsequently instilled. Wells maintained that this was evidence that hypnosis was a powerful agent of influence. He argued that if one could use hypnosis to induce dissociation in hypnotic phenomena such as amnesia, it could be used to induce dissociation from morality. He believed, however, that such effects were contingent on working with highly hypnotizable individuals. Hence he sided with Rowland and Estabrooks in arguing against Erickson, who maintained that hypnosis was an impediment to the induction of antisocial acts.*

In the letter from Wells to Brenman in which Erickson was copied, Wells mentioned Brenman's replication of his findings and her contradiction of Erickson's study. The citation for Brenman was her 1942 article, "Experiments in the Hypnotic Production of Anti-social and Self-injurious Behavior," Journal of Psychiatry, 5:49–61.

The following correspondence from 1940 concerns a preprint sent by Wells to Erickson of an article on antisocial behavior induced through hypnosis: "Experiments in the Hypnotic Production of Crime" (Wells, 1941).

From: Wesley R. Wells
August 19, 1940

Dear Dr. Erickson:

Thank you for your two letters of July 23rd.[Note: These letters could not be found in the Erickson files.]

I have at last sent in my article to the editors. I sent you the second draft. The final draft, or what had been intended as the final (third) draft, turned out to be over 60 pages in length. I then shortened it to 50 pages. No essential changes were made, however, except for a footnote correction in which I referred to your letter and your statement that the 50 (75) subjects of your article had been selected from 500. The result of this correction, however, is merely to put the blame for your failures more squarely on your lack of adequate technique.

You say that you hypnotize 90%, and 70% "can be put into a profound somnambulistic trance." My point is that, by your own admissions, you have never put any subjects into a really profound somnambulistic trance. Also, you must never have seen any really deeply hypnotized subjects, otherwise you would recognize your own failures. These two statements would hold true of Hull, I believe, also.

Since writing the article, and since writing to you last, I have learned that Estabrooks, of Colgate, warned you, before the publication of your article on antisocial behavior, not to make the interpretation which you made. He warned you to leave open a line of retreat. The main point of my criticism of you is that you boldly assert that, since you have failed to get certain results, such results cannot be obtained. The fallacy of such an argument should be obvious to you now, as it was to Estabrooks.

I did my experiments without any reference to you. You had not then published your article. In writing up my results in full this summer, however, your article of 1939 has been one which I could not overlook.

I did add, in my final draft, one further reference to your work. In an added discussion of the matter of control experiments, I discussed experiments in the use of hypnosis for purposes of surgical anesthesia. I referred to Hull's account (Hull, 1933, page 252) of your attempted hypnotic anesthesia for purposes of dental surgery. I contrasted with it two cases where I have administered hypnotic anesthesia for purposes of dental surgery with complete success. I did not say this in the article, but I say it to you now in this letter, that it seems unfortunate that the account of your failure to induce hypnotic anesthesia should have been referred to by Hull, without an account of successful cases of hypnotic anesthesia. Perhaps you have succeeded since Hull's book was published in inducing complete anesthesia. If not, you would certainly be interested to do it or to see it done just once. Your subject "whimpered and squirmed," according to Hull, sufficient evidence that the anesthesia was not complete . . . I can plan to attend the September meeting of the American Psychological Association at State College, Pa. If you are there, I hope that we may have an opportunity to discuss some of our common problems.

Sincerely yours,
Wesley R. Wells

Editor's Note. The exact wording of Hull's text was: "The patient whimpered and flinched . . ." (p. 252). Also, in Erickson's copy of Hull's book, Erickson typed and pasted an appended correction: "Patient underwent extraction of six teeth at a sitting; showed no apparent pain reactions until the attempted pulling of the fifth tooth. She then flinched and whimpered. Reinforcement of the anesthetic suggestions permitted completion of extractions without any further pain manifestations." M.H.E.

To: Wesley R. Wells
August 22, 1940

Dear Dr. Wells:

I regret very much that your manuscript and your letters seem to be directed to the purpose of making a personal attack upon my intelligence, integrity, and experience, instead of directly to the much more worthy purpose of making a contribution to science. Really, I do not know how your attack on me furthers your points and it seems to me so useless and futile to clutter up the literature with ad hominem arguments. They are neither pleasant nor fruitful reading, and they contribute nothing of merit to the problems under consideration.

I do wish that, instead of attacking me as a person, you had preferred to criticize my experiments as investigative procedures. A direction of criticisms to experiments as such I think is highly to be desired since such criticisms often constitute genuine contributions in the furthering of science. That is why, in criticizing Rowland's experiment, I limited my remarks to the experiment itself, and why I wish you, too, would prefer to give critical consideration to my experiments as such rather than to direct so many denunciations at me as an experimenter.

However, you have apparently made your choice and so all I can do is to ask you to tell me where you intend to publish so that I may prepare a reply. Would it be possible for you to loan me a copy of the revised draft of your paper for my secretary to copy and then return to you?

One other matter concerns your reliance upon the extremely misleading and incomplete account of hypnotic anesthesia which Hull put into his book. I related the experience to Hull early in 1928, but apparently, in 1933, he merely relied upon his memory of that previous account instead of securing a valid factual account from me, even though we were in active correspondence at the time.* And since Hull gives that account as his own restatement of another person's experience rather than as a quotation, I

*There is no record of this correspondence in the Erickson files.

am rather astonished that you did not avail yourself of our correspondence to secure a first-hand account of the facts instead of using Hull's second-hand account as another weapon against me. Also, I wonder what pertinence Hull's unfortunate misstatement of my experience has to your experiment.

I shall be interested in meeting you at the APA convention.

Yours sincerely,
Milton H. Erickson M.D.

Copy to Dr. Erickson
From: Wesley R. Wells
September 7, 1940

Dear Miss Brenman:

Though I am at home now, beginning next week I shall be at my quarters in Syracuse at least most of the time, except weekends, and my mail address should be as above, or at the University.

I returned last evening from the A.P.A. meetings at State College, Pa. I left one day early. I had seen nearly all the people I wanted to see, and was getting tired and anxious to get back at my work at home. I was sorry to miss the address of the retiring president last evening, and I was sorry to miss Maslow's paper, for the sake of finding out who he is. Over 1200 were registered at the meetings. Maslow was on the program for yesterday afternoon. I would have liked meeting him, to ask about your hypnotic work this summer with his classes. However, I found your letter of August 31 when I arrived home, and I was very much pleased indeed to get your own report of your experiments. You had not written since the very beginning of your work a month ago or more.

Lest I forget less important items raised by your letter, I shall take them up at the start, and then write about my conversation with Erickson and your own experiments.

. . . Now for the really important part of my letter, pertaining to your experiments, and my impressions of Erickson. I had a talk with him for an hour. I am glad to have met him, of course, but our conversation was very unsatisfactory. However, I learned some things. He knew Hull at Wisconsin, but thinks very poorly of him. He says Hull reciprocates this feeling. Yet Erickson's article on antisocial behavior puts him in the same class of would-be debunkers of hypnosis that Hull belongs in.

My experiments were planned and done before I had ever seen Erickson's article. Consequently Erickson claimed that what I had done was easy and obvious, and proved nothing; while it would be impossible to have repeated his experiments with success. I was going to write you this, advising you when the opportunity arose to repeat some of Erickson's experiments. He said I had given my subject permission to pick the pocket, since it was my own coat. I wrote you earlier that you had better use someone else's coat than your own. It would, of course, be as easy, since the subject is made to see it as his own coat. I used my own coat since it was warm weather and no other coats were hanging on the wall. I took my own overcoat there on purpose. But Erickson claims that he was trying a much harder thing in trying to get a subject to look into a handbag belonging to a third person, though without stealing anything. I am glad that you have repeated some of these experiments of Erickson's. You found them very much easier than mine, I am sure. You say, "It was extremely easy to obtain positive results." Well, you have done something to stop one of Ericoson's arguments. You have done specific instances of what Erickson said could not be done.

I'll send you Erickson's letters. Please return them, but there is no hurry about it. On the whole, I think even less well of his competence and his knowledge of the theory and practice of hypnosis, and his knowledge of psychology, than before talking with him. For example, he does not know the difference between an illusion and hallucination. He said that in my illustration of making the hypnotized subject see, posthypnotically his friend's dog as a fox instead of a dog, and then shooting it, the man would see the fox somewhere else than where the dog was. Erickson was loud and dogmatic in asserting that it would always work out this way. But I said illusion and I meant illusion. I did not say he would see the dog chasing a nonexistent fox, or rather not see the dog, but see a nonexistent fox ahead of the real dog. This would have been a case of negative hallucination and of positive hallucination. In the case of illusion, there is an object present which is misperceived, but it is perceived where it is, and when the man shot the seen fox, the dog would be shot. But there was no use arguing with Erickson on this point.

When you get the reprint of my article in from two weeks to a month, you will find an added section on control experiments. I say that it would be a farce to do a control experiment in such an experiment as ours. You will see what I mean when you read it. In fact you expressed to me the same thought last spring. But for the sake of quieting this objection that no control experiment had been included, in the future it would be wise to go through the farce of repeating the same instructions to the same subject, but without hypnosis. But anyone who can understand the situation, and who reads my article and yours, will see the absurdity of requiring control experiments in such cases.

Erickson argues in one of his letters, and also orally two days ago, that real crime has been brought about by experimenters who have not used hypnosis. Of course, I admitted to him in discussion that crime is usually brought about by nonhypnotic methods. But in our experiment we used hypnosis and not these other methods, not suggestion, undue influence, etc. Erickson claims that he has produced complete anesthesia for purposes of surgery and obstetrics, and I believe that he had done so. But it would be as logical to say to him that I know of thousands of cases of operations in hospitals in which anesthesia has been induced by ether and other chemical agents, with no hypnosis; therefore, it was not hypnosis which produced the anesthesia in his own cases.

I don't know as I would care much for your mere notes on the Brooklyn College experiments. But whenever you get your article or articles written up, even in an early draft like the one I sent you, I hope you will send me a copy. I was disappointed not to get a letter from you with comments on my own article. I am sure you might have made helpful criticisms. I shall be very glad to read whatever you send, and to make comments that might be helpful. Also as to the matter of publication. You may be too busy to write up your work for publication for months to come. I can't do writing for publication while classes are in session. But when you do get this done, I shall be glad to help in the way of finding a publisher, if I can do anything to help.

Erickson thinks I have something against him personally. Now I had done my experiments before I knew anything of his own experiments. When I read Rowland's article, I was pleased, and considered it a real contribution. My attitude was, "Of course, hypnosis can do what Rowland has done by means of it." His results agreed with what I would have expected. But Erickson's article should not have been published, according to my opinion. I believe I am interested in advancing in some slight degree the cause of hypnosis. An article like Erickson's causes glee among the debunkers, among the skeptics. No matter who wrote the article, the article needed criticism, just as Branwell, Schilder and Kauders, and others needed criticism. If Paylor, one of my old acquaintances and best friends, had written the article, I would have felt it my duty to criticize it. Erickson says he wants to write a reply to my article and to publish it in the same journal. He will probably do so. I shall caution him for his own good reputation not to make himself too ridiculous by repeating some of his criticisms of two days ago. I'll tell him that you have already repeated some of his own experiments, getting what he claimed he could not be got.

I would advise you to go your way without expecting to convince Erickson. His attitude seems to be that since he has got extreme results in one or two types of work, anesthesia, analgesia, deafness, etc., therefore, all his results are extreme. I am reminded of the doctor who could cure fits but nothing else, and yet, because he could cure fits, he thought he could cure everything that anyone could cure.

You say the fault is not with Erickson's technique, but with his failure to select the best subjects. When you wrote, you had not received my letter in which I said that Erickson had written that the 50 (75) subjects of his experiments had been selected from 500. Certainly, if he was able to tell the good subjects when he worked on them, many of these must have been top-notch subjects. I am convinced that his technique is bad. I don't believe he distinguished the art of hypnosis from the art of suggestion (any more than Taylor does). Not having seen the production of extreme results in this field, he does not recognize how poor his own results are. This is what I think. But the only point is, he was justified by his experiments in concluding only the following: "The conclusion warranted by these findings is that I have thus far been unsuccessful in inducing hypnotized persons to commit actual wrongful acts," etc. Instead of this, he "stuck his neck out," against Estabrook's advice, to publish his experiments but to leave out this conclusion. He wrote, "The conclusion warranted by these experimental findings is that hypnosis canot be misused," etc. The facts are that the literature records a good many instances where hypnosis has produced antisocial behavior; in my experiments I did what Erickson said is impossible; you in your first year of hypnotizing have done similarly. And the best thing about your work is that you repeated some of Erickson's own experiments so that he has absolutely no comeback. Yet two days ago he had the nerve to say that his conclusion was very cautiously written. If he had only inserted the words "by myself" after the assertion, "hypnosis cannot be misused to . . . commit actual wrongful acts," etc., it would have been all right. That is, I readily accept the proposition that he has not yet succeeded. But I do not believe that it would be impossible for him to learn a better technique and better theories and then refute his own earlier experiments.

I hope you will send him a copy of your article before it is published. Your paper will be like this: you have repeated my experiment, getting similar results. Then you have repeated some of his experiments, getting opposite results.

I do not see how Erickson could have made such an imprudent statement as his conclusion. "I tried it. I couldn't do it. Therefore, it can't be done." This is the exact logic of his article.

I shall write to Erickson. I have made copies of this letter, and I may send him a copy of the last part, portaining to his work, to save the time of rewriting some of these points. Can you think of any way to make Erickson see that his logic is fallacious? For the good of hypnosis as I see it, I wish Erickson would broaden his contact with hypnotic techniques, and apply himself in trying to get extreme results in fields other than that of anesthesia.

By the way, he says that he really produced complete anesthesia for purposes of dental surgery, and that Hull simply falsified the facts on page 252 of his book, where he said Erickson got amnesia afterwards for the pain, but no anesthesia. I feel sure Erickson did get anesthesia or analgesia; some time I want to bring into some article an account of this falsification by Hull of what had been transmitted to him by letter. It is just in line with Hull's seeming interest in discrediting hypnosis. Hull is so ignorant of the type of psychology needed to understand hypnosis, i.e., subconscious processes, dissociation, recall amnesias, and recognition amnesias existing with perfect retention, that argument with him is useless. He was chairman of the session where a Syracuse Ph.D. man, Leuba, who learned hypnosis from me ten or more years ago, read a good paper on hypnosis. Hull's comments for the most part were cynical, lacking in understanding of the situation.

Now Erickson is sincerely interested in advancing the cause of hypnosis. Hull is hopeless. I hate to think that Erickson is hopeless. I wish that he might have an opportunity to study your technique and your experiments as you perform them. I am even so bold as to think that I could teach him how to hypnotize as well as you do it. It would indeed be much harder than it was to teach you. He knows many things which are not so, whereas your mind was mostly a blank to start with, so far as actual methods were concerned. But it is of course unlikely that he will ever learn how to get extreme results in all fields. He has been working too long and has too good an opinion of his methods to want to learn better methods.

I am really very grateful to you for getting interested in this problem. I hope that you will be able in future years to return to experimental work in this field. And I hope that you may be able to write up your results effectively before too long a time. My article will be in the *Journal of Psychology*, January 1941, vol. 11, pp. 63–102.

Wesley R. Wells

Ament

Erickson was adamantly opposed to stage hypnosis and throughout his career he attempted to curtail its use. Philip Ament, D.D.C., wrote Erickson on March 19, 1956, informing him that a Buffalo, N.Y., city councilman was "interested in passing an ordinance . . . to the effect that stage hypnosis will be against the law." Erickson's reply is a succinct representation of his basis of objection to the stage practice of hypnosis.

To: Philip Ament
April 1, 1956

Dear Dr. Ament:

I have just returned from a seminar in New York and will answer your letter hastily.

I have been interested in hypnosis for over thirty years. I have written extensively on the subject, as regards both experimental work and clinical work. I have had a great deal of experience with a wide variety of patients, as you already know.

It is on the basis of my experience that I wish to make the following statements: Stage hypnosis is detrimental to the general public for the reason that many unstable persons volunteer as subjects in a desperate hope to get some help, either directly or indirectly. As a consequence, they are misled, misinformed and confused and often alienated in relation to a therapeutic method that would ordinarily be helpful to them. Additionally, stage hypnosis gives the public a misconception of what hypnosis really is and what its uses are and, in this regard, is actually a disservice to the general public.

The use of hypnosis by charlatans and would-be practitioners of the healing arts constitutes the same liability to mental health that surgery would be in similar hands, although the danger is not so readily recognized. During the course of my experience, I frequently have had to clarify the disordered and confused thinking of many patients, who had been abused by the deceptive, misleading and often callous use of hypnosis by stage hypnotists and unqualified users of stage hypnosis.

For these reasons, which could be elaborated upon extensively, I faver strongly the passage of laws and regulations limiting the use of hypnosis to professionally qualified men. I would include in such professionally qualified men licensed psychologists possessing the Ph.D. degree or the equivalent thereof, dentists and physicians, and I would also favor the use of hypnosis under the supervision of the Psychology Departments of any accredited institution of higher learning.

I hope this letter meets your wishes.

Sincerely yours,
Milton H. Erickson, M.D.

VI

AN ERICKSON OLIO:

Various Correspondents—Professional and Nonprofessional

Colleagues

Erickson's June 17 reply to Griffith Williams' June 13, 1942, letter provides classic illustrations of the principle of utilization. Zeig (1992) defined utilization as "readiness of the therapist to respond strategically to any and all the aspects of the patient or the environment" (p. 256). Utilization is effected to advance trance and/or therapy goals. It was a cardinal concept in Erickson's psychotherapy. Utilization is to Ericksonian therapy as interpretation is to psychoanalysis. Rather than exposing the understructure of resistance, though, the therapist harnesses resistance and turns it in constructive directions.

In 1942, the concepts of "double bind" and "prescribing the symptom" did not exist. Yet Erickson clearly delineated the construction of binds by utilizing the "resistant" (unawakening) behavior. Through this means, he meticulously created a series of steps designed to lead the subjects constructively. Whether utilizing a

hallucination (hypnotic phenomenon), "sophistry" (intellectual adroitness), tran-
sition from hypnosis to sleep (biological process), or acting out (personality trait),
Erickson strategically channeled the practicable forms of resistance toward the
hypnotic goal of reawakening.

From: Griffith W. Williams
June 13, 1942

Dear Dr. Erickson:

I am trying to collect material on some of the difficulties encountered in research on hypnosis. One of the difficulties that always interests the layman is that of the inability of the experimenter to dehypnotize his subject. I can find but very scattered references to this phenomenon in the literature.

Have you had any first-hand contact with situations of this type? They sometimes creep into the newspapers, but unfortunately I have not kept a file of these. I have written to Paul C. Young about this as I believe he had some such situation on his hands some time ago, but I have not as yet received a reply.

If you have a file of newspaper references or an opinion concerning the nature of this phenomenon, I would appreciate very much receiving such information. Apparently the situation occurs infrequently but it is a genuine phenomenon. Do you think that the subjects who cannot be dehypnotized may have been hysterical in the first place? Furthermore, is the difficulty in dehypnotizing a form of regression to a type of behavior that would take them out of immediate contact with their environment? I also have a suspicion, but one that would be very difficult to confirm, that narcolepsy may be a form of self-induced hypnosis in some ways comparable to this difficulty in dehypnotizing.

These are some of the questions that bother me and I would welcome whatever information you may feel that you can give. I have been rereading your study of unconscious mentation by autonomic writing. I was intrigued by it when I first read it, and my interest has been increased on rereading. It seems to me that if many studies of this type could be produced, we could get far more insight into the nature of the dynamics of behavior than we have at the present time. I am puzzled, however, as to how experimental situations of this type could be set up. Anyway, congratulations on a splendid study.

Cordially yours,
Griffith W. Williams

To: Griffith W. Williams
June 17, 1942

Dear Dr. Williams:

I was very happy to receive your letter, both because I am glad to hear from you and because the problem you discuss is one in which I have long been interested.

However, I shall not try to answer your specific questions. Instead, I shall write you in a rather sketchy fashion and thus to outline my own experience with the problems. It is my hope that we can carry on a more extensive correspondence and perhaps formulate some satisfying ideas on the total subject.

However, at the outset though, I would like to suggest that you abandon all ideas about narcolepsy, hypnolepsy and cataplexia being related to hypnosis or self-induced hypnosis, I have made extensive investigations in this regard and I can assure you that they are not related in any way.

First of all, those subjects who refuse to awaken from the hypnotic trance constitute actually only a simple problem in technique. After a few difficult experiences I learned to have a lot of fun with them by letting them think they were successfully refusing to awaken from the trance and I took advantage of this refusal to carry on a good deal of experimentation in this regard. Actually, one can employ a number of technical procedures in handling their refusal. With highly intelligent subjects who can follow my logic, after they have convinced themselves that I cannot awaken them, I explain in essentials, "I have suggested sleep to you slowly, progressively, until, in response to my suggestions you fall into the condition of sleep. In other words your present state is conditional upon my suggestions. Therefore your present status is conditional upon what I say, what suggestions I offer. Now I am suggesting that you try hard to stay asleep, that you try to keep from awakening."

Thus, I have reversed the situation entirely. I have taken command of the resistance to awaken and made it obligatory for him to remain asleep in accord with my verbalized wishes. As a consequence of this sort of sophistry it becomes impossible for him to awaken unless I suggest it and it likewise is impossible for him to remain asleep without my suggestion. And in the trance state the subject has little opportunity to unravel the sophistry employed.

Or, after explaining how his trance state is conditional upon my suggestions that he go to sleep slowly, gradually, completely, becoming aware that he is sleeping sounder and sounder all the time, I then point out to him that in a similar way I can suggest that he begin to get ready to awaken slowly, to awaken bit by bit and so build up waking suggestions in a cumulative fashion. With the extremely obstinate subject I find that in this way I can force him to maintain a state of sleep by accepting my suggestions that he awaken—that is, he stays asleep, accepts my suggestions but these compel an awakening—a utilization of the two horns of the dilemma.

Or again I seemingly accept the refusal to awaken and then slowly build up to the performance of some act by the subject. When this act is adequately built up and after I have given the cue for that act and it is in the process of performance, I let him discover that its completion culminates in awakening. However, so far as the subject is concerned the process of behavior is already under way and more or less automatically he carries it through.

Then again, subjects may find the trance state so pleasing that they may decide to remain in the trance and to dispense with me entirely. Thus, in giving a demonstration before a psychology department I asked my subject to hallucinate the movie *Rasputin*, which I knew he had seen. And as he hallucinated it he discussed it with me and talked about it. When there had been a sufficient demonstration of this hallucinatory behavior I attempted to awaken my subject but he informed me quite irritably that he wished I would stop talking, that he was interested in seeing the movie through to its completion, that if I wished to leave the theatre, I was at liberty to do so, but that he intended to remain until the end of the picture and that he intended to see it through a second time. I seized upon this as a nice opportunity to demonstrate technique to the group and after I was certain the audience realized the difficult situation, I joined in with my subject in presumably watching the movie and he quite pleasantly began renewing his comments on it with me. Watching for a favorable opportunity I suggested that something seemed to be going wrong with the film, that apparently the projector was somewhat out of order and I expressed the hope that the operator would be able to repair the projector. After three or four such remarks I made the suggestion that the projector was running much too fast, that the pictures were getting blurred and out of focus, that apparently something was seriously wrong with the projector and that undoubtedly there would be an enforced interruption and again I expressed the hope that I was mistaken but qualified it by the statement that I was afraid I was right in my judgment. Thereupon I proceeded to give rapid suggestions to the effect that the projector was running much too rapidly, that the pictures were becoming increasingly blurred and finally that the machine had broken and the picture had stopped. My subject found himself unable to resist these suggestions and I offered the suggestion that we might sit quietly and wait patiently until the projector was repaired whereupon we could continue watching the film. In the meantime we might take up various other problems.

The above is but a single example. I have had that sort of thing happen several times with different subjects before different groups and the measure of employing an external factor or force with which we have all had common experience has been most effective in permitting me to control the total situation.

The greatest difficulty in handling the awakening process occurs when the subject is reoriented to an earlier period of his life. In this connection see footnote on page 592 of the reprint entitled, "The Successful Treatment of a Case of Acute Hysterical Depression by a Return Under Hypnosis to a Critical Phase of Childhood," published in *The Psychoanalytic Quarterly* [Erickson & Kubie, 1941]. One needs only to insure that he maintains contact with his subject, as mentioned in that footnote, and, keeping in mind the actual psychic realities being experienced by the subject, proffer suitable suggestions.

Then too, a most simple measure is to review for the subject the differences between natural sleep and hypnotic sleep, especially if the subject's educational background warrants it, and then suggest the transformation of the trance into natural sleep since he wishes to sleep. This permits a ready loss of rapport, a lapsing into natural sleep and a ready awakening. Additionally, as an experimental setup it is grand.

Otherwise, one can simply suggest that they continue to sleep even as they did last night, last Monday night, etc. And since the subject insists upon sleeping, all his emphasis is upon *sleep*, such suggestions are readily accepted and unwittingly he proceeds to sleep as he did last Monday night—a sleep from which he could be awakened.

Then again I use a variation of the horns of the dilemma. When my subject has convinced me that he is going to stay asleep despite my suggestions I accept his behavior at face value and proceed to give him suggestions to the effect that he resist awakening, that he exert every possible effort against awakening. As you can readily understand, resistance cannot be offered against something which is nonexistent and so the more resistance he offers to awakening the more reality he gives to awakening as an impending possibility. This simply creates a vicious cycle from which he escapes either by awakening at my request or by yielding to the tendency to awaken. A somewhat analagous situation is the induction of hand levitation in an unresponsive subject by encouraging him carefully to resist any possible movements of his hand, and as you probably know from experience, this often facilitates hand levitation.

In other words, simple technical approaches solve the problem invariably and comfortably and you have a beautiful experimental situation.

The background for the above statements derived from experiences with the following types of subjects:

(1) Subjects who secretly determined before they went into a trance that they would not awaken from it until they got good and ready.

(2) Subjects who agreed with others to do the same thing but without letting me know about it.

(3) Subjects whom my colleagues had approached with this idea as a definite experiment to be conducted on me, sometimes with and sometimes without my knowledge.

(4) Subjects who found the trance state so pleasing that they decided to dispense with me entirely.

(5) Subjects who were given suggestions by me or others that they resist effectively any suggestions to awaken as a definite experiment intended to discover adequate ways of handling such a problem.

(6) Subjects who through reorientation to earlier periods of life lost all contact with the hypnotist.

(7) Subjects who deliberately faked trances to deceive me, usually with somebody in the audience aware of the intended hoax.

(8) First-hand accounts from the unfortunate participants in news stories (one such was publicized extensively in *Time* a few years ago).

In the three newspaper stories on which I got reliable information, the subjects were all hysterical neurotics, the hypnotist inexperienced and the results were hysterical episodes and not a trance on the part of the subjects, and the severe panic on the part of the hypnotist increased the hysterical reactions. In all three instances the trance phenomena were very slight.

Additionally, I have had three experiences with hysterical girls. In each case I was giving a lecture and demonstration before a professional or semiprofessional group. Each time the hysterical girl attempted to create a horrible scene by crying, screaming, declaring inability to awaken and that sort of thing. One instance I handled, since it was a medical group, by promptly demonstrating the girl as an example of acute hysteria, pointing out how her behavior differed from hypnosis. As you can guess it was a very successful evening for the group and the girl could do nothing but go home afterwards with the satisfaction of having been successfully demonstrated on my terms and to the satisfaction of everybody. Another girl I handled by suggesting hysterical aphonia and hysterical paralysis which would persist until after she had fallen into a natural sleep. I further suggested that, when she awakened from the natural sleep, she would be so embarrassed at her behavior that she would hope everybody would forget about it and that this hope that others would forget about it would make her want to forget about it. I also gave a few therapeutic suggestions so that she could talk the matter over with me later and get an adequate understanding in an appropriate situation. The third girl was handled by suggesting that her frightened screaming would change in character until it would become transformed into a long drawn-out exclamation of pleasure and that this pleasure would derive from a wealth of happy pleasant dreams and fantasies in which she would absorb herself and which she would protect from outside disturbances until the end of the lecture hour. I also suggested after the lecture hour that she sees me privately in my office for a little psychotherapy. (However, my psychiatric experience serves me greatly in this sort of thing.)

I hope this letter is of value to you. Should you wish to use any of the material you are welcome but I would like the privilege of seeing your manuscript. Also, should this material be of value I would like to check through my records for the additional points I have omitted from this hasty letter.

> Sincerely yours,
> Milton H. Erickson. M.D.

As mentioned earlier, by the mid-1940s, Erickson had attained extensive notoriety. His reputation was such that clinicians began sending challenging patients to him for consultation. One such example was the couple Dr. Muncie described in this letter of referral. The consulting question, however, is unclear. Erickson thanked Dr. Muncie for the referral and responded to his request for an elaboration about the treatment.

To: Wendell Muncie
July 8, 1946

Dear Doctor Muncie,

Please accept my most earnest thanks for the Alabama people.

The first interview indicated that there was no possibility of using hypnosis.

Instead, there was a systematic and orderly effort at complete reorientation of all thinking, feeling and behavior. The results were satisfactory. In less than a week I was able to tie up the package and send it back. I really had anticipated a much more serious struggle in view of the severe pattern of two years and seven months, but apparently the method of conscious reorientation I employed was entirely satisfactory.

Again, many thanks.

> Sincerely yours,
> Milton H. Erickson, M.D.

Editor's Note: On July 15, 1946, Muncie wrote to Erickson asking what points Erickson covered with the husband. He also asked how Erickson decided that hypnosis should not be employed. Muncie closed by saying how delighted he was with Erickson's results.

To: Wendell Muncie
July 18, 1946

Dear Doctor Muncie,

To reply to your letter is most difficult since it is hard to convey clinical understandings by mere words.

In the first place the man was very pleasingly agreeable and intelligent and he so thoroughly intellectualized everything that it was not possible to get at his real emotions. Additionally, in an obscure and almost obsequious manner he really demanded that he be met on an intellectual plane and he merely verbalized appropriate emotional responses.

Second, he was so impersonal in all of his psychomotor behavior. He crossed his legs, shook hands and leaned forward earnestly to listen and put on his hat, all in such a mechanical, well-controlled fashion that there was no real expression of his personality, nor of his emotional realization of the severe problem he had. Third, his actual emotional concern over his problem was related more to an intellectual appreciation of anatomical and physiological functioning and to the social implications of these items without relating them to his own feelings of personal pride and self-esteem or, if you wish, personal narcissism.

On the contrary his wife felt humiliated, embarrassed, resentful, and seriously distressed, disappointed and wounded. He only verbalized these things and gave such full earnest attention intellectually when these items were discussed that he made no emotional response within himself. His wife, however, would be half listening attentively and the other half would be struggling with her own unrecognized and repressed emotions.

Since hypnosis is primarily an experiential process for the subject I felt any trance I secured from him would be limited by intellectualizations. Therefore, I let him cover his problem with me by intellectualization of his general attitudes.

Therapy then became a matter of "cutting back" in his pattern of intellectualization and I then confronting him in minute detail with the probabilities and possibilities of his actual emotional responses in his early childhood. This made it necessary for him to recover past emotional experiences in order to intellectualize his understandings of them. Thus he was forced into the situation of evoking real emotional memories as the means to an intellectualization. This then gave me the opportunity of granting him permission to engage in prepubertal behavior as a self-exploratory and self-investigative process by which to secure more material for further intellectualization. Following this, permission was granted indirectly for pubertal, early adolescent and late adolescent behavior, and along with this permissiveness I also threw in an attitude of parental interference and objection so that he would have the opportunity of defying me unconsciously.

The result was that his first success was really based on a defiance of my objection.

This was followed by a minute examination of every emotion, reaction, and sensory experience that had resulted in his success with the result that he became acutely aware of personal feelings in such a situation, and he needed to become aware of them in order to intellectualize.

I then capitalized upon the attitude of parental objection by reforming it into a general forbidding of traveling around the country over the Fourth of July, which he took great pains to violate by driving all around the city of Detroit.

While he gave an accurate description of his travels about the city of Detroit, I carefully let him appreciate that I was vaguely displeased with his actual disregard of my instructions not to drive about the countryside and he in turn felt pleased and satisfied that he had driven about in exact accord with my instructions, driven about without violating the actual words of my instructions. In turn he obviously developed an excellent feeling that he could do things in his own way and meet all the demands of a forbidding parent at both a social and personal level. This was then followed by his assumption of all responsibility for discovering the extent of his capacities, including two successes within the span of an hour although I had specifically specified he must not succeed in a space of time less than several hours although I admitted there was no good reason for my interdiction.

The follow-up was then a careful letting of him to make clear to me, of course actually to himself, that he really did not need help from me, and that actually I had served only a useful purpose in letting him discover his own capabilities.

I hope the above clarifies somewhat my handling of the problem. Again thanking you very much for this opportunity.

Sincerely yours,
Milton H. Erickson, M.D.

———————————*JR*———————————

The summary of Erickson's consultation in his letter of July 18, 1946, to Wendell Muncie demonstrates the flexibility of his approach. This case could be considered an example of hypnotherapy without trance. Here, Erickson used features of the patient's personality, pride, narcissism, oppositional behavior, and intellectualization to artfully guide treatment. From his description, it is obvious that Erickson capitalized on the patient's "dissociated" state (emotion from intellect) to effect small, progressive changes. In the process, he encouraged resistance in order to increase his therapeutic leverage. This was a carefully circumscribed resistance, however, one that allowed for constructive behavior. The patient was admonished not to drive in the "country," but he managed to find an intellectual way around Erickson's instruction by limiting his driving to the city.

This case description aptly demonstrates how Erickson utilized existing personality patterns, took what the patient brought, and promoted small steps toward desired ends. Note that his interventions were geared toward modifying the patient's associations. It seemed that Erickson discerned the patient's thinking style and strategically guided him to establishing constructive associations. Behavioral tasks and directives (in this case, accessing childhood memories for "intellectual" scrutiny) would be precise steps for reassociative, internal life. Therapeutic tasks were not designed necessarily to "desensitize," but rather to reassociate.

Bernard Raginsky was one of the leaders in hypnosis in the 1950s. A physician who practiced in Montreal, he was active in the Society for Clinical and Experimental Hypnosis and an avid supporter of the society, which was occasionally plagued with financial problems. Raginsky tabbed Erickson "Mister Hypnosis."

Milton Kline was the founding editor of the International Journal of Clinical and Experimental Hypnosis. *He and Erickson had been in considerable conflict and, at the time of Erickson's September 21 letter, their feud was in full bloom.*

Harold Rosen was influential in hypnosis circles as well, but eventually, became dogmatic regarding the dangers of hypnosis. Erickson countered Rosen's polemics on many occasions, both verbally and in writing.

To: Bernard B. Raginsky
September 21, 1956

Dear Dr. Raginsky:

As you undoubtedly remember, Leslie M. LeCron was a member of our panel for Seminars on Hypnosis, but during the course of his association with us, we became increasingly unhappy about it, because we felt that he resorted to practices not in accord with professional ethics. This became increasingly an item of open discussion with him in our post-seminar meetings and the resentment that he developed led to his resignation at San Francisco.

At that time, I informed the other members of the panel that it was Mr. LeCron's intention to have his wife, whose only experience has been that of a third-grade school teacher, become associated with him professionally as a psychologist. I am enclosing a photostat of his recent announcement to this effect.

Additionally, since April I have been interviewed by three charlatans, who all are advertising hypnotists. Each stated his intention of setting up an office in Phoenix and expressed a wish to affiliate with me in somewhat the same fashion as they had been affiliated with LeCron. One of them had an eighth-grade education. Two had purchased Ph.D. degrees, one from a metaphysical diploma mill in Indiana and the other from a diploma mill in Los Angeles. All three separately described LeCron's office and gave details of cases worked on by LeCron, which cases were known to me. I have no reason to doubt the veracity of their statements to me. To date, none of the three has located in Phoenix.

I doubt very much if Mr. LeCron should be continued in membership in the Society for Clinical and Experimental Hypnosis and I am equally doubtful that he should be continued as a member of the editorial board of the Journal. I further doubt that the special branch of the Society for Clinical and Experimental Hypnosis that he is organizing in California should be recognized until its membership has been thoroughly scrutinized.

One additional item concerning the Associate Membership concerns Dr. Richard N. Clark [address provided].

This physician is a very competent, honest, sincere man; however, ill-advisedly he has contributed a foreword to the book *The Hypnotism*

Handbook, written by Charles Edward Cooke (without any degree) and A. E. Van Vogt, a science fiction writer.

I have met Mr. Cooke and I have had correspondence with him. I have also seen a considerable number of patients whom I felt have been seriously harmed by this untrained lay therapist. Mr. Cooke endeavored to have me write a foreword for his book and I refused, because I felt that it was completely unprofessional and utterly wrong to do so. Mr. Cooke assured me that Mr. LeCron had given him a great deal of professional advice and guidance in writing the book. The veracity of this statement I do not know; however, there is the foreword by Dr. Clark and I was assured by Mr. Cooke before the publication of the book that Dr. Clark was writing such a foreword at the suggestion of Mr. LeCron. I do not believe that any members of the Society for Clinical and Experimental Hypnosis should lend their names to such books as the one written by Cooke and Van Vogt.

The book is published by the Griffin Publishing Company of Los Angeles, California, and I have been assured by several people that this is a small printing firm, which publishes solely at the author's expense.

I am sending copies of this letter to Drs. Milton Kline, Harold Rosen, and Frank Pattie.

Sincerely yours,
Milton H. Erickson, M.D.

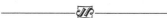

Erickson was a diligent defender of hypnosis. His October 30, 1958, letter represents another example of the care he took to rebut uniformed attacks on the approach. Also, note that Erickson wrote a substantial letter to V. G. Henry, ending in an appreciative, personal tone, rather than addressing the misinformation in a more public forum.

Henry wrote a letter to the American Society of Clinical Hypnosis, which was forwarded to Erickson, who was president at the time. He was conducting a busy private practice in Phoenix, leading the effort to solidify the fledgling society's status, and editing its journal. Still, he took the time to address comprehensively the alarmed members' concerns.

To: American Society of Clinical Hypnosis (Attention: Seymour Hersh-
man, M.D.
From: V. G. Henry, Jr.
October 18, 1958

Dear Doctor Hershman:

I am writing you this letter to call attention to an article that came to
my desk yesterday that appears in a small booklet published by a phar-
maceutical company. [Identifying information supplied]

Perhaps you also received this little booklet, but the last article in this
issue involved quotations from a paper by Dr. B. T. as given at the 114th
Annual Meeting of the American Psychiatric Association, San Francisco,
California, May 16, 1958. It states that Dr. T. is in the private practice
of psychiatry in Long Beach, California. Following are some of the quotes
from his article in this magazine.

(1) "Hypnosis does not provide as good results as can be obtained
through brief, intensive psychotherapy."

(2) "Hypnosis, by its very nature, does not help the individual to mature. Rather, it fixates his development at a point of immaturity."

(3) "In the process of hypnosis, patients must give up their own control
of reality and entrust this vital function to the hypnotist. They cannot
always regain control easily and in a healthy fashion."

(4) "In hypnosis, without any real pressing of the patient to regress,
there is, nevertheless, regression. It is in this process that many severe
emotional disorders may be precipitated by evoking feelings which the
individual is not prepared to deal with."

(5) "In the past nine months I have seen several patients with acute
emotional illnesses provoked by hypnosis. These patients had been subjected to hypnosis as dental anesthesia, to effect symptomatic relief of
emotional problems, or merely as entertainment stunts."

(6) "In view of the hazards and questionable efficacy of hypnosis, I
believe that it has little value in psychiatry specifically or even generally
as a psychotherapeutic technique. I believe that it is dangerous as a routine
procedure for anesthesia in obstetrics, surgery, and dentistry. Its routine
use in children is certain to stunt emotional growth."

(7) "Because hypnosis deprives man of the opportunity to resolve his
difficulties through active mastery and imposes on him a passive, infantile

adjustment, I believe that it must be employed with the greatest caution."

Dr. T.'s article was quoted in the Indianapolis papers soon after their meeting in San Francisco. While this particular article I am quoting from probably will only arrive on the desks of doctors and perhaps some dentists, the lay still has had an opportunity to hear of Dr. T.'s beliefs. I would like to suggest that perhaps a rebuttal could be made by someone in our group, perhaps Dr. Erickson, giving our side of the picture. I know nothing of Dr. T., what his status is in the psychiatric field or as a physician; but certainly his views are contrary to what most of us believe.

Very truly yours,
V. G. Henry, Jr., M.D.

To: V. G. Henry, Jr.,
October 30, 1958

Dear Dr. Henry:

I like to think that I am rather well acquainted with the literature on hypnosis and with the literature on psychotherapy, but unfortunately so far as my knowledge is concerned, the name of Dr. T. was unknown to me as related to hypnosis until I saw his name listed on the program for the American Medical Association.

In looking him up in the American Psychiatric Association directory I notice that his training does not include any special training in hypnosis. On reading his paper I note that he makes some rather dogmatic statements that signify to me a profound unawareness of the use of hypnosis and the nature of hypnosis.

You list his statement: "Hypnosis does not provide as good results as can be obtained through brief, intensive psychotherapy." This statement is warranted only if he adds the qualification of "in my experience." He certainly cannot speak from my experience or the experience of many others who have had good results.

He states, "Hypnosis, by its very nature, does not help the individual to mature. Rather, it fixates his development at a point of immaturity." This is an incredibly naive statement. Hypnosis is a special state of awareness. Naturally a state of awareness does not mature a person; neither does it educate a person, nor does it age a person. It is merely a state of awareness, in which a person can be given psychotherapy. For Dr. T. to criticize it on the basis that it does not mature a person is as absurd as saying that drinking water does not mature a person.

Also, he seems to imply that the purpose of hypnosis is to effect maturation. Does he feel that hypnotic anesthesia for surgery on a patient, aged sixty, is a procedure for maturation? Does he feel that psychotherapy in the correction of a sorrow or grief that has become pathological is a matter of maturation? Does he feel that enabling a cancer patient to adjust to his pain and impending death is a matter of maturation? Does he feel that hypnotic delivery is a matter of maturation? One wonders why he made such a statement in the first place.

In the third quotation you list, he stresses that "in the process of hypnosis, patients must give up their own control of reality and entrust this vital function to the hypnotist. They cannot always regain control easily and in a healthy fashion." This makes one wonder whether he has ever had any experience with hypnosis, because it is so contrary to fact.

In the fourth quotation, there is the dogmatic statement that the patient must necessarily regress. This again makes one wonder if he has had any experience with hypnosis, other than armchair speculation. He also states in that same quotation that severe emotional disorders may be precipitated. I think that anybody possessed of adequate psychiatric training would not precipitate an emotional disturbance and I do know that hypnosis properly is employed to prevent emotional disturbances. So long as the professional man employing hypnosis keeps within his specialty, there is no possibility of harm deriving from the hypnosis.

Concerning the fifth statement that he has seen several patients with acute emotional illnesses provoked by hypnosis, I wonder if he is as careless in documenting his cases concerning hypnosis. Even in the reporting of historical facts, he was remarkably inattentive to accuracy in readily verifiable statements.

With regard to his depreciation of its use, it would be much better if he were to speak from a body of knowledge than from what seems to be an intensity of armchair opinion.

His statement that a special state of awareness stunts emotional growth is in itself a rather remarkable statement that one ought to be wary of making, lest he bring discredit upon himself.

Concerning the last statement, namely, that hypnosis imposes a passive, infantile adjustment, one wonders again where he acquired such incompetent and unwarranted ideas.

However, the history of medicine, like the history of every other scientific endeavor, is replete with the dogmatic declarations of the uniformed. I can remember many of the outrageous statements made about psychoanalysis. We all know about Fulton's Folly and the Wright Brothers' Madness. One of the most charming pieces of "scientific" literature I ever read was an earnest "factual," laboriously well-written exploration of the dangers of riding at speeds of fifteen miles per hour on the proposed new railroads, since the human body could not stand air pressures of that sort and thus unwary people could easily suffer asphyxiation! Unfortunately, I failed to make a notation of the author and the book in which it was published and I have never had a chance to go back to those library stacks. However, I do assure you that it was an entrancing article and so logical. I expect it was not only read but rather widely believed at the time.

I shall be delighted to hear from you again.

Sincerely yours,
Milton H. Erickson, M.D.

On September 1, 1960, J. Wesley Edel, M.D., a Baltimore general practitioner, wrote to Erickson to consult about the case of an overweight female patient. He included a number of documents (letters and reports) for Erickson's review. The patient was formerly under the care of a psychoanalyst, well known to Erickson, who held controversial views regarding hypnosis. This analyst was well situated in the American Medical Association and used that as his pulpit to criticize hypnosis.

Edel's patient apparently derived no benefit from the analytic therapy and, according to Edel, the analyst "established resentment and anxiety about the use of hypnosis in her case." Edel continued, "I feel I have been able to establish [a] warm, therapeutically effective relationship." His inquiry to Erickson concerned whether or not he was "justified in continuing with this case."

To: J. Wesley Edel,
October 1, 1960

Dear Dr. Edel:

I have gone through the case material you sent me most carefully and thoughtfully.

There is no question in my mind about the wisdom of handling the patient. Let me explain:

In the parent-child situation, there were many emotional interplays that were destructive. As a result your patient learned to seek comfort from overeating. This served an emotional purpose at that time. As the years passed, this overeating became a habitual pattern. Finally it became a habit employed to meet situations, since it was a well-learned habit and being irrelevant to the situation, would not be corrected. Therefore, it was readily at hand to be used at any moment for any type of stress.

A parallel much more fitting and meaningful than the quite inappropriate one that Dr. R. suggested concerning physically destructive activity in relation to cardiac disease is as follows:

A 12-year-old boy can sneak out behind the barn and smoke cigarettes in defiance of his parents. Then 15 years later he is smoking them as a habit, no matter how well adjusted and completely "psychoanalyzed" he may have been in the "child analysis" and "adult psychoanalysis" he received during those 15 years.

He continues the smoking free of parental defiance, but, because of having learned to like cigarettes, he will still have the habit. In moments of stress he will light a cigarette, not because it is a personality defense but because, in moments of stress, one needs to do something and smoking is a token initiation of still further action.

The fact that the patient is smoking free of conflicts does not dispute the question of health considerations related to smoking. But it is a habit just as much as many other patterns of behavior of all kinds become habitual and may need correction as a harmful habit.

Now for your patient and your therapy of her:

Your patient has a habit of many years' duration. It no longer constitutes the personality defense it did in her childhood and early youth. It is an unnecessary habit that has persisted in the absence of other, better learnings, but more than that, it is a personal physical liability. As such, it should be corrected and it cannot be assumed that correction of the obesity will intensify the personality problems unless one falsely and deliberately assures the patient that correction of the obesity brings other problems or that it cures the other problems. For example, the diabetes mellitus patient should not be encouraged to keep his crop of boils resulting from increased blood sugar until his diabetes is cured. One treats the immediate problem of lancing and draining the boils and then institutes therapy for the diabetes mellitus. A fair parallel of Dr. R.'s admonition is, "Do not alter the drunkard's state of intoxication until you have first eradicated the underlying personality problems." In other words, allow the patient to stay drunk (or fat) and "analyze" for years to come.

As for the patient necessarily developing a new and worse symptom if a long-established habit is removed, let us examine that old well-kept defeatist superstition of the unthinking.

I have never heard of a patient developing a broken ankle because of the symptomatic relief of an aching or broken tooth; thousands, in fact, millions, of headaches have been symptomatically removed without the patient setting about to develop a worse symptom; the symptomatic correction of a broken arm received in a reckless automobile accident never (I state this dogmatically) leads to a replacement of the symptomatically relieved broken arm by two broken legs; just consider that much of medicine and dentistry is based effectively upon symptomatic relief.

A much more intelligent comprehension of therapy is that symptomatic relief from unnecessary illnesses, habits, and practices clears the way and makes possible further (or deeper) therapy that the patient may need.

As for your patient I strongly recommend that you secure her aid and co-operation in removing the obstructive layer of fat maintained by a habit built up long ago. I am positive that you will not tell her normal weight constitutes good parental relationships or anything like that. Instead I am sure that you will do no more than tell her, "And now, instead of using your strength to carry around tonnage and using time to maintain that tonnage, you can now use that strength and time to advantage in dealing more effectively with your personality needs, much more effectively than when you were draining off strength and time on weight problems."

You as a general practitioner are entitled, in fact, obligated, to meet the patient's needs instead of saying in effect, "I'm very sorry about your extreme sunburn, but some personality inadequacy caused you to overexpose yourself to the sun, and your sunburn must not be treated symptomatically until a sufficient number of years of analysis have corrected the deep underlying self-destructive trends hidden in the profound recesses of your personality."

I do not understand why, in all other branches of science, each new thought, each new discovery is hailed with a delight that constitutes the motivation to seek for new and better thoughts and discoveries, while in psychiatry, it is otherwise. As our friend Dr. R. so emphatically teaches, any statement once made must stand as a final declaration indefinitely. For example, in 1890, Freud made certain declarations. Now his followers want to let the years and decades pass with not the tiniest deviation of original statement or understanding, because to them, the pronouncements of the past constitute the absolute truth of all eternity. So think and teach many "psychiatrists."

As for you, more power to you and to your patient. You are jointly working to achieve a common goal, the patient's success and happiness.

May the misunderstandings of those who would maintain ritualistic beliefs yield to scientific advancement.

Sincerely,
Milton H. Erickson, M.D.

Erickson taught podiatrists to use hypnotic communication techniques within the scope of their practice. He did this at a time when many in the medical establishment did not find favor in podiatry.

A podiatrist, Charles Ormond, wrote Erickson with a concern about a radical procedure used by a colleague, called foot strapping. Ormond speculated that the procedure's effectiveness was the result of suggestion rather than the actual physical technique. Ormond began his letter by reminding Erickson that he and his wife had invited Erickson to their home for a chicken dinner.

To: Charles S. Ormond
February 26, 1962

Dear Dr. Ormond:

First of all, my regards to the Preparer of The Best Chicken and Dumplings.

Concerning your letter about the foot strapping, periodically in the medical field there develops a new school of therapy of a miraculous type centering around some special foot procedure. Two previous such cures that come to mind was the ankle twister who set up business in Canada near Detroit and cured everything from hemorrhoids to dandruff by ankle joint manipulation. Then the other one was the "sole pressure point cure." The proper massage, pressure and stroking of various spots on the sole of the foot cured everything. Both of these cults lasted a year or two, reputable men threw up their medical practice to become ankle twisters or pressure spot massagers, and then the wave of gullibility died down and a lot of otherwise intelligent people were out of pocket, embarrassed, and some professional men ruined.

I can only suggest that the man's enthusiastic confidence and his proselytizing zeal are effective psychotherapy. The will to believe is a terribly strong force and many a fraud is practiced in earnest honest belief, but it is still a falsity and all the belief in the world will not make it scientific.

My practice and advice are always to steer away from contact with such people. The cult soon dies for a while, then comes to life in some new form—ankle twisters, soleful massaging, foot strappings, what next?

I hope you and your wife have a delightful time in Seattle.

Sincerely,
Milton H. Erickson, M.D.

With regard to the following letter to Clifford Morgan, Ph. D., there is no other correspondence on this matter, and Mrs. Erickson does not remember activity around the writing and compilation of abstracts during this period. There is no record of a response to Erickson's request and he did not assist with Psychological Abstracts.

To: Clifford T. Morgan
January 25, 1963

Dear Dr. Morgan:

In a recent issue of *The American Psychologist*, comment was made upon the incompleteness of the coverage of articles on hypnosis currently and for several years back. I think this is most regrettable in view of the constantly increasing number of articles in medical, dental, and other scientific journals. Hence I would like to be of service to *Psychological Abstracts* in this regard.

As for my qualifications, I am a Fellow of the American Psychiatric Association, of the American Psychological Association, and of the American Psychopathological Association, among other Fellowships.

For about 17 years, early 1930's to late 1940's, I abstracted regularly for *Psychological Abstracts* articles, books, journals, medical and psychological, and since I had done extensive work in criminology, on that subject as well.

I would like to volunteer my services to abstract regularly *The American Journal of Clinical Hypnosis*. In this regard you may be hesitant since I am the Editor. I am also willing to abstract *The International Journal of Clinical and Experimental Hypnosis* and I assure you I will perform those duties promptly. My original reason for discontinuing abstracting was a prolonged disabling illness, and then the demands of building a private practice in psychotherapy occupied my energies.

I am corresponding editor of two Spanish journals on hypnosis and receive regularly abstracts for the Journal I edit from all parts of the world.

I would, if there is any possibility, like to have you accept my services.

For immediate references, I would like to refer you to Carl P. Rogers, Ph.D. (Department of Psychology and Psychiatry, University of Wisconsin), to Ernest R. Hilgard, Ph.D. (Stanford University), Roy M. Dorcus, Ph.D. (University of California at Los Angeles), Donald G. Marquis, Ph.D. (Massachusetts Institute of Technology), Norman R. F. Maier, Ph.D. (University of Michigan), none of whom are on my Editorial Staff, and I shall be glad to answer any questions you may wish to put to me.

I hope very much that I may have the privilege of being of service to you.

Should you consider it inadvisable for me, as Editor-in-Chief, to be an abstractor, I would like to suggest André M. Weitzenhoffer, Ph.D., now located at the University of Oklahoma and formerly of Stanford University. Dr. Weitzenhoffer is an associate editor of the Journal and has extensive abstracting experience.

May I hear from you please?

Sincerely,
Milton H. Erickson, M.D.

Enclosure: Editorial masthead of *The American Journal of Clinical Hypnosis.*

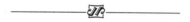

Sheldon Cohen, M.D., a distinguished member of the American Society of Clinical Hypnosis, served as the third editor of the official organ of the society, The American Journal of Clinical Hypnosis, *from 1975 to 1982. Erickson wrote, to Dr. Cohen, asking him to review a book for the Journal because he had volunteered his services in that regard. Subsequent to his request for a specific review, Erickson congratulated Cohen on publishing an article on drug toxicity and supplied some of his own experiences with reactions to medication.*

To: Sheldon B. Cohen
December 23, 1963

Dear Dr. Cohen:

Incidentally I wish to express my sincere appreciation for your contribution to medical enlightnment, "Brain Damage due to Penicillin." I am exceedingly pleased that this paper was published in the JAMA. I believe that acute brain syndromes as a result of drug reactions are far more frequent than the average physician realizes and are almost invariably misdiagnosed.

I have several times been called as psychiatric consultant and recognized the symptoms as a toxic delirum to some drug, which was relieved by withdrawal of the medication.

For example, I regard Librium as one of the safer tranquilizing drugs and I sometimes prescribe it. However, I was called to advise in the following case: A young man, stable basically but under considerable domestic tension, was supplied by another physician with Librium, which he took only infrequently and in small dosages. In the presence of my son one evening he took a capsule and suddenly began "to pass out." My son and the man's wife took him to the emergency room of a nearby hospital, admitting procedures were being completed, when he suddenly roused and manifested an acute disoriented delirious state, obviously toxic, as later described to me. The hospital desk employee immediately stated that they refused to take mental patients as hospital policy, and she would not even call his physician, suggesting a sanitarium or the police. My son and the wife then took the man to a private mental hospital where he was admitted but diagnosed as definitely psychotic, and the wife was advised that long hospitalization would probably be necessary, with shock treatment. She decided that in that case, she could afford three days' private hospitalization but after that, financial considerations would make the state hospital her only recourse. However, the next day the young man was shaky and tremulous but entirely lucid and well-oriented, and was discharged. I then saw him and he obviously showed residuals of toxicity from which he was rapidly recovering. He has never touched the drug since (three years ago) and has shown exceptional good balance and judgment.

I have also observed two very serious cases of long-continued brain disturbance from antibiotics. One patient developed a severe encephalitis as a result of the drug, perhaps generalized since it caused personality disturbances, although the neurological signs were localized. The other eventually recovered fully, I believe. I have also seen complete physical collapse of over a month's duration from an antihistamine drug reaction; and to the physician's disgust, I got the patient's husband to engage another physician (a patient of mine), who promised not to give her any antihistamines. However, he figured that I was probably wrong about chlortrimeton [the antihistamine] and she had to be hospitalized again. Now her husband won't let her take aspirin or baking soda without my permission. I had to have her husband sign her out of the hospital against permission to keep consultants from prescribing.

She is now OK.

One of my friends when first in practice was told by a beautiful young girl that she had a headache and told him that she was sensitive to aspirin and not to prescribe it. He knew better, lied to her, and five minutes later called the police and the undertaker. He is painfully sensitive to "drug idiosyncracy" but he doesn't put the term in quotes, just in large red letters with a skull and crossbones for quotes.

Also, not so long ago a resident at the local county hospital pooh-poohed a woman's statement that penicillin would kill her. She lived five minutes after the shot.

Hence you can see why I like your article.

I am awaiting your decision on the book and hope you are interested.

Sincerely yours,
Milton H. Erickson, M.D.

A. Levitsky, an esteemed colleague of Erickson's and, at the time, an associate editor of the American Journal of Clinical Hypnosis, *presented Erickson with a challenging case of a severely disturbed patient. Erickson replied by citing two of his own cases, in which the treatment he offered was striking. The extent to which Erickson went in treating patients was extraordinary. It is hard to imagine that Levitsky could effect the kind of therapy that Erickson used.*

Did Erickson's therapy meet the proper "standard of care" to maintain professional dignity? How can Erickson's treatment be justified? Here, there are a number of clinical issues that can be clarified: Erickson was working in life-threatening situations. At such times, it is not professional dignity that is the primary issue, but rather the health of the patient. Although Erickson's measures were extreme, the patients had extreme problems. One could take the position that the severity of the therapy should be proportional to the severity of the problem.

No contemporary practitioner would do what Erickson did. Modern ethics prohibit such treatment. How then can we understand the ethics of Erickson's approach? It is not that the ends justify the means, but that one cannot view Erickson's techniques through the lens of contemporary ethics. The range of psychiatric interventions available today had not yet been developed when Erickson practiced.

Note Erickson's emphasis on resources. He was certain that his patients had within themselves the resources necessary to accomplish the treatment. He believed that they had the psychological power to change psychotic thinking, and so merely put them into situations in which they would irrefutably confront the fact that their ideas were unsound. Erickson was convinced that the patients had biological re-

sources that could be activated, and, he noted, his drastic methods were an appeal to the patients' inherent self-protective mechanisms. It was not his design to trick them, but rather to let them experientially discover previously latent abilities.

The case of Herbert is described in three sources: Conversations with Milton Erickson, Volume 1 *(Haley, 1985);* Uncommon Therapy *(Haley, 1973); and* My Voice Will Go with You *(Rosen, 1982).*

From: A. Levitsky
May 23, 1963

Dear Milton:

I want to play a long shot and consult you on a difficult problem in psychotherapy. I realize very clearly that you might not be able to help—in which case nothing will be lost.

The case is that of a 30-year-old Presbyterian minister who developed a psychosis some three years ago and is an inpatient at our hospital. He had the delusion that God had ordered him not to eat. He became depressed and suicidal. Probably the best diagnostic label is psychotic depression with paranoid features, although paranoid elements are hardly discernible.

Family Background: The father and mother are highly intelligent "nice" people. They are genuinely concerned about the son's illness. They are aware of their own excessive perfectionism. The most pathological element I have been able to discern is the family custom of parading around the house in the nude—a "liberalism" not in keeping with other subtle puritanical and somewhat Pollyanna-ish attitudes. However, I must say that in my many contacts with the parents I have come to like them.

Course of Treatment: The patient has been in treatment for 1½ years. We employ an unusual technique, multiple therapy with three therapists, all of them men. One of us, Dr. Miller, is both a clinical psychologist and a Methodist minister.

1. At the outset the patient made an excellent relationship and seemed to get off to an encouraging start in the psychotherapy.
2. Soon, however, his food compulsion returned in force and he became

so overwhelmed by his inability to stick to his resolution not to eat that he made a fairly serious suicidal attempt. He became bizarre, started to soil and manifested negativistic actions, such as overturning trash cans and taking occasional nonserious jabs at patients and personnel. However, he always remained in contact and never developed a thinking disorder. For many months he refused our interviews and so we would simply come up on the ward and accept his refusal and leave.

3. For months he was tube fed and spoon fed.

4. A year ago he started to make marked improvement. He began to visit his home regularly, had many social activities, and he and the therapists would occasionally go out to lunch together. He was given a responsible job assignment in the hospital, which he did well. He attended a college class and passed with a good grade. We were much encouraged.

5. Just recently there has been a sudden change for the worse. He had had an eight-day pass to attend a postgraduate seminar for pastors. He discussed some of his problems with the group and developed the feeling that he had not been behaving "with integrity." Suicidal thoughts have returned and we now have him on suicidal precautions.

Summary: His main theme is that he was called upon not to eat and true Christian integrity would have demanded that he stick to his guns. Being fed forcibly is okay, but helping himself to food is bad. Thus, he has committed an unforgivable sin and has no hope. I feel that the patient needs to go through some severe crisis before he really improves. It is likely that he requires a profound ordeal, perhaps some sort of punishment, in order to feel that he can be restored to grace.

I do not know whether this information puts you in a position to advise us. Any suggestions will be highly welcome since we feel sort of stuck. I am enclosing summaries of a recent interview. One summary is by myself, one by Dr. Miller and one by the patient himself. I look forward to hearing from you.

Sincerely,
A. Levitsky, Ph.D.

To: A. Levitsky
June 11, 1963

Dear Abe:

Concerning your letter of May 23rd, I have given it much thought but little energy. I've been getting the last of the page proofs of the July issue corrected. We changed printers also, which meant new and earlier deadlines.

Concerning your patient, I have no real suggestions to offer but I can cite some examples.

Arthur P. Noyes, M.D., was superintendent in Rhode Island. A female patient insisted that God had forbidden her to take sustenance. She promptly vomited every tube feeding and lost weight progressively. Dr. Noyes told me to take charge and that the sky was the limit.

My procedure was effective. I had her dressed in panties, brought in a pitcher of high caloric liquid food with a rich content of raw cod liver oil, the feeding tube, a bevy of nurses giggling with amusement at my plan, and several large pans of crushed ice and an empty pan.

She passively allowed me to tube feed her, vomited it all right back up, which I caught in the empty pan. I poured it back in the pitcher and tube fed her again. Up it came and was caught in the empty pan. I put it back in the pitcher, assured her that this time she would keep it down and poured it down her. As I withdrew the tube, the nurses at my signal seized handfuls of crushed ice and gave her a thoroughgoing rubdown, which included stuffing ice into her panties.

The patient tried to get away from the nurses but they were having too much fun—and besides they were evening the score for the many times they had mopped the floor. After 40 minutes they dried her off and dressed her. I came back (I watched for about 15 minutes before I left) and let that woman tell me in simple plain language what she thought of me for twice pouring vomitus into her stomach. I made no explanation or defense.

At the next tube feeding time, I returned with the full equipment and nurses.

The woman looked it over coldly, announced that the Lord had shifted the burden of the sinfulness of food upon my shoulders, asked for a glass, drank the entire amount, expressed uncomplimentary comments upon the taste of the raw cod liver oil and my lack of judgment in food preparation.

She joined the other patients at the table the next meal.

But I don't think she liked me.

The next case was a man who had stood in his nightshirt in a corner of the ward night and day for 6 months. He was tube fed twice a day despite his delusional insistence that he lacked a G.I. tract in its entirety, did not know how the floor became soiled because he had no G.I. tract and hence it had neither a beginning nor an ending.

For one week I tube fed him regularly, each time assuring him that on the next Monday he would get proof from within himself that he had a throat and a stomach.

That selected Monday, I tube fed him carefully, adding that shortly he would have proof from within him that he possessed both a throat and a stomach. His invariable contention was that tube feeding was merely a Houdini act, entirely pretense.

That morning's tube feeding, which, besides the usual high caloric liquid, included a large amount of baking soda and raw cod liver oil, was poured into the tube at intervals to insure the forcing of air into his stomach, and was polished off with vinegar.

The first raw cod liver flavored burp was not long in forthcoming after I withdrew the tube.

That evening, the time of his second tube feeding, I came in with two supplies and explained that if he still had no throat or stomach, I would tube feed him as I had in the morning. Otherwise, if he had a throat and a stomach he could have the contents of the second pitcher. His eloquent reply was, "You're goddam right I've got a belly and a throat. I've been belching rotten fish all day."

He smelled the second pitcher, inserted the tub himself, poured down the feeding himself.

After several days of this cooperative behavior, I explained daily that shortly I would teach him how to lie in bed.

This was done by putting him into a dry hydrotherapy tub with a restraining cover. Thus it was not a bed, but he was lying down. I saw to it, however, that on each side of him in the adjacent tub were highly disturbed noisy patients. Each morning he took his stance in the ward corner and tube fed himself.

Finally I offered him his choice of any bed on the ward or in a private room. He mumbled that as long as he had to lie on his back all night, he might as well use a bed instead of a dry hydrotherapy tub with "screaming nuts" yelling all the time.

Since he had always been exceedingly careful never to step into his excrement or the urine puddles, I offered to teach him that he had an exit to his bowel. He scoffed at the idea, gave himself his tube feeding unaware that I had loaded it with a cathartic.

Then I restrained him with no resistance on his part on his back in the bed. He merely snorted, "Back to your old dry tub routine:"

I left orders for the night men to check every half hour but to remain deaf to all entreaties.

The next morning he was released and made a beeline for the ward toilet. Unfortunately it was locked and as the attendant fumblingly searched his pockets for the right key, the patient put his whole soul into a competent description of that attendant and all his forebears, none of it complimentary.

As he finally took his seat on the commode, I showed up and argued insistently that he had no lower end of his bowel. With withering scorn he asked me what in hell I thought he was doing.

By this time I thought it would be well to discontinue tube feeding and for a week I explained to him that on a specified Monday morning there would be in the locked breakfast room two glasses of milk and a glass of water. He informed me that God had deprived him of the ability to swallow and that he would have no interest in the milk or water.

He took his tube feeding as usual, not knowing that I had loaded it with atropine and salt. I ordered his room locked and the toilet locked and the water turned off at all the drinking fountains.

The next morning he pounded on the door demanding to go to the toilet. That was locked. Then he rushed to the fountains. They were dry. He rushed to the breakfast room, demanded that it be opened. The attendant did so and he rushed in regardless of my presence and drained all three glasses and asked for more. I countered with the question of when I should teach him to eat solid food. He glared at me, then proceeded to give a devastating account of my whole genealogical tree, all its side branches and there was not a complimentary thing that he could say about any one of my forebears. His adjectival wealth was tremendous.

I then explained that he had made such a good start in voluntary swallowing, his accomplishment should not be wasted.

So that day (It was mid-winter in cold Rhode Island) I had him warmly dressed and marched up and down the grounds by relief attendants, giving him water whenever he said he would swallow fluid.

That night, still unfed, he literally fell into bed sound asleep at once.

The next morning two attendants marched him into the most aromatic corner of the kitchen and there he stood all day smelling, drooling and receiving only lukewarm water.

That night as he fell into bed to sleep I asked him what he wanted for breakfast. After looking searchingly at me, he said, "Ham, eggs, toast, steak, hashed brown potatoes, jelly, milk, coffee, pie and fruit."

He was allowed to eat his breakfast early and then I took him to the aromatic corner of the kitchen.

The head cook was a marvelously kindhearted, jovial woman, and tremendously fat. Acting under my orders she prepared a special meal for her "birthday," set up a table near the patient, set two places and invited him to join her in her "private" celebration. He did, and nobly too.

I assigned him to kitchen work and soon he was up to his previous prepsychotic weight of 240 lbs. He had dropped to 80 lbs.

He was discharged as a patient, hired as an assistant chef and worked there for 15 years, dying suddenly of coronary thrombosis in his late 60s.

Whenever I visited Rhode Island, I always looked up Herbert, and we jointly had many a hearty laugh at the measures I had employed.

Perhaps in some way the foregoing material will be of value to you in suggesting some measure in which symptoms can be met and an interpersonal relationship, however repugnantly it begins, can grow into a warm friendship.

It took that woman many months to forgive me for pouring vomitus back into her stomach but she became a most ardent friend and she too laughed at the measures I had employed.

I look upon mental illness as something drastic often needing equally drastic measures that serve to meet the patient's needs in an incontrovertible manner.

That woman did not want to vomit; God made her. She was helpless. And then I poured back into her stomach the vomitus that had been twice vomited. And if you want to have an experience you won't forget, have someone wash your face with crushed ice while others massage your back, your belly and your crotch with more crushed ice.

Oh yes, I had psychotherapeutic talks with them, but then they were fully prepared to give me their attention.

It is of the utmost importance at all times to maintain most rigidly and dominantly your own nonpsychotic identity despite the seeming folly of your actions. This is the paramount force in this type of therapy.

Regarding this specific patient, the therapy that has been done with him has been too considerate, too amenable to his psychotic arguments and hence has got nowhere. Why has his statement been accepted that his precious "integrity" is so valuable that he can demand that his world revolve around it? Why should he have his ideas of "giving and receiving" so respected that he can continue to find virtue in his imperious demands to be fed spoonful by spoonful? Let him at least see that others can regard this as grandiose demands for slavelike service rather than an acceptance as a humble attempt to "maintain integrity."

You will note that I had no respect or consideration for their wrong behavior and that I called upon every innate inherent need for, and learning of, self-protection.

I can cite many similar cases whose psychotic behavior was harshly offended against, my nonpsychotic behavior made dominant, and their inner self-protective needs enhanced to the state of recovery and they all became my friends eventually.

I'm sorry to have been so slow in answering but I have really been most busy.

Sincerely yours,
Milton H. Erickson, M.D.

Stanley Milgram, an American psychologist, conducted one of the most famous experiments in the history of psychology. Perplexed by the phenomenon of blind allegiance in Nazi Germany, Milgram (1963, 1965a) investigated the dynamics of obedience to authority. In the central experiment of a series, subjects, in the role of "teacher," administered shocks to experimental confederates, who were purportedly learning word lists. With each mistake the 'learners' made, the voltage of the shock (which, unbeknown to the subjects, was not real) increased. Despite such acted pleas by the "learners" to "Let me out!" (of the strapped chair they were in) and "I've got a heart condition!," 65 percent of the all-male subjects applied (false) shocks into the "dangerous" voltage zone listed on the panel of the

apparatus. They acceded to demands of the experimenter to continue the protocol. Milgram concluded that obedience to authority has a far-reaching influence on behavior.

Considerable controversy raged in response to Milgram's experiment. Many protested what they viewed as the coercion of subjects in the study. Impetus for decreased deception and increased informed consent of experimental subjects translated into tightened ethical guidelines for human research. Milgram continued to study obedience and other topics, such as authoritarianism and information overload.

Estabrooks (1943) posited that hypnosis can be used to prompt the comission of crimes and that subjects can be hypnotized without their consent.

To: Stanley Milgram
November 4, 1963

Dear Mr. Milgram:

I was exceedingly impressed by your article "Behavioral Study of Obedience" in the October 1963 issue of the *Journal of Abnormal and Social Psychology*. I believe this is a very important contribution, with rather far-reaching implications. Investigations which have been done in attempting to evaluate the effect of the hypnotic relationship in influencing behavior harmful to others or contrary to the subjects' moral standards, have, in my opinion, given far too little consideration to the effect of the laboratory situation and the implicit obligation of the subject to fulfill his commitment to the experimenter.

Your experimental study opens a field of interpersonal relationships and a field of situation-relationships that have long been neglected or, at best, only superficially approached.

During World War II, the Office of Strategic Services was greatly interested in anything in the literature pertaining to the topic you have presented so well and was bitterly disappointed at the paucity of reliable studies.

I was called in to do considerable work on both types of relationships for immediate use in propaganda work in relation to both Germans and Japanese, but this work was not for publication. Hence, you can see that I feel a sense of personal indebtedness to you for your study.

I should be very much obliged to you if you could send me as many copies as you can spare of the reprint, 6 or 8 if possible. I enclose stamps which I believe will cover the postage.

My congratulations and appreciation of this remarkable report and your penetrating analysis of the factors involved.

Sincerely yours,
Milton H. Erickson, M.D.

From: Stanley Milgram
November 12, 1963

Dear Dr. Erickson:

Thank you for your very kind letter of November 4. I shall be very happy to send you reprints of the article "Behavioral Study of Obedience" when the printer makes them available to me. I'm sure I can spare the eight copies you request. When subsequent articles appear, I'll send reprints on to you.

You mention your wartime experiences with the OSS. My own interest in the topic of obedience dates back to the Second World War. I have still not quite gotten over the fact that Hitler's insane orders were carried out with dispatch and efficiency by people who were probably quite normal. My original interest was in setting up an experiment here, and then replicating it in Germany, to see if there were any measurable cultural differences in the area of obedience to authority.

I very much appreciate your comments.

Sincerely,
Stanley Milgram

On April 10, 1967, Milgram wrote to Erickson stating that a colleague had informed him that Erickson had cited him in an article in the American Journal of

Clinical Hypnosis. *Milgram requested a reprint of that article, which led to Erickson's reply of April 14.*

To: Stanley Milgram
April 14, 1967

Dear Dr. Milgram:

Under separate cover I am sending you four reprints of my article "Laboratory and Clinical Hypnosis: The Same or Different Phenomena?" [Erickson, 1967].

I have been very much impressed by your studies which I am convinced have many implications which merit investigation. I have long claimed that the vast majority of experiments on the so-called antisocial uses of hypnosis are invalid, since the experimenters did not realize the pressures of compliance in a laboratory setting, or, if they did make an effort to compose a naturalistic setting, they still did not realize the weight of authority in a structured situation. It is this, rather than the use of hypnosis as such, which accounts for the positive results which have sometimes occurred, and it is this condition which is so exceedingly difficult to control or to equalize in the waking and hypnotic trance conditions.

I shall be very much interested in your further research in the field of authority and obedience.

Sincerely yours,
Milton H. Erickson, M.D.

To: Stanley Milgram
April 1, 1969

Dear Dr. Milgram:

I have just read your article, "Some Conditions of Obedience and Disobedience to Authority" and the critical evaluations of it. I was rather startled at the inadequacy of my appraisal of your work and astonished that the sociologist did not know that the social group is made up of individuals and that the whims of an individual can lead the social group into appalling destruction.

Your studies are demonstrating experimentally and in controlled settings that ordinary individuals not only evade responsibility for their own actions but accept and abet this evasion as a part of life.

For years and years, nurses and doctors have been covering up and concealing and falsifying the records on patients. During my internship I saw a surgeon who opened the abdomen of a man expecting to find a tumorous growth, even though I had told him that it was my firm conviction that the "tumor" was actually a badly distended bladder. He was so furious at finding that I was correct and that he should have catherized the man before operating that he took off his surgical gloves and threw them on the floor of the operating room, and contrary to the protests of the anesthesist he probed furiously around in the man's abdomen with his bare hands, proceeded to make use of the catheter and finally to sew up the abdominal incision. I wrote up my eye-witness account of this since I was then on surgery and was supposed to write up the surgical account. I put all the facts in the case record, the names of the nurses, the names of the anesthesiologist, the surgeon's name, and his assistant's name as well as my own. I described everything correctly. I typed it up on my own typewriter, adding the fact in the clinical notes that the patient died of sudden acute peritonitis within the next twenty-four hours. To reward my honesty the superintendent of the hospital, who learned about the matter through other channels, and had the record checked, called me into his office and told me that I was discharged as an intern and that he would personally see to it that I would be blacklisted in every hospital in the United States, and that I would not be able to complete my internship anywhere in an accredited institution. He also stated that he was going to blacklist me with the American Medical Association. Additionally, he stated that he had had prepared a much more proper report on the operation and on the cause of death, and would notify the Colorado State Board of Medicine that I was not ethically prepared to practice medicine. I asked him in return if he had noted that I had had six eye-witnesses initial that original report, and I asked him what I should do with the carbon copies, which I had retained and which were also initialed by the eye-witnesses. I then stated that one of the carbon copies that I possessed would be placed in the patient's record and would remain there during the rest of the time during which I completed my internship.

This is only one single example, but have you ever read the "accident reports" written in hospitals and seen the coat of whitewash put over them? I have, and I have known about this sort of thing for forty-five years; and I have noted that the same "accident" has occurred repeatedly on patients being treated by the same doctors and the same nurses and the same attendants. Actually, I never won a popularity award in any hospital where I worked.

Have you thought about the countless numbers of "battered child" reports that are just recently coming to light? The battered child is not something that is unknown to the police, to doctors, to parents, and to hospital authorities, but it has been covered up to my knowledge for forty-five years. Only recently has there been any interest in this syndrome. When my granddaughter broke her collarbone, my daughter insisted that the doctor make a complete examination of her body. She also told him that her father had told her to make such a request on the occasion of every accident, to impress upon doctors that the battered child may come from any family and that a good physician should on his own responsibility make a complete examination in every case.

Fairly recently I had a young mother come in to see me and her statement was, "I don't want to be the mother of battered children, and my husband doesn't want to be the father of battered children, but one of our children has a painful burn deliberately inflicted and another one has a scalded foot. We both love our children, but when they misbehave, both my husband and I lose our heads. When we took the children to the doctor he made light of this whole matter so my husband and I are coming to you for psychiatric help and we are going to ask you for the name of an honest pediatrician." Both parents were emphatic in stating that neither grandmother would ever be allowed to see her grandchildren.

This is but one of many examples I could quote to you. What about the late-teenager who deliberately gives LSD and various other drugs to siblings under the age of twelve to "prove" (or testing unconsciously) that drugs are not harmful? Nobody knows nor is there any way to find out how many sugar cubes in restaurants have been given "a touch" of LSD as a practical joke on someone not even known. The police know about this sort of thing but they do not like to talk about it, and I have seen two boys under the age of twelve who were badly damaged from such treated candy passed out to them by a teenager who, when accused, said boldly, "I can get kicks in a lot of ways and nobody can prove it." Both boys accused the same teenager. Neither patient knew the other. I have seen many presumably respectable members of society who have told me of unbelievable atrocities that they committed for the pleasure of "getting away with it."

Man's inhumanity to man is something that "good" people do not want to learn about. Dr. O. [a renowned psychiatric researcher] is a prize example of the person who is interested only in the methodology by which unpleasant facts are discovered, and not in the unpleasant facts. Dr. M. [a renowned psychiatrist] is an example of a man who likes to display his knowledge of seldom-used words, his very great wit, his sharpness of intellect where he uses it, but is amazingly uninterested in seven wives who sought divorces because they could not endure physical cruelty. He talks freely when he is drunk.

Upton Sinclair's *The Jungle* is not dead. Consider the disregard of safety measures and the undue concern about profits. The coal miners of West Virginia have recently demonstrated that neither the mine communities nor the legislators have any regard for human life. My own intimate knowledge of copper mining in Arizona has disclosed that profits, not lives, are the only things of importance. What about the patent disregard of safety measures in the automobile? Also take into consideration the endless battle of the Food and Drug Administration. Human lives are expendable and profits are desirable and the tendency is to look away from these facts, or in Dr. O. fashion, to direct attention to the superiority or inferiority of the paint job on an automobile rather than the question of defective brakes. This is but a single illustrative example.

Undoubtedly you have read the news stories of the Pueblo. I read those of World War I, World War II and the Korean War, and I have had detailed personal accounts of innumerable tragedies where not even wishful or hopeful thinking accompanied those who, sometimes in large numbers, were sent deliberately on useless and fatal missions.

Although I have read most of your articles on this subject, I am not familiar with the one cited in the critical evaluation by Orne and Holland, namely, "The Lost Letter Technique: A Tool of Social Research," *Public Opinion Quarterly*, 29, 437–438, 1965. Will you send me a reprint of this article if you have one available? Thank you.

Sincerely yours,
Milton H. Erickson, M.D.

Editor's Note: There is no record in Erickson's file of Milgram's response.

To: Stanley Milgram
June 20, 1969

Dear Dr. Milgram:

Due to physical disabilities which restrict me to a wheelchair I do not attend the motion picture theater. However, my wife occasionally sees some movie which particularly interests her.

In the nearby town of Tempe, there is a theater which particularly caters to the students of Arizona State University, which is located there, about twelve miles from Phoenix. This theater has been presenting a series of so-called "underground" movies at midnight every Saturday for quite a long period of time. Having received a brochure of advance programs in May, my wife was intrigued by the description of the movie entitled "The Experiment" and hence made it a point to attend last Saturday at midnight. I do not know if you are aware that your work has served as the basis of an "underground" short movie but knowing that you are interested in every reference to your work, my wife picked up a couple of extra brochures for you, and thought you also might be interested on her comments on this twelve-minute production. She felt that it was actually above the average for this type of movie. It dramatized an oversimplified but not grossly inaccurate representation of your experimental work. After the procedure was described, only one subject was shown and he, of course, continued to inflict punishment on the victim in spite of his own distress at so doing. The movie ended with a shot of marching feet of uniformed soldiers. You were not mentioned by name; however, the scientist who conducted the experiment was presented as being rather ruthless and callous, and perhaps also unduly pleased with the results of the experiment.

These movies seem to be made primarily by graduate and undergraduate college students, as part of their projects in fine arts classes or as independent productions. I think it is rather interesting that your work was made the basis of this production even though your name on the brochure is so oddly misspelled . . .

In relation to the social implications of your experimental work, I wonder if you have also had your attention called to the article in the Summer, 1969, issue of *American Scientist*, "Bystander 'Apathy' " by Bibb Latané and John M. Dorley. The authors conclude that even as panic and violent behavior can be socially communicated and increased, so too can social inhibition and reluctance to intervene in incidents which must first be subjectively interpreted as an emergency situation and the course of one's own action decided upon. Non-intervention, as shown by this experimental work, appears to be highly communicable, with the subjects typically redefining a situation so that no action need be taken when others present do not seem to be concerned.

Sincerely yours,
Milton H. Erickson, M.D.

Editor's Note: In a brief letter dated July 1, 1969, Milgram thanked Erickson and expressed his interest in seeing the movie.

The Erickson–Milgram correspondence demonstrated that Erickson's interest was societal as well as psychological. He looked at the world through a "wide lens," acutely aware of exigencies that affect the conduct of day-to-day life. Clearly, he realized that psychopathology did not necessarily cause inhumanity, that so-called normals could engage in contemptuous and deadly acts.

Moreover, Erickson called for action in response to acts of inhumanity. Throughout his career, he was steadfast in his confrontation of unethical behavior in colleagues. The anecdote recounted in his April 1, 1969, letter regarding his hospital internship attests to his unflinching resolve, a characteristic prominent in his efforts on behalf of ethical hypnosis.

Ronald E. Shor, Ph.D., was a prestigious academic researcher in hypnosis and a long-time professor of psychology at Harvard University. A developer of the Harvard Group Scale of Hypnotic Susceptibility, in addition to his research, he wrote

notable theoretical works on such topics as the levels of hypnotic depth. He also introduced the concept of the generalized reality orientation as a way of understanding hypnotic experience. It seems that Shor contacted Erickson and other researchers during the course of compiling information for a history of hypnosis.

In 1931, Richard Husband and his student, Davis, devised a scale of hypnotic depth that is of historical importance. Husband's letter is included in light of his work in hypnosis.

From: Richard W. Husband
October 2, 1959

Dear Dr. Shor:

I am afraid you have caught me completely off base with your searching questions on my published study on hypnosis.

In the first place, this was never a burning interest of mine. The study was started under Clark Hull, and when he went to Yale and I took his place at Wisconsin, I inherited Davis as a thesis student. The study was already planned, so I supervised the experimentation and writing of the thesis. Then Davis had trouble writing it in publishable form and length, so I did that.

Secondly, it was thirty years ago this academic year that the study was done, and since I never did anything more on that area, I am afraid it had just vanished from my mind.

Davis left the field of psychology after he got his M.A., and is now a sales executive with DuPont, I see him now and then, including just this August. He is living in West Chester, Pennsylvania. I doubt very much if you would get a comprehensive answer from him either.

Sorry to be so negative. I can't even think up an intelligent bluff, so I might just as well confess my ignorance, instead of letting you find it out if I should fluff around. Thanks for your interest anyway.

Yours,
Richard W. Husband

To: Ronald E. Shor
February 19, 1964

Dear Dr. Shor

I am not aware of the beginning of Dr. Hull's interest in hypnosis. I do know that until I was in his class of premedic psychology, the extent of his work was merely no more than to demonstrate, once each year in early spring, to the class, nothing more.

I volunteered among others for an evening session to secure subjects for my next day's class. I was a poor subject solely because I was interested in learning, unfortunately not in experiencing.

Hull's method was to have the subject sit in a straight-back chair with the head leaning back as far as possible, the eyes fixed on a small blue glass knob on a small pencil-like stick held a few inches above the bridge of the nose and suggesting that the lids close slowly, that the subject breathe deeply, and that the subject go sound asleep. Out of about 6 hours' work with 10 or 12 subjects, he finally succeeded in getting one of the volunteers into an excellent somnambulistic trance as I can now look back and recognize it. In fact, I recognized it shortly thereafter because I used that same fellow premed and discovered that he could do a lot of things that Hull had never attempted.

The evening of the next day when Hull gave his very simple demonstration, I took that subject and another fellow premed who had not volunteered but whose peculiar behavior during the demonstration to the class intrigued me, to my room, and put one in a comfortable position in a chair and the other on my bed since I had resented my own neck discomfort when Hull worked on me.

I merely suggested that they feel comfortable, breathe deeply, that their eyelids would close bit by bit and they would start to go to sleep and then go "way deep sound asleep." Essentially I followed Hull's verbalization but discarded the using of a glass knob as an eye fixation point. To me, that seemed unnecessary.

Fortunately, both subjects proved to be somnambulistic subjects and I immediately began to try to find out what they could do. One of the first things was to ask them to stay "sound asleep" but to open their eyes and talk to me and to answer questions. To my amazement, I found that both could see me and hear me but they did not see each other. This was accidental. I had explained this using the words that "when you open your eyes, staying sound asleep, you will talk to me and answer my questions." Both opened their eyes, looked at me and I, looking at Charles, said, "Tell me your life history as a boy." To my utter amazement, both began relating their life history, neither apparently hearing the other. This so amazed me that I was at a total loss. I could not understand it. Finally I said, "That will be enough history." Then looking at Charles still lying on the bed I said "Will you just sit up there?" Charles promptly sat upon the bed and George said, "But I am sitting up." I promptly proceeded to record all of this at once.

I then placed their arms and legs in awkward cataleptic positions, told them I was leaving the room but would return shortly. I went into the student room next to mine, told a fellow student that I had two classmates in my room and would he come in and talk to them. Lester accompanied me back to my room, was dumbfounded by their peculiar positions, asked them what was wrong with them, "sitting like that." Neither seemed to see or hear Lester. Lester looked alarmed but I told him everything was all right—I was a junior, he a freshman, hence he accepted my assurance. I asked him to put their arms and legs down. He attempted to do so and encountered resistance, and asked them what was wrong but they did not respond. He then asked me if they were deaf and blind. Lester was a predental student and was obviously distressed by what he could not understand. I said, speaking as if to the wall, "I am going to ask who is in the room. Now tell me." Both Charles and George each said, "I am," while Lester looked puzzled by the apparent absurdity of the question and said nothing but was astonished by their answers. I asked further, "Who else?" Both Charles and George said, "You are." Lester then looked alarmed. I asked, "Who else?" Again the two replied, "That's all." "Nobody else at all?" "No."

Lester, more alarmed, started for the door, saying, "Those fellows must be crazy and I'm getting out of here." I stopped him, explained that they were students from my premedic class in psychology, that we had seen the professor do hypnosis on Charles that morning and that I had invited Charles and George (the other one) to come to my room to let me hypnotize them. That relieved his fears and he enthusiastically asked me to hypnotize him. Placing him in a chair, I proceeded to do so and within about the next three minutes he too was in a profound somnambulistic trance and he easily opened his eyes and apparently saw only me.

I tried the same questions with him about who was in the same room prefacing my question fortunately by saying by custom, not intent, "Lester, who is in the room?" He answered "I am." I next asked unthinkingly, as I had before, "Who else?" To my utter surprise, all three answered, "You are." I followed through with the succeeding question, "Who else?" All three replied "No one."

I corrected the catalepsy in Charles and George and said, speaking generally, "Rest comfortably, I am going to do some writing, and I want you to close your eyes and rest comfortably all over."

I promptly wrote out a full account of the activities, and this done I had a heyday.

At that time I was one of Hull's students in experimental psychology and tremendously interested in the subject, even thinking somewhat of becoming an experimental psychologist. Because of this I had had Hull assign to me many more experiments than had been assigned to my classmates. Furthermore, I had spent many a Saturday and Sunday in the experimental psychology laboratory doing various experiments that both Hull and Jastrow (who was then head of the department) outlined for me. Jastrow had given me a reprint of his paper on ideomotor activity, which he had published as an original discovery. Then by accident, he discovered that a Frenchman had published a similar paper in the 1850s. Jastrow was humiliated no end by his error, and knowing of my enthusiastic interest in his paper, he called me into his office and told me of his error and discussed the importance of scientific honesty. I know now that he didn't want me to think he was dishonest. The man's profound distress made a great impression on me. I had, as a result of his paper, set up an experiment in the experimental laboratory ideomotor activity. This first setup was horribly crude. It was always easy to round up volunteer subjects and on a Saturday afternoon or a Sunday I would go to the lab with a subject and place him on a stool at sitting height facing a long table. I had arranged a lighting system that cast a well-defined shadow of the subject on the wall. The wall was inconspicuously marked in short measured lengths. On the table there were at variously spaced distances nuts, apples, bananas, chocolates, and oranges. With Hull's help (he was a wizard mechanically) I had a graduated spring-powered plunger that served to propel a rubber hall down a track made for it on the table and the properly graduated push by the plunger would cause the ball to roll an approximately exact distance. This apparatus was screened from the subject's view.

My instructions to the subject after a few trial runs with initial subjects to insure adequate performances on my part were essentially as follows:

"Sit straight upright (the table was low and all of its top in easy view). I'm going to roll a ball down that track you see and it will stop at or near one of those piles, I'll roll the ball a lot of times. If it stops three times beside any or each of the piles a total of 3 times, every such pile is yours. If it stops before or goes just beyond, it's not. To be yours the ball will have to stop between the two white lines beside the various piles and those white lines are far enough apart so that they represent a distance of twice the diameter of the ball. Now I'll place the ball by hand so that you can see what I mean and I will demonstrate the positions of the ball before the pile of snacks, beside the snacks, and just beyond.

"When we begin, just sit up straight, watch the ball carefully and when it stops, no matter where, just take two deep breaths, and then I will roll it again."

Each time I rolled the ball, I noted the subject's shadow moving along the wall as he involuntarily leaned both to the right and to the left in his desire to have the ball roll clear up to a pile or to slow it down when it seemed to be rolling too fast to stop at a desired pile. It was soon learned that the subject's involuntary leaning behavior would disclose his preference of the piles. During the course of the experiment, the subject's stool was randomly placed along the length of the table, sometimes in front of each pile, sometimes halfway between piles. Both Hull and Jastrow came to the laboratory to watch this experiment, which was never published because my interest was in experimenting in various ways, rather than in publishing. Besides, I then and still write papers with much rewriting and consumption of time. Fortunately this experiment on involuntary movement had been done long before I began my experimenting with hypnosis.

After I had written up the events of the evening with Charles, George and Lester, I really began searching for things to do with them. I worked with them until about 4:00 P.M. having started at 7:00 A.M. One of the first things was to call to mind my ideomotor experiment that had so interested Hull and Jastrow. I drew an analogy between that and the eyelid closure. I then suggested that they open their eyes and imagine a ball was rolling along the floor and that they would wish intently that it would roll clear to the wall of the room even though they would imagine that the ball was slowing up just after it was halfway there. All three repeatedly showed the same involuntary not self-recognized leaning behavior I had seen in my laboratory experiment. Then I began wondering about imagining seeing the ball with their eyes open. Their behavior convinced me that they were actually visually hallucinating a ball. I also noted that they took two deep breaths when the ball stopped rolling but each at a different time. I had suggested that sometimes the ball would stop short, sometimes would actually reach the wall. If it stopped close there should be taken two deep breaths. If it hit the wall there should be taken three deep breaths. Each obeyed but each took breaths at different times and their breathing did not agree. One might breathe twice, the other, two or three times. Since I had told them to *imagine* seeing a *ball* and to note if it hit the wall I was forced to the conclusion that they must be visually hallucinating the wall even if they were *imagining* seeing the ball. So I asked them to tell me the color of the ball. Two said it was red, one said it was blue. That raised an immediate question in my mind. I explained that I was putting two or three thumbtacks in the sides of the ball and every time a thumbtack clicked against the floor they were to count it aloud to me. Each counted a different number of clicks.

As each thing was done, I wrote it down.

I remembered a girl I had known in grade school who had learned the trick of chattering her teeth as if suffering from the cold.

I suggested that they get so cold that their teeth would chatter. Lester succeeded. I asked him what he was doing. He answered, "I gotta get this team home before the blizzard gets worse." Lester came from a farm in North Dakota.

The reply opened new vistas for me. I asked, "What are you going to do next summer?" He answered with chattering teeth, "I'm going to leave this goddamned farm and go to the University of Wisconsin."

After writing that down, I thought carefully and then asked, "How far you got to go yet?" "Ten miles and the blizzard is getting worse." "Think you will make it?" "Maybe I better stop in at the Williams place two miles from here and put up there." I told him that sounded like a good idea and when he had put the horses in the barn (remember I am a farm boy myself) he would find the Williams at home and the house warm.

Shortly I noticed his body making odd partial movements which I couldn't understand. I asked what he was doing. He replied that he was unharnessing the horses and would put them in the extra stalls and get into the house and get warmed up. Very shortly he turned his gaze on Charles and George and said "I knew you wouldn't mind if I crove in and put the horses in the extra stalls. The blizzard is getting worse and I'm just frozen and I didn't think I could make it home. I'll just phone Pa so he won't worry. Oh yes, ma'am, thank you (turning to Charles), "I sure would appreciate a cup of coffee. It will thaw me out."

Then I realized he was hallucinating George and Charles as a Mr. and Mrs. Williams.

While writing this down, I was suddenly struck by a bewildering thought and as soon as possible I asked him, "Who am I?" His reply was, "I don't know. A friend of the Williams's I suppose. Wait a minute. You were with me about 2–3 miles back, and you must have got in the wagon when I stopped at the store. You were talking to me. Funny, I never asked you who you were. I guess I was too worried about the blizzard that was starting up. Who are you?"

I replied, "Ask Mr. Williams."

He looked at George, turned back to me and said, "He says you are someone named Erickson but I don't know you. Any relation of the Ericksons that live 10 miles north of us?"

"Ask Mr. Williams."

He turned to George, started to frame a question with his lips but paused, turned back to me after apparently listening and said, "Mr. Williams says you are some one named Erickson."

"Ask him where from." He turned toward George, turned away, said "Thank you, ma'am.' It sure looks good." (The coffee) After going through the behavior of drinking, he answered, "He says you are from the University of Wisconsin. That's where I'm going next year. Say, I told you that back a piece on the road."

While recording this, the question arose of how to get him from the Williams' home in North Dakota to my room in the rooming house.

Finally the thought came to me, "Say, what is your name?"

"It's Lester T—."

"Tell me, what kind of a room would you like to have when you get to Madison?"

He proceeded to describe his actual room as a favorable possibility. That gave me my opportunity. I remarked, "That sounds like it would make a good room—in fact, it *is* a good room isn't it, and you like your room don't you?"

He was back in my student room, apparently alone with me.

Subsequent inquiry, weeks later, about the Ericksons living ten miles north of his father's farm (an actuality) and the Williams living 8 miles away and Mrs. Williams having blonde hair and Mr. Williams having black hair (such was the case with Charles and George respectively) bewildered Lester no end. And then I asked if he had stopped in at the Williams place a year previously during a blizzard. He confirmed these items as facts, looked even more puzzled, obviously, and about a week later he accused me, "Say you have had me doing some hypnosis and you have been prying into my private life. I don't like that."

A full account was given to him but he said, "Maybe you asked other things. I'm never going to let you hypnotize me again."

Later he volunteered if he could have some friends present to watch my behavior and prevent any prying. Nevertheless I failed completely. Subsequent trials also failed.

More than 30 years later, when I was addressing a state dental meeting, a rotund bald dentist walked up to the platform and asked me to hypnotize him. I could not understand the peculiar smile on his face. He added, "And after I'm in the trance, tell me that I have something special to tell you."

He went into a trance readily and I spoke to him as instructed. He opened his eyes in a deep somnambulistic trance, and said, "222 North Brooks Street, a hellishly cold blizzard, the Williams are 8 miles from home, I phoned my father, the coffee was good, the Ericksons live 10 miles north of my father's farm. Now you remember. Wake me up." I did so and he related the incident, including his former mistrust of me and his current knowledge that one cannot pry into a hypnotic subject's history unless the subject is willing.

But to return to that evening. I tried everything I could think of on George, Charles and Lester, including anesthesia, paralysis, depersonalization, amnesia, hypernesia, writing down in full each procedure. Night after night I worked on them until they rebelled at working so hard. I got three other subjects—worked at least 20 hours on each and failed miserably to induce a trance in any of them. Then I ran across two more good subjects and tried everything I could.

Then I took my written reports to Hull. He took them home, studied them, turned them over to Jastrow, who also studied them. Then Hull arranged a special demonstration by me for all professors and instructors in the Psychological and Philosophy departments and the medical school who were interested and his graduate instructors as well. He asked me to bring Lester, George and Charles and he told me he would bring subjects and that I could ask for volunteers. Both Hull and Jastrow felt that I had gone overboard, as they later told me, and for this reason they had arranged this meeting. At that meeting Hull and Jastrow handed me a protocol I was to follow. It was in essence that first I take a number of unknown subjects one at a time, work with them until I found one or two equal to Lester or George or Charles. I was then to elicit from them the type of behavior comparable to that secured from Lester, George, Charles, and others I had included in my report. Now knowing that they doubted me I was delighted to demonstrate.

Fortunately Hull had picked some good subjects who were worked with separately, the others being kept in another room where they could not know what was being done. Each was eagerly awaiting his turn to be called, an item I did not realize then, which was of great aid to me. We started at 6:00 P.M. The session continued until 2 A.M. Hull, Jastrow, the medical school professors of physiology, the psychiatrist Dr. Lorenz, Dr. Loevenhart of the pharmacology department, all suggested the elicitation of things I had not thought of.

The evening proved so informative that Jastrow, the head of the Psychology Department, and Hull agreed that a seminar should be given the coming September, that I should spend all my spare time carrying out hypnotic experiments the rest of the semester, keeping careful notes. I was given an A in a couple of psychology courses and excused from them so that I could spend my time on hypnotic experimentation. Both Hull and Jastrow offered a few suggestions but for the most part I was on my own. In addition I was to spend my summer on every hypnotic experiment I could think of, making careful notes. Then beginning in September at a weekly seminar from 2 to 4 P.M. I was to present my material systematically for the group from 1/2 to 1 hour, and then the graduate students would discuss it. Usually the seminar would continue until 6 P.M. and there were frequent Sunday gatherings. My presentation consisted of my notes, demonstrations, and using available subjects to answer clearly or to illustrate the discussion and various points raised. The second semester the entire seminar group conducted a whole series of experiments chiefly to replicate those I had done. These were again repeated in large part at Yale. And those were primarily the studies included in his book.

Through a misfortune in no way my fault, actually a malicious act by someone else of which he accepted untruthful information without any investigation, Hull became very antagonistic to me although when he got into trouble at Yale through Mildred Mitchell's poor judgment and the antagonism of a bigoted psychiatrist, Hull again wrote to me for support, which I gave. He also had the poor judgment to sponsor briefly a layman who is still exploiting it. The combination of these events embittered him regarding hypnosis and he not only dropped all his interest, but even resented being connected with hypnosis in any way. He would never join in any meetings and did not wish his book to be mentioned.

His ill-based sudden antagonism to me is why no credit whatsoever is given to me in his book. The only mention of my name is a distorted account of a demonstration of dental anesthesia before the national anesthesiologist meeing. I was put on the program, although a medical student, by Dr. Ralph Waters, dean of anesthesiology in the United States who was and continued throughout the years to be interested in my work. Hull's brief reference to it implies that it was simply a session in a dental office, and the facts themselves are given wrongly.*

Now this has been a hurried letter. I hope out of it you will get the information you want.

So far as I remember I had nothing to do with Davis.

As for the duration of Hull's interest in hypnosis I don't know when it began. It was definitely highly superficial until that experimental binge of mine extending over 6 months and then he became highly interested.

His greatest fault as a researcher was a lack of clinical sense. He thought that a single playing of one of Estabrooks' records would produce an equally deep trance in all subjects, yet he knew that varying numbers of exposures on the tachistoscope were required for different subjects to achieve the same amount of learning.

> Sincerely yours,
> Milton H. Erickson, M.D.

Incidentally, I am writing up for publication a lot of this old material—I got the idea from Hull—he had several bookshelves with written-up work

---

*The reference to Erickson in Hull's book *Hypnosis and Suggestibility* (1933) is decidly unflattering. Hull states that Erickson told him of a "supposedly painless tooth extraction"; however, Hull reported, the patient (an adolescent girl) "whimpered and flinched during the extraction." (See the correspondence with Wesley Wells [page 228] for Erickson's correction of Hull's perceptions.)

not yet in final draft awaiting his spare time—lots of the material in practically final form. So I followed his example.

Hull dedicated his book to 20 associates "in remembrance of our united efforts to established hypnotism on a secure experiential basis." Erickson was not one of these associates. However, Mildred B. Mitchell (mentioned in Erickson's February 19, 1964, letter) is on Hull's list.

To: Ronald E. Shor
March 2, 1964

Dear Dr. Shor:

An item that may be of interest to you, which I overlooked in my letter to you, is this: When I was a student dealing with hypnosis, George Sellery, Dean of the College of Liberal Arts at the University of Wisconsin, conducted a prolonged and bitter campaign to have me expelled from the University as an undesirable student, and to have the study of hypnosis eliminated from the University curriculum. This caused me to seek out Dr. A. S. Loevenhart, Professor of Pharmacology who was a dedicated experimentalist; Dr. M. Maek, Assistant Dean of the Medical School and Professor of Physiology; Dr. Joseph Jastrow, Professor of Psychology, who was then Clark L. Hull's superior; Dr. W. F. Lorenz, Professor of Psychiatry; and Dr. Frank C. Richmond, Chief of the Psychiatric Field Service of the State of Wisconsin, who was also a licensed lawyer in Wisconsin, to protect me from explulsion. All of these men were profoundly interested in scientific research, and I had made their acquaintance in my first year at college in an endeavor to make sure of exactly what I wanted at the university. With their protection, I was safe and it was their influence that enabled Dr. Hull to have included in the official curriculum a Seminar on Hypnosis.

I am sorry that I overlooked mention of this in my first letter. These men were most influential for hypnosis, and later it was through their

assistance that I got accepted as an intern, since Dr. Sellery was still untiring in his efforts to secure adequate punishment of me.
    Hastily,

                                                      Sincerely,
                                                      Milton H. Erickson, M.D.

From: Ronald E. Shor
March 19, 1964

Dear Dr. Erickson:
    Thank you very much for your helpful, informative, and fascinating letters. While my own historic survey will be written too concisely to more than to summarize a few key highlights of the incidents you describe, I would very much hope that you will soon write them up for publication in detail. After spending months studying the history of our field, I have come to the firm conclusion that only two men in the twentieth century have an assured place in the history of the scientific understanding of hypnosis—yourself and Hull. Hull initiated a continuing tradition of academic quantitative research; you are by a wide margin the boldest, most ingenious, and influential figure in the clinical tradition.
    I came to suspect that Davis' depth scale derived from your inspiration when I learned that Davis was Hull's student. As you point out, Hull had little or no clinical sensitivity. Even though you personally are highly critical of uni-dimensional scales of hypnotic depth, the kind of diagnostic clinical approach which Davis' scale represents seemed to me much more likely to have derived from your methods than from Hull's.
    It might prove useful when you write up these important events to clarify more fully your academic status at the time of these incidents. For example, what is premedic psychology? I note that you received your B.A. in 1927 and *both* your M.A. and M.D. in 1928. Was this some kind of combined Liberal Arts undergraduate plus medical school training?
    I gather that Hull's perfunctory classroom demonstration of hypnosis was your first experience with the phenomenon. But had you been interested in hypnosis or other altered states of experiencing in any way before then?

To perhaps help refresh your memory in recalling further valuable details, I am also enclosing the brief report by Williams on Hull's work on hypnosis. You probably are familiar with this report, but the photocopy will save you the trouble of digging it out.

Thank you again.

Sincerely,
Ronald E. Shor, Ph.D.

Editor's Note: In his text The Practice of Hypnotism, Volume I, *Andŕe Weitzenhoffer (1989) described scales of hypnotic depth. He indicated that the Davis-Husband Scale, published in 1931, outlined five depths of hypnosis, from insusceptible to deep trance. Test suggestions and responses, varying from relaxation to negative visual hallucination, are listed. The Davis-Husband Scale was the first American attempt to quantify the depth of hypnotic trance.*

To: Ronald E. Shor
March 27, 1964

Dear Dr. Shor:

My B.A. degree was officially granted in 1927 so that I could apply for my internship with a statement that I had a B.A. degree. I was actually in the class of 1924 but had postponed submitting the required thesis since I had obtained permission to combine it with my master's thesis. Internships were hard to get then and I wanted a teaching one. Hence it was granted in 1927 but conferred in June 1928, the same time as my M.A. and M.D.

My college record is a mess. I worked my way, I was not content with just an M.D. degree as were most of my classmates, I talked heads of departments into letting me sign up for courses given at the same time as medical courses. I would guarantee a final grade of 90, if 89 it was to be a flunk, and they took me up on it. That way I got a lot of course credits but not hour credits. I skipped prerequisite courses and took advanced courses on the same basis, knowing that my medical school hours would permit me to graduate. For example, I signed up for first semester German, skipped my classes almost completely but let the professor find me spending that hour in the German library using a dictionary and reading German novels. I stated that I wanted a reading not a speaking knowledge and that I did not have the time to listen to my classmates make mistakes. I got away with it and passed an exceedingly stiff German exam by translating German novels.

Sometimes I took courses without the formality of registering but by talking the professors into letting me audit unofficially or by reading and then taking a final oral or written examination from them to see if I had done adequate studying. I remember taking Sociology completely unofficially but I was already signed up for two other courses for that same hour. I was always in hot water with Dean George Sellery of the College of Liberal Arts for my unorthodox ways and he repeatedly tried to expel me for taking two courses at the same hour but he was at a loss to explain my good grades. Furthermore, I enjoyed annoying him and the Dean of Men, Dr. Goodnight, was a staunch friend of mine who declared that a university was for educational purposes, not the enforcement of administrative rules.

I doubt if this letter will be of any value to you except to disclose something about my drives as a student.

Hastily.

Sincerely yours,
Milton H. Erickson, M.D.

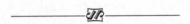

M. Erik Wright, Ph.D., M.D., a psychology professor at the University of Kansas, also was a renowned author and a practitioner of hypnosis. The following letter from Erickson seems to mark the beginning of Wright's tenure as president of the American Society of Clinical Hypnosis.

The first three paragraphs, which describe Erickson's postpolio syndrome (a malady that had not yet been identified at that time), are highly personal, and demonstrate the close relationship Erickson had with Wright. By 1965, Erickson was using a wheelchair to get around.

Shortly after the split between the American Society of Clinical Hypnosis and the Society of Clinical and Experimental Hypnosis, overtures were begun to unify the groups. Erickson was philosophically amenable to the idea but had grave misgiving on other fronts.

To: Erik Wright
November 19, 1964

Dear Erik:

Finally able to be a bit up and about. This spinal nerve root syndrome residual of polio and resulting from spinal column torsion is an old, old story for me. During college and medical school days, I was hospitalized repeatedly and made a specialized object of study by neurologists and psychologists because of the peculiar motor and sensory changes and losses I experienced each time.

For this episode, my losses have been the rest of my right biceps, and some of my left biceps, minor losses of both triceps, and sensory losses in right leg. Mayo's chief neurologist, a few years ago, while visiting Phoenix, had a picnic mapping out and identifying specific nerves, damaged and destroyed.

As for my attitude, well, for a long time I have known that I better hope to live long enough to acquire my own wheelchair. That time is pretty close now, if not already here. Three years ago, in relation to an episode then, my local neurologist, after extensive studies including myelographic, was positive that the wheelchair era had arrived; but I assured him that muscle compensation and re-education did amazing things. Gruesome as it sounds, it has been somewhat interesting over the years to watch my muscles, one by one, slowly fade away. I suppose that is where I learned to watch closely for minimal cues in observing human behavior.

Now, concerning your letter of November 2 about the bettering of the relationships between the two societies, I am greatly in favor of it. In fact, I am willing to do any reasonable thing to promote it. In the past, when such committees were organized, I received letters (I still have a large file of the correspondence) suggesting:

1. The dissolution of ASCH.
2. Turning over the Journal to IJCEH.
3. Turning over the treasury of ASCH to the SCEH. . . .

4. Revision of our membership list, dropping a number of members, reducing many Fellows to Associate Members.
5. Elimination of our officers and editors, or reducing them in grade.

In return, we would be allowed to become, with the exception of a few outstanding members who merited better, associate members of SCEH and our subscription list would be taken over by the Journal of SCEH.

In return they would give us their blessing and let us pay off their accumulated indebtedness, at this time between 4 and 5 thousand, of which I knew for an absolute fact, although not the precise figure. There was also some other indebtedness, just what I do not know or its extent.

Now at the present time, I know factually that two men have privately underwritten $5000 of SCEH indebtedness; a mixup in the printing bills disclosed that the IJCEH subscription list is less than one third of ours; I have been reliably informed, but without proof thereof, that IJCEH is periodically bailed out by private funds; I have been responsibly approached with the proposition that I dismiss my associate editors and replace them with SCEH men (this proposition is less than a year old) and that I take steps to become Editor Emeritus while SCEH takes over. My response was one of stupid friendliness. I was then informed that SCEH was about to collapse, that the October meeting would be a failure, and that private funds would be required to finance that meeting.

It was frankly added that they wanted to save face, and that since SCEH was historically the older society, everybody would gain by having one society, and one with a history as long as possible.

It was freely admitted that the ASCH foreign membership far exceeded IJCEH and also freely admitted that their publicity department was infinitely superior to that of ASCH. This was pointed out to be an extremely important gain for ASCH.

In return for efforts at amalgamation, I am to have conferred upon me many signal honors, awards, etc.

At this very special trial balloon meeting with me, I was extremely noncommittal but friendly. Before the meeting began, there was chitchat about tape recorders, among other things, and this enabled me to call attention to a briefcase strategically, apparently innocently placed, which I openly and innocently recognized as containing a tape recorder and I asked for a demonstration of it and of the remote control, since I was interested in securing one for myself. I think my innocent curiosity had a distressing effect, well concealed, upon my interviewers.

With this preliminary material, intended only to disclose bad faith on the part of an intrenched few, I have this to say.

I am in favor of the two societies amalgamating. I am not in favor of taking on any of their indebtedness despite our present financial situation. I know how some of that indebtedness was incurred and it smells.

I am not in favor of a false tripartite division of hypnosis into three different varieties. I have been consulted by lawyers about the possibility of malpractice suits because a dentist used medical or psychological hypnosis instead of dental hypnosis. This legal approach has been made to me from three different states. I don't like it. The proposal to give credence to specific boards is wrong. To have one board passing on hypnotic training is one thing; to have three boards is to create out of thin air important positions for friends and is another.

In other words, let there be amalgamation but let's cut away the furbelows and gingerbread.

They also insisted that we recognize M.A. degrees that they accepted for full membership as full members of ASCH. Should we modify our constitution? I think not. There might, however, be the possibility of a lower level of membership, such as affiliate member. We could, perhaps, include ministers, lawyers, speech therapists, etc.

In brief, they have had only demands to make of us so far, and according to their higher echelons (at least eight men have so informed me), the continued existence of SCEH and its Journal is most precarious. I do not blame them for seeking an advantageous arrangement. But I do not favor any losses of any sort to our society.

A recent (since September) influx of private funds has given them a little additional time and strength, but that source of support will soon be exhausted (I am so fairly reliably informed). . . .

. . . But now that you are President, I fully expect that your tact and diplomacy will effect a good handling of the SCEH affair.

I have no personal interest. I favor anything that advances hypnosis. I have all the personal recognition in hypnosis that I want, with one exception. I would like to complete 10 years editing of the Journal. I need no committee memberships, etc. I want to edit, to support my family, to promote hypnosis. That's all. I'll agree to anything you work out because my knowledge of you gives me complete faith in your integrity. So, go to it

Erik. . . . [Erickson suggests some names for the amalgamation committee.]

. . . I don't envy you your job, but I am confident that you will do a good job. My best wishes.

Sincerely,
Milton H. Erickson, M.D.

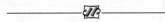

Milton Erickson served as editor of The American Journal of Clinical Hypnosis *from its inception in July 1958 until July 1968, when he turned the reins over to William Edmonston, an academic psychologist at Colgate University in Hamilton, N.Y. Erickson solicited Edmonston's review of a manuscript in 1965, even before the editorship was transferred.*

The following letters are interesting because they preceded by six months the publication of one of Erickson's important papers: "Special Inquiry with Aldous Huxley Into the Nature and Character of Various States of Consciousness" (Erickson, 1965a). It seems Erickson heeded Edmonston's editorial advice, as the footnote was dropped from the article and the introduction was far from "folksy." Erickson's paper was published during Edmonston's tenure as second editor of the Journal.

Huxley, one of the leading intellectuals of his time, rose to fame in the 1920s and 1930s as an author; Brave New World *was the best known of his earlier works. His interest in consciousness persisted after his collaboration with Erickson.* The Doors of Perception *and its sequel,* Heaven and Hell, *published in 1954 and 1956, respectively, recounted Huxley's experiences with hallucinogenic drugs.*

From: William E. Edmonston
January 4, 1965

Dear Milton:

I read the enclosed manuscript with much interest and would like to make the following suggestions. It would seem preferable to begin the manuscript with an account similar to that appearing in the second footnote, rather than the present preamble. I would suspect that the present preamble is a bit too folksy for the journal publication.

I certainly agree that it is immensely unfortunate that the notebooks were burned in the Huxley home, but I wonder if you could not be more specific and detailed in your account of the episodes in the account of that fascinating day. For example, to what phenomena of deep trance did Huxley respond and to what degree? Can you recall more of the discussions of the initial light, medium, and deep trances? It would seem to me that a further explication of these discussions would be highly informative to our readers. Also, I wonder if the contrast between a deep trance and a "deep reflection" could not be made more explicit.

I guess what I'm trying to say is that by the time I finished reading the manuscript I had a feeling of unfulfillment, a lack of closure. Perhaps I entered the manuscript with extraordinary expectations, beyond the limits of reality and doomed by their own excess to disillusionment. Two things I think would make Huxley's experience more meaningful to me: (a) much more detail of the intellectually stimulating discussions throughout that eventful day, and (b) some more reflections from you, as the author, on the meaning that the readers might attribute to the events you describe. These two additions would add to the ms.'s fascination and increase its meaningfulness . . .

Our best to you and the family for the new year.

Sincerely,
William E. Edmonston, Jr., Ph.D.

To: William E. Edmonston, Jr.
January 6, 1965

Dear Bill:

I'll go over my material carefully. I agree with you about the Preamble. I know Huxley was going to include it some way but how is now an unanswerable question. I haven't got his literary talent:

Yes, I felt let down by the ending and made up my mind to comb my notes more thoroughly. I'm sure I can enlarge the exposition of my notes.

Do you happen to have an extra day-stretcher lying around loose? A mere 24 hours per day is definitely insufficient.

Sincerely yours,
Milton H. Erickson, M.D.

————————— 𝒥𝒽 —————————

Erickson seems to have written the following letters to William Edmonston on his own initiative, and there is no record of any response. Edmonston, a junior colleague, served as Erickson's chosen successor as editor of the American Journal of Clinical Hypnosis.

The letters are frank exposés of political machinations and personalities in the academic and professional world. They could even be seen as harsh critiques. They are presented here to provide insight into Milton Erickson, and not to disclose old controversies and open old wounds.

Erickson was keenly aware that many people have a natural tendency to be self-serving, and clearly wanted Edmonston to know about the designs that some had on hypnosis, and on the ASCH and its Journal. He was forthright in describing the Machiavellian and meretricious maneuvers of the unscrupulous, and the lengths to which they would go to carry out their schemes. To get his point across, he provided abundant examples. Erickson reasoned that Edmonston would face inherent problems in his new role as editor, and he did not want him to have any naive misconceptions.

Consider, also, Erickson's personality. He was meticulous; his attention to detail was evident in all of his work, including that as editor of the Journal, and he encouraged Edmonston to behave similarly. Erickson also was frugal by nature, and he urged Edmonston to keep expenses to a minimum. Moreover, Erickson was powerful and could be autocratic, and he advised Edmonston to unglove an iron fist when necessary.

To: William E. Edmonston, Jr.
November 9, 1967

Dear Bill:
For years—since the publication of the second volume of the *American Journal of Clinical Hypnosis*—[he mentors three prominent members of

ASCH, identified there as X, Y, and Z.] with others, by a devotion to "THE GREAT BIG LIE," have endeavored to take away the editorship. All three have been highly resentful of many lecture invitations I have received. They have built up a story about enmity between Frank Pattie and me and that has been pounded home over and over again. Actually, Frank and I worked together with great pleasure for several volumes and then the university requested him to write a book. Since Frank discontinued the work, he and I and Mrs. Erickson have carried on an extensive correspondence. I don't know how well you know Frank, but he has a most marvelous sense of humor. I am enclosing some correspondence from him to Betty and a letter from him to me which you can read, I hope with a great deal of amusement, but I do want you to return them. His book review will be utterly charming and there are going to be quite a number of people who will be surprised with his quotation of the authors in a review we will publish in January. [Pattie, an associate editor, reviewed, and panned, a book on Mesmer in the January 1968 issue of AJCH. He later wrote an authoritative biography of Mesmer.]

When I accepted the editorship, in the beginning, I was confronted by the prospect of completing successfully with an established journal and I had no experience in editing. Nevertheless, the first volume of the Journal was a success. I kept the price down solely to insure a good circulation and financial success. When X found out that the Journal was successful from the very first, he made many plans to transform it into a lay magazine and he had a cover design made and paid for by the Society on his own, fully expecting that I would give up the editorship. When we had to give up the original publisher, X convinced the Executive Committee that we should have the Journal published in Chicago. X booked a commercial printer unacquainted with a lot of things connected with scientific publications. In one year's time, we lost $2,000 on the Journal, yet the Journal not only is still being profitable to the Society, it is three times the size of the journal published by SCEH, so far as content is concerned. We publish a much larger number of foreign articles, we publish abstracts, and the abstracts they publish are only of their own articles, and rarely do they publish book reviews, and despite this fact, with the exception of one issue, our Journal, no matter how late, has always been earlier than that journal. Yet, I am informed by fairly reliable sources that their editor is paid $2,000 an issue and he delegates most of the work to others. Our present circulation is over 3,000, which is remarkably extensive for a

Journal of our type and has three times the circulation of the SCEH Journal and this has been achieved by my holding the price down, first to six dollars and then to eight dollars, and by giving still lower rates to libraries and institutions. This latter have brought us more subscribers and a much wider circulation in all parts of the world. The SCEH "International Journal" is unknown in many countries where we have regular subscribers.

Our members get their Journal by just paying their dues to the Society. The dues for the other Society are larger, they make requests for special assessment, they charge their members for admission to the Annual Meeting, they require the sale of tickets to banquets, which are not served. They charge a special fee to the members in the International Society and they issue a directory of its top officials and committees and members. It is a very small directory and includes names of dead and former members. By accident, our press, which also prints their journal, sent me a long overdue bill for the printing of our competing journal which indicated not only the size of the journal printing-wise, but the number of subscribers printing-wise.

X, Y, and Z want to take over the AJCH. They wanted to change it, to transform it and they are quite right in their accusations that I never asked the Executive Committee to approve of the Associate Editors. I had good reason not to ask for approval. I knew that it was important for the success of the Journal to have as many universities as possible listed on the masthead. This was a vital matter in the acceptance of a second journal on hypnosis. I dropped Y from the editorship when I discovered that he, in his insecurity, and in his desire to insure tenure, had joined the rest of the faculty in opposing the teaching of hypnosis at the dental school. After he secured tenure, I did not feel that he merited reappointment and so I substituted Kay Thompson. The listing of Dr. Fredericka Freitag led, together with my lectures at the Aerospace Laboratory in Dayton and at the Aerospace School of Medicine in San Antonio, to a much more receptive attitude toward hypnosis by the Air Force. It led to the Air Force's permitting two officers of the Air Force to publish in the Journal and the Air Force has permitted my son-in-law to write an extensive paper on the use of hypnosis in the Air Force, which had been ruled against in a book of regulations outdated years ago. Partially on the strength of my son-in-law's paper, he has been given a greatly desired temporary detached duty which was an assignment to the Armed Forces Staff Officers College. Every officer in the Navy, the Army, the Marines, and the Air Force hopes for such an assignment.

Our Journal is accepted behind the Iron Curtain. We have received requests for permission to reprint articles, not only mine, but those of others, for republication behind the Iron Curtain, in South America, in Germany and in various other places.

Arizona State University made a study of six volumes of both journals to appraise hypnosis. They contacted me for copies of our Journal, which were readily supplied. They wrote to the other journal and to various universities for the volumes for those six years that were to be studied but without result. They finally asked me if I could furnish them, which I was able to do. The evaluation of the two journals was decidedly complimentary of ours.

X and Y wanted to be permanent trustees of the ERF [the education arm of ASCH] and they thought I would join them in that. There was to be a committee of fourteen members, three permanent. I spoiled that for them because I did not think that any person should be a permanent member and they resented it highly. I also think that the editorship should not remain permanently in the hands of any one person. I think the good of the Society is more important.

I have aroused the hostilities of every self-seeking person in the Society. I have rejected manuscripts and caused much hostility. For example, Dr. L. and X published an article somewhere in which the statement was made that one-third of the questionnaires on which the study was based were rejected because of incompleteness of information, another third were unaccountably lost and the data were based on the remaining one-third. Actually, the manuscript based on all the data was sent to me originally by X and his secretary included a letter from a medical ghost writer which advised him that he should get some experienced aid on percentages. André Weitzenhoffer reviewed the manuscript and gave extensive advice for major revisions. X convinced Dr. L. that he had actually lost a large portion of the questionnaires, not knowing that I have in my desk drawer a complete record of all the actual information. Dr. L. was most resentful toward me when I learned that he was being used dishonestly by X, but the Dr. L./X paper is filled with inaccuracies and misinformation.

When you are in the high, responsible position in any organization, you are bound to incite hostility, but I assure you that the learnings you acquire are worth putting up with the slings and arrows that come your way. Long before I was the editor, I had corresponded with editors of various psychiatric journals because I was curious about editorial problems. I also knew Carl Murchison [then editor of the *Journal of General Psychology*] as a personal friend and listened to his discussions on all his problems as an editor. All of this information served me well.

Every year X tries to get the Journal published somewhere else. Waverly Press publishes at least one hundred and fifty scientific journals. If an author makes an error that slips by the editor regarding scientific terms and various references, they often correct it. More than once they have corrected references appended to various papers because the authors had misspelled the authors' names. This kind of service is very useful and very helpful, but I can assure you that mistakes occur in journals everywhere. Betty and I have found misprints in *Science*, and in the *American Journal of Psychiatry*. The publisher of the Shor-Orne book has a running head which is a terrible error. For example, on page 307, the running head is "Three Dimensions of Hypnotic Death," [it should read, "Three Dimensions of Hypnotic *Depth*"], and that error occurs only once in the paper. In correcting proof for the October issue of the Journal, in the title of my paper, they have "futher" instead of "further" studies, and the word "pantomime" in various publications is spelled with a "n" and was so in one of my papers in the running head, although it was correctly spelled in the typewritten copy and proof . . .

. . . Dr. W. promised me a book review in October if I would be content to wait until April, but he didn't specify that it would be the April after the next April. Book reviewers have to be written to over and over again. One book reviewer assured me that he has four book reviews that he is planning to polish up "next week." Another has several book reviews that he will send me "tomorrow," which have not arrived for many long months. A few book reviewers are very prompt. There are some volunteer book reviewers who don't wait for a review copy to be received. They review the book that they have purchased and send the book review to me.

I have received many letters of criticism from authors objecting to my publication of the paper they sent in because, in thinking it over a year later, they had discovered some changes they would have liked to have had included in the article.

Betty just told me to tell you that there are some rewards and not to scare you by just telling you the miseries. I think you should know the miseries but it will be your pleasure and satisfaction to discover all the joys that far outweigh the miseries.

My secretary suggested that I tell you, "Don't chicken out, carry on."

I assure you, Bill, that I think you are in a most advantageous situation, and you will find some who will be interested in learning something about reading and choosing papers, some who will be interested in proofreading, there will be some who want to learn how to write scientific papers and you can have your burdens greatly lessened in this way. Clark L. Hull's book was literally a book put together by Hull and based in large part upon published papers or typewritten reports of his students. He became angry at me on a purely personal matter and ripped out of his manuscript all references to me except for one he misquoted, and he became very angry at me when a number of the students at Yale protested the lack of acknowledgment of the assistance I had given him, both at Wisconsin and at Yale.

Editing a journal brings you into contact with a great many people, even people in other areas of scientific research. These are some of the rewards that enable you to ignore a lot of criticism.

Since I have my office in my home, I also have the editorial office there. It was only through Betty's persistent efforts that we managed both the nonmember and our overseas subscription sales. The regular subscriptions were finally transferred to the Central Office, and she hopes to transfer the foreign ones eventually as well. When the Journal was printed in Kentucky, Frank Pattie paid token wages to his family for doing all the bulk mailing, inserting the Journals into the envelopes, sorting them, bundling them and there are a whole series of commercial terms describing this art. Having Frank use his home and by using my home, we kept the original cost of the Journal down, which was very necessary because X handled the money of the Society and he was outrageously extravagant in its use.

Be very wary about anything that X urges upon you. For confirmation of this advice, you can write to [Erickson names distinguished SCH officers], who have frequently been much outraged by X's behavior. Seminars on Hypnosis came to an end because X deliberately destroyed the Philadelphia, and the New Orleans, and the Dayton, Ohio, seminars. The Seminars on Hypnosis debacle led to a blacklisting of Seminars on Hypnosis in hotels throughout the United States. He ran up a bill of $1,600 for unused private rooms and did not show up for the teaching at the last three seminars, and he ran the Society into the red one year. Nevertheless, the man does have an ability to promote many things successfully, but once they are a success, he endeavors to destroy them.

This is something that many in the academic world do not fully realize can be true. I saw it happen in two different departments at the University of Wisconsin. I saw it happen in the Department of Biology at Wayne State University, in the Psychology Department at the University of Michigan, and I saw it happen at Yale University, and all of those academicians did not know what had happened and didn't really understand how a destructive departmental member can actually make it necessary for a department to reorganize from the ground up. That reminds me, the Psychology Department at [two southwestern universities] were both completely disorganized, each by a single member, and they are still in the process of building up. As an editor, you will have an opportunity to recognize this and you will be better able to understand and see clinically some of the things that are happening around you.

I left Michigan in 1948 for my health. Before that particular health accident happened to me, I was aware that I would have to leave Michigan because heads of departments of the 11,000-bed hospital were all moving away. I was one of the last to go and in 1949, the man who had built it up from a political cesspool to a nationally recognized hospital died, and it took just one year for the hospital to go back to being a political cesspool, and only within the last eight years has it achieved a good reorganization.

I realize I've given you very little specific instruction in this letter. That will come later.

Yours,
Milton

To: William E. Edmonston, Jr., Ph.D.
April 4, 1968

Dear Bill:
Early in the 1930s, somewhat by chance and somewhat by curiosity, I became interested in the problems of editorship and also the importance of editorship. From various psychologists I learned that the editorship of a journal could lead to the presidency of the American Psychological As-

sociation. In appraising you over the years I have felt that you would have this potential.

Long ago Margaret Mead and I impressed upon Abe Maslow the tremendous importance of accepting freely and easily and comfortably any criticism of his publications. We were both greatly impressed by Abe and his capacity to think, even though we frequently disagreed with it. We both agreed and told Abe that someday there would be a more than usual recognition of him as an outstanding man in the field of psychology, but neither of us realized that the APA presidency would come his way.

In getting acquainted with editors of both psychological fields and medical fields, I learned a great many things. One was that under no circumstances should a journal allow itself to become the medium of controversy by permitting authors to be aware of what some other author was intending to publish. This is possible only when the journal is practically the sole organ of a very large scientific society. Even then, it is undesirable. Fishbein, who was the Editor of the *Journal of the American Medical Association*, apprised me at length of the folly involved in permitting authors to see the papers published by other authors prior to publication. This folly lies in the simple fact that both authors then develop animosity toward the editor and the editor is used as a battleground. Also, I was informed that the editor had to be hard-headed and obstinate if he were to continue as such and if the journal were to continue. In fact, the editor has to be extremely arbitrary or the journal will fail.

This is true not only in psychology and medicine but it is true of journals in other scientific fields, such as geology, journals concerned with the use of wood, journals concerned with horticulture. For that matter, when *Time* magazine was first published, the betting was 10 to 1 that it would not last more than two years. I had a great deal of discussion by correspondence with the editor of *Time* magazine. When I published a paper in the *British Journal of Medical Psychology*, the editor sent me a letter telling me that my manuscript was the very first in his many years of experience that he did not have to rewrite at all. That while I made the error of using "second" instead of "secondly" and "behavior" instead of "behaviour," he thought it would be captious on his part to find fault since such usages were obviously Americanisms.

I had a long correspondence with the editor of *Mental Hygiene* in which he poured out his woes because it was the policy of that journal to ask permission of authors to make changes in their articles. He stated that his life was made horrible by repeated letters of damnation for correcting a misspelled word, inserting a comma where it belonged and for making new paragraphs. This correspondence resulted from a request to me inquiring if he could make a change in a manuscript of mine, and I had written to him that his long editorial experience qualified him to do much better than I could in preparing a manuscript for publication.

Actually, I do not know how many editors I have talked the problem over with, but it was fully a score, and this curiosity of mine served me well in developing the Journal, even though I did not know until the late 1950s that I would ever become an editor-in-chief.

One of the things that is the bane of existence for an editor is the author who submits a manuscript for publication and then bombards you with revisions of it, and revisions of revisions of revisions, until even the postman gets weary of bringing you the new revisions.

Another problem is that when you let authors correct galley proofs, they always find new and better sentences and new and better paragraphs that should be inserted, and paragraphs and sentences that should be omitted. They even do so with page proofs. After they have revised their entire article when it is in galley proof, and revised it even more extensively when it is in page proof, you are then bombarded with endless criticisms for having published it in the final form which they themselves sent to you. This is my reason for not sending out galley proofs or sending page proofs to authors and my severest critics are authors who have sent manuscripts and then revisions and then revisions for me to insert in the revised manuscript.

It is astonishing to discover how many scientifically trained men quote a source of information, misquoting the author entirely, and even spelling the author's name wrong. One of my reasons for sticking to Waverly Press is that they have a cross-index system which they use constantly to check references and the names of authors referred to. Waverly. Press publishes at least 150 different journals and they specialize in this type of publication. . . . Their employees are extremely loyal to them. . . . When X managed to get the Journal published by a firm in Chicago despite my protests, every author suffered seriously; for example: the price of reprints would be quoted according to the number of pages, however, there was no mention that new rules required that each reprint had to be set up afresh since the type of the Journal had to be dismantled at once and reprints, according to union rules, had to be reset as entirely new work. Furthermore, a general commercialized publisher is simply not interested in scientific publications. If it is convenient for them, part of a bibliography can be omitted. The editor has no rights, no matter how carefully he proofreads the page proof. They rely on their own proofreaders, who are merely professional proofreaders and not informed on scientific matters.

Journals such as ours have a relatively small circulation compared with commercial publications, therefore, our Journal takes last place in their consideration. Waverly Press depends upon scientific journals. The only other possible printer is the one-horse-town publisher and very few of those are left. When our Journal was first issued, we had one such publisher but it was initially a one-man firm who took immense pride in his work, no matter how long it took, and we were dependent on his good health.

I received many criticisms because of the late appearance of the various issues of the Journal. Some of the most emphatic and eloquent were from those who have promised to send a manuscript, and send a promise regularly with every request from me, even if it took three years or longer for them to get around to sending the manuscript.

You are also at the mercy of the Program Chairman, [some of whom] deliberately tried to sabotage the Journal. The only manuscripts [one of them] sent me were mimeographed sheets of news releases, or preliminary summaries.

The editor is also at the mercy of the most selfish men in the Society. They are the ones that want to hang unto some official position year after year, for example: X has insisted on holding some office for ten years and excluding other men. Z insists on keeping his present job in spite of the fact that for two years he has lost money for the Education and Research Foundation regularly. Y has insistently demanded that he have an official position. The good and the welfare of the Society have little meaning for these various selfish people. In ten years' time, Y has never sent a single dental abstract. I had to rewrite every one of his papers.

Despite this long letter of unpleasant content, Bill, I want you to be editor because I think it will prove a desirable force in molding your future, and that while it may be painful to be editor, you will eventually reap many rewards.

Sincerely yours,
Milton H. Erickson, M.D.

To: William E. Edmonston, Jr.
January 30, 1969

Dear Bill:

I am in sympathy with your desire to evaluate all contributions solely on their merits without reference to the identity of the author or the orientation and approach of the paper. However, I think you should be made aware that in practice this idealistic standard lays the way open for exploitation by those whose standards are not so high. I think the best way to inform you about these pitfalls is to recount two separate true stories.

The first concerns one Benjamin Peter [Ed note: a fictitious name], Dr. Carl Murchison; and Dr. Clark L. Hull, who was my professor of psychology at the University of Wisconsin. Sometime in the year 1941, Peter, freely admitting that he possessed no academic degree, submitted a paper for consideration to Dr. Carl Murchison who was then the Editor of the *Journal of General Psychology*. The paper concerned hypnosis and Dr. Murchison sent it to Dr. Clark L. Hull for review since Dr. Hull was well known as the author of what was then considered to be the only modern, scientifically oriented textbook on hypnosis. Dr. Hull, while I don't think he was particularly bowled over by the paper, thought "it contained some interesting ideas" and approved publication. Peter turned out to be a most ruthless and self-seeking character who is actually still deriving profit from this mistake. The *Journal of General Psychology*, of course, was an entirely respectable publication. Dr. Murchison, in an attempt at academic whimsy had included in his directions to contributors at the time a statement something as follows: "The Editor has no wish to receive and evaluate book reviews which are assigned to undergraduate psychology majors as assignments by their professors, hence, no unsolicited book reviews will be considered for publication unless the reviewer possesses a Ph.D. in psychology."

Mr. Peter had enrolled in [a] university and had dropped out during his first year with failing grades and incompletes. However, shortly after the appearance in print of his paper, which, incidentally, was a very much oversimplified interpretation of hypnosis, he opened an office on Park Avenue, designating himself as a psychologist and charging fees of $1,000 and up for patients (and this was in the 1940s). He somehow managed to become a fad. *Life* magazine gave him a rather extensive writeup as did *Readers Digest, Time*, and several other popular publications. In each and every one, he admitted that he did not possess an academic degree; stated that he had intended to major in psychology but found that he was "wasting his time watching rats run mazes" while the troubled world was crying out for his invaluable services. He invariably coupled this statement with the fact that in spite of his lack of a degree, he had published a paper in a technical psychology journal so prestigious that contributors were warned not even to submit book reviews unless they possessed a Ph.D. in psychology. He also repeatedly claimed that the prestigious and respected Dr. Clark L. Hull, a noted authority on hypnosis, had "*sponsored* him."

Dr. Murchison was outraged. Dr. Hull attempted vainly to counteract the claim, to disavow it, etc., but could not escape the fact that he had indeed recommended publication. He finally became so embittered that he completely washed his hands of hypnosis, and turned to study of learning theory for the rest of his academic career; did not even mention the subject of hypnosis; and continually embarrassed his colleagues by his extreme reaction against the entire subject. The underground story has also gone around, which you might have heard, that Hull disavowed hypnosis after a lawsuit connected with a Yale student and there was some such case which contributed additionally to his bitterness. However, he had already turned against the entire subject.

Peter continued to prosper; however, as the years passed, he became aware that certification for psychologists was the coming thing and that he had better get on the bandwagon. Accordingly, he went back to the university where he was previously enrolled and completed a four-year course and was awarded the B.S. degree majoring in psychology. I managed to obtain a transcript of his courses and grades and was struck with admiration for the manner in which he had managed to fulfill the requirements for a major with the absolute minimum of courses requiring any solid academic work. His transcript is filled with sandbox and Mickey Mouse courses. The State of New York eventually, in 1961, passed a certification law for psychologists, but as such laws invariably must, it contained a "grandfather" clause. The "grandfather" clause provided that one must have at least a B.S. in psychology and that if this was the highest degree, it must be accompanied by twelve years of experience as a psychologist and an endorsement by two practicing psychologists. If one had a master's degree, a lesser number of years of experience was required. Peter, of course, had the years of "experience" and found it possible to get two psychologists simple enough to recommend him on the strength of his publications. He had later brought out this paper in expanded form as a very slim book, which had given him additional publicity. As a side-light, in 1946 I was invited to contribute a chapter to a volume being edited by Salvatore Russo. This book, *Modern Hypnosis*, edited by Kuhn and Russo, appeared in 1947. His first listing of contributors was so uniformly well selected and of good status that I consented. However, as he expanded the volume he tentatively included a chapter by Peter. I immediately wrote and stated that I could not appear in any volume to which Peter was a contributor and would have to withdraw if Russo continued to include this chapter. His initial reaction was to rather huffily inform me that as editor, he, of course, was the only judge of his contributors' worth and that he regretted my withdrawing. However, completely independently of my communication, he found himself receiving similar withdrawals from other writers, and I received a second letter not long after, very apologetic. He had undoubtedly suddenly realized that he was choosing Peter over his best-known contributors, and asked himself, "What am I doing?" Russo gave me the additional interesting information that he had checked carefully through certain sources available to him and found that Peter's works were all ghost written by the same person who was ghost writing books and articles for Elsa Maxwell and other similar personalities. I believe this was the excuse he used to get rid of Peter's contribution, since he was printing only original works.

Incidentally, Russo, in his independent investigation, discovered that Peter had solicited reprints, and turned them over to a ghost writer, whom Russo interviewed. In reviewing Peter's book, some paragraphs had a suggestive tone. I looked through a lot of the psychological literature and was able to discover a number of original sources which the ghost writer had misquoted, misconstrued, or had deliberately altered to "formulate" Peter's presentation.

Several years after, Peter became aware that he had exploited hypnosis thoroughly and that the coming thing in therapy was going to be the other half of his initial piece of writing, namely, the conditioned reflex. He brought out a book on [his model of] therapy, of which I have a copy and I agree with Frank Pattie's judgment, after we had both looked it over, that it is "unbelievably awful." Somehow or other, however, he was able to convince the very prestigious Dr. Horsley Gantt that he knew what he was talking about, probably because, although Gantt is an expert on [certain aspects of psychology], he obviously knows nothing of therapy. Also, I strongly suspect from the laudatory review that Gantt wrote that he may have been becoming senile. This, however, has launched Peter in a new and even more profitable direction. In view of his publications and this laudatory review, he was able to convince Dr. Ian Stevenson and Dr. Joseph Wolpe that he was qualified to appear on a program which was being presented at an eastern university in 1964 on Conditioned Reflex Therapy. I wrote to Dr. Wolpe and apprised him of Mr. Peter's career. However, as you may be aware, Wolpe is exceedingly naive in many respects, and Dr. Stevenson even more so, having gone completely overboard in various offbeat directions, such as reincarnation, etc. Hence, Peter was retained on the program. The moral of this long story is that if Dr. Murchison and Dr. Hull had been more wary and had turned down the initial publication on the grounds that Peter was unqualified, he would have at least been hampered in his subsequent career, and furthermore, could not *still* be claiming that the late Dr. Hull was his sponsor.

The next story that I want to tell you briefly concerns Dr. Louis Wolberg and one L.S., who brought out a book on self-hypnosis. Wolberg in a careless moment wrote S. a few helpful comments, since he felt "there were some good ideas" in this projected volume. Then he found to his horror that not only was S. completely unqualified, but that he was using Wolberg's statements in his book and in other self-promotions in every possible way, and has also embarked on various teaching and other ventures for which he has no qualifications whatsoever.

Weitzenhoffer, on his own responsibility, curious about S.'s book, discovered when and where S. had worked unsatisfactorily as a garage mechanic, an insurance salesman, and as a general handyman. Wolberg helped him to prestige and fortune as did the Journal of SCEH. Shortly after S.'s book appeared, Wolberg sent me a picuture postcard of a string of fish on a line with the rueful comment that "If I had kept my big mouth shut, it never would have happened."

The moral of this long letter is simply that the identity of the writer and his knowledge of his background are not at all irrelevant to the editorial judgment, when the Editor must decide as to the accepting or rejecting of papers. It would be fine if we could consider only the subject matter and its presentation but, unfortunately, reality precludes this ideal state of affairs.

LeCron, has, of course, a number of completely acceptable publications to his credit. In view, however, of the turn his recent writings have taken, I believe we may well be wary of him.

As editor, I did not even approve of *citing* of papers and books by such authors as Peter, S., et al., in the legitimate authors' reference lists, and I deleted them (always informing the authors, of course). This is not a harsh or arbitrary decision. These men are not above utilizing such a mention for the rest of their careers, e.g. "My papers are cited as basic references in the *American Journal of Clinical Hypnosis.*"

Writers upon whom I exercised this complete editorial ban (and I strongly advise you, tor the sake of the Journal, of our membership, and of the exploited public, to do the same) include: [Erickson lists nine names].

I will be glad to detail the careers of any of these on your request.

Sincerely,
Milton H. Erickson, M.D.

Erickson's June 15, 1965, letter to Wolfgang Luthe, M.D., of Montreal is re-markable because Luthe and Schultz were confounders of autogenic training and methods that were similar to hypnosis in many respects. Erickson apparently ad-mired their work and wanted to protect their approach from beng tainted by such personages as Dr. B., whom he considered a primary example of an unscrupulous practitioner of hypnotism.

Erickson also expressed his concern about Dr. B. in his December 16 letter to Wright, then president of the American Society of Clinical Hypnosis.

To: Wolfgang Luthe
June 15, 1965

Dear Wolfgang:
I had intended to write to you earlier, but unfortunately since our meeting in Paris I have not been able to keep up on my correspondence. I took part in the Workshop in Detroit, but have since been hospitalized, having extensive studies made and am now at home doing quite well, but I am on a very limited working schedule as yet.

I am writing to you at the present time in the hope that you can use your influence with Dr. Schultz to prevent him from associating himself with a most unethical and undesirable group. I am enclosing a duplicator copy of the folder recently circulated by this group. I am sure you are familiar with the difficulties all of us in the ethical, professional societies and teaching organizations have had with Dr. B. Although his medical degree is a legitimate one, his flamboyant and theatrical publications, advertising and courses have rendered any associations with him and projects under his sponsorship completely unacceptable. You have no doubt run across previous examples of Dr. B.'s exploits; and the type of book which he authors is very adequately evaluated in the book review by [Erickson provides the citation]. Furthermore, at various courses and congresses organized by Dr. B. hypnotists and promoters of stage hypnosis have frequently taken part.

In the present three-week course which Dr. B. has organized, another faculty member is Dr. P. of England. Many years ago Dr. P. was well-regarded in professional circles, but his publications and associations have steadily gone downhill, and as you may see from the book review cited above, were completely unacceptable to serious scientists.

Another faculty member, Dr. V. of Rotterdam, is completely unknown to me, but I am not impressed by his qualifications as listed in this folder.

The physician, Dr. M., seems to have somewhat more impressive credentials, but if he were actually recognized in the field of hypnosis in France, it seems to me that we would have heard his name mentioned at the recent International Congress in Paris.

The two other physicians on the faculty are also foreign members of the American Society of Clinical Hypnosis. If they were the only such, I would have no hesitation about raising the question with the Ethics Committee of their participation in the program. However, I have no intention of so doing at the present time because the question would inevitably be raised as to Dr. Schultz's participation.

Dr. R., as you no doubt know, is highly regarded in psychiatric circles; but since the publication a number of years ago of his book on hypnosis, he has not produced any serious research or writing that I know of. Instead, in spite of the many very adequate evaluations which have been published by various men pointing out the many serious errors of implications and conclusions and the numerous omissions of pertinent facts, he seems to have done nothing but repeat over and over the various dubious conclusions of this book. About two or three years ago, as you may know, he announced his resignation from the psychiatric profession, in order to enter a religious order. However, in Paris he was again resuming his crusade and his presentation on Dr. B.'s program is another such repetition.

As for Dr. M. I have been very dubious about his abilities and his professional judgment all through our correspondence, which has gone on for a number of years. Had I known that he had applied for membership in our Society, I would have raised some questions at that time. However, up to now I have actually had nothing definite against him except the rather haphazard, somewhat confused type of writing in the papers he had submitted for publication and which have been rejected. I am sure that Dr. Schultz is completely unaware of the dubious nature of the American Institute of Hypnosis, and I hope he will withdraw his participation on grounds of his physical health, if nothing else, since I understand his health is not too good. After a reasonable length of time, I would then feel more free to bring up the question of Dr. R.'s and Dr. M.'s association.

It is particularly unfortunate that this publicity is distributed at this time since the German Society of Medical Hypnosis has almost completed the formalities of affiliation with the American Society of Clinical Hypnosis. The formal business in this matter has been carried on by Dr. Klaus Thomas, who is at the present time taking a special residency at St. Elizabeth's Hospital in Washington, D.C. I feel we should go about this as discreetly and tactfully as possible, because there are always certain people who would take pleasure in making an unpleasant issue of such a problem.

I am hoping to hear from you on this matter.

Sincerely yours,
Milton H. Erickson, M.D.

P.S. An examination of the Directory and my files shows that I was mistaken—Dr. R., while a member of the International Society for Clinical and Experimental Hypnosis, has never become a member of the American Society of Clinical Hypnosis. However, I hope emphatically that Dr. Schultz will withdraw from participation in Dr. B.'s course, and that the publicity already given to his name will not lead to criticism or condemnation of him, since I believe he has been misled and deceived as to the status and credentials of the organizers.

I am enclosing a snapshot, as I promised you in Paris, of our dog, Roger, in a "hypnotic trance," with a treed cat as the center of concentration of attention.

To: Erik Wright
December 16, 1965

Dear Erik:

I am sending you an example of the sort of stuff that opportunistic charlatans promote.

Because this man, [Dr. G.] like Dr. B.* has legitimate university degrees (although much less impressive ones), some might object to the term "charlatan," but I think when you look through this material you will agree with the characterization.

For example, Lewis Wolberg found that he had enthusiastically endorsed the book by the charlatan Mr. S., ex-handy man, ex-garage mechanic, ex-insurance man, ex-stage hypnotist, ex-yardman, ex-etc., because he courteously wrote that "the manuscript may have some interesting ideas" when he was asked for an appraisal of it. Lewis remarked to me, "If I had only kept my big mouth shut and ignored the request." That enthusiastic endorsement as worded by Mr. S. led an SCEH reviewer to give the book a long thoughtful appraisal, unaware of Mr S.'s lack of a college education; and his paraphrasing carefully material from reliable sources to give worth to his own stage hypnotist ideas.

I had a patient several years ago whose mother, a psychiatric social worker, was a completely psychotic paranoid. She had developed a grand detailed new system of therapy which she proceeded to draw her clients into, in a sort of multiple folie-a-deux. Because it was based on Freud's theories, although it improved, developed, and went far beyond them, she sent a great folder of single-spaced typed manuscript to the hotel where Dr. A. A. Brill was stopping. He was kind enough to send her an acknowledgement—something like, "Thank you for sending me your interesting manuscript, which perhaps I shall be able to find time to look over."

From then on, her folder has been headed with the statement, "I have received an enthusiastic personal letter from Dr. A. A. Brill himself, who calls my work 'interesting' and who states that he is eager to go over all the developments in detail that I have made."

This woman, of course, is not a conscious charlatan but has now convinced herself that Dr. Brill was her ardent disciple. She did exactly the same thing with Dr. Ernest Jones, with the same results. She had duplicated copies made for distribution and she showed them to me. I refused to write anything for her . . .

My reply to Dr. G. will be written by my secretary on plain paper without using my name. It will not even be concluded "Very truly yours," which would enable him to say, "Dr. M. H. Erickson has thanked me for sending him my material and says he is very truly mine." Dr. G. seems to be smart enough to know that when he reprints letters from people who have even mildly endorsed him, and then lists all their important affiliations, somehow it all becomes confused in the readers' minds and the halo effect of the legitimate associations spreads over all . . .

Sincerely yours,
Milton H. Erickson, M.D.

*A well-known hypnosis teacher who affiliated with lay hypnotists whom Erickson believed to be unethical.

Erickson pulled no punches in the advice he offered students and colleagues. It is apparent from his June 28 letter that he wanted to dissuade Tugender from a course that Erickson believed unwise. Little indirection here! Yet Erickson substantiated his opinion and offered Tugender the opportunity to contact directly those who were adversely affected by Dr. M. In his private communications, Erickson was frank, and he did not hesitate to offer his opinion when it was solicited.

From: Henry S. Tugender
June 22, 1965

Dear Dr. Erickson:

Enclosed herewith is a tear sheet from "This Week" the national syndicated weekly included in selected newspapers. I have decided to send it to you since you may be interested in seeing how the lay press treats our favorite subject—hypnotism. Also, they have mentioned you near the end of the article. Perhaps you have seen this already . . .

I wrote a letter to Dr. M., who is the Director of Clinical Training at a university. I merely wrote to him complimenting him on a book review he had written in the *Journal of Clinical and Experimental Hypnosis* and in passing mentioned what had occurred. I was pleasantly surprised when he answered my letter and practically invited me to continue on at his university. I have since received an outline of the courses and hynotherapy is included, as well as operant conditioning, which was held so highly in esteem in Arizona. They also countenance Freud and other approaches. I like their eclecticism. I believe I will apply there. As is usual, I must have letters of recommendation. You wrote a "beaut" in relation to my position here and perhaps you may be inclined to write one again. I can forward to you the carbon copy of your last letter which you had sent to me to save you "creative" toil. I know that Dr. M. would be impressed mightily to receive a letter from you on my behalf.

How is the family? Fine, I hope. Give Mrs. Erickson and the children my best wishes and I hope that one of these days I can make another trip to Arizona and drop by and say "hello." I really became quite fond of the State of Arizona and in many ways it was with a great deal of sorrow when I couldn't return to school there. However, [this university] looks quite good—especially since they include hypnosis in the curriculum. We can readily ascertain Dr. M.'s interest—and influence therein.

Sincerely,
Henry S. Tugender

To: Henry S. Tugender
June 28, 1965

Dear Henry:

To write to you in full about Dr. M. and to recommend you to him is to run the serious risk of losing your friendship and gaining you an ardent friend in Dr. M.; or else making him your implacable enemy and causing you to wonder why I had ever been instrumental in wasting your time. Or, and this I doubt, seeing you become a convert and spouter of that kind of terminology that permits a baby to be described simply as a "reality apparatus indicative of the existential meeting of ego apparatuses in a struggle between the forces of the id and the superego resulting in the culmination of the basic psychodynamic compulsion of the thalassic return with consequent introjection and subsequent extrojection."

Now: Dr. M. started out as a perfectly wonderful chap. He became an excellent contributor to hypnosis and psychotherapy although he was naive in many ways and too trusting to be rigidly scientific. But he worked hard and was honest.

But ambition descended upon Dr. M. and he became convinced that an impressive vocabulary was the way to fame, scientific achievement, and leadership among men.

He soon discovered that this formula lacked an important element, namely, "political finesse," by which term is meant saying the pleasing expedient thing to everybody and disregarding any question of truth, merely dressing up statements so they resemble the truth; and hence, behind the barrier of resemblance to the truth, avoid being charged with falsification. As an example, do not say falsely, "The man did not get his medical degree." Instead, say sympathetically, "Isn't it too bad he never got the medical degree he so much desired." This is a true statement. The man desired to get his medical degree in the year X at University Y but the war interfered and he got his degree in the year W at University T. Omitting these last facts makes everybody sympathize with the poor joker for not having a medical degree. Dr. M. is an expert at this type of thing and he pulled the above on one of our Honorary Foreign Fellows with the result that the man was put to much trouble by the local medical society, proving that despite the unavailability of some of his records because of World War II, he really had a medical degree. Dr. M. was then engaged in a campaign to destroy the American Society of Clinical Hypnosis prestige abroad.

As the years have passed, Dr. M. has become smoother, cleverer, more skillful and you either become his ardent follower and believer or you don't wake up because there is a knife in your back.

He will tell you that I am a wonderful person. If you agree with him, you will get a marvelous recommendation a year later only to be turned down because of the horribly black record you have which he forgave you again and again, always hoping for the best. The reader of your letter of recommendation will admire Dr. M.'s patience and forbearance and willingness to believe in you, will read your record and then order the clean-up squad to rush you to the highway and to scrub up every spot you may have stepped on.

Everyone who has worked with Dr. M. has either become a duplicate Dr. M. or been thoroughly wrecked professionally if he dared to think independently.

Do you want a letter of recommendation? Dr. M. will gladly accept it but with the intention of re-educating you from any respect for me or for the purpose of destroying you.

That's the way it stands. Personally, I would take a job as a street cleaner rather than have Dr. M. on my staff.

Please let me hear from you. Oh yes, if you want to know others who have had unfortunate experience with Dr. M., I can furnish you with names; but most of them want to hide their scars.

Sincerely,
Milton H. Erickson, M. D.

Hypnosis—yes, Dr. M.'s kind of hypnosis—that's it, and that's all and I would reject any paper of original research he offered as unsound. But he can rewrite other men's ideas excellently.

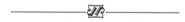

Gilles de la Tourette's syndrome (also called Tourette's disease) is mainly characterized by autonomous motor tics. Spasmodic movements, especially in the upper part of the body, range from eye blinking and grimacing to spontaneous squatting, skipping, jumping, and/or head banging. Vocal tics are also frequent: clicks, grunts, barks, yelps, coughing. In one-third to 60 percent of these cases, patients compulsively call out obscenities, the pathognomonic feature of the disorder.

The cause of Tourette's syndrome is as yet unknown. Central nervous system (CNS) dysfunction has long been suspected, but CNS abnormalities are found in only about half of those with the disorder. Contemporary treatment generally consists of a combination of an antipsychotic medication, such as haloperidol (as

in the case described), and psychotherapy. Prescribed medications, however, re-
quire constant monitoring, and they are not always effective. Symptoms of the
disorder wax and wane, making management all the more difficult.

Although this condition was first described by the French neurologist Gilles de
la Tourette in 1885, rational treatment has been slow in coming. Patients tradi-
tionally had been viewed as peculiarities, their symptoms commonly ascribed to
demonic possession or mental illness. Institutionalization or lives as social outcasts
had been the rule for sufferers of Tourette's. But by the late 1960s and early 1970s,
more attention was being focused on the psychiatric management of the syndrome.
The November 21, 1970, letter from Erickson to Florence Sharp describes his
tailored approach to its treatment. Erickson saw the patient, a young girl, for one
session and then referred her to Dr. Sharp, an esteemed colleague who practiced
psychology in California. (Sharp later collaborated with Ernest Rossi in publishing
Erickson's lectures.) The following background data on the girl (identified as R.G.)
were provided by her mother.

Erickson (1965b) had written an earlier paper describing the psychotherapy of
two adults with Tourette's syndrome. Both cases were reported as successes with
remission of symptoms. In the article, he also reported attempts to treat two
adolescents with Tourette's as being "utter failures." Evidently, Erickson referred
only to youths (as in the letter to Sharp) when he contended that he had treated
only one case successfully.

Data on R.G. provided by her mother

After seeing you in 1970, Dr. Carroll in Santa Barbara gave [R. G.] Hal-
dol; he does not have in his records the amount. As I remember, it was 2
pills at night and 1 in the morning.

Then he sent us to UCLA where she spent 7½ months. She came home
on weekends. They say her brain waves were normal and her chromo-
somes are normal. She did mind better. When she was discharged, they
told me to get her with her peers.

He had a friend living across the street from us who, through a divorce,
moved to Tucson, remarried and had 6 children. They asked us to send
the child to stay with them for a while. We thought this was wonderful
as she would be around other children. They enrolled her in school and

she started out in a special education class. [R.G.] was doing quite well and had been moved out of the special class into some regular classes.

She was in a Spanish class and the teacher said she was nervous and sometimes he let her sit up by him. He also said she had a natural talent for language and to keep her in it. Her home room teacher said she was doing well there, was very bright. He also said the whole family, 6 children and all, slapped her constantly for her swearing.

However, the people where she was staying decided to wash her mouth out with horse manure for swearing, and as they were going down to get the manure [R.G.] slapped the lady and the lady and the husband gave her quite a beating. Both eyes were black, her nose bled for several days and 2 teeth were cracked.

We came down and the school said she could continue going to school so we sold our home in Santa Barbara and moved to Tucson. When we got here, they took her out of that school and put her in High School in a special class.

This seemed to be the final rejection. She started slapping herself and beating on her ears until they bled. Then she did absolutely nothing in school. She didn't want to go to that school, but back where her friends were. She put socks on her hands so she couldn't slap herself or anyone else. Put a sweater half on so she couldn't slap.

Then she started yelling, "Fuck you, you God-damned neighbors." She goes out in the backyard and yells this at the top of her lungs.

The neighbors are filing suit to make us move. They say they can't sell their house and we are responsible for their loss.

[R.G.] did not do this until she got kicked out of school. This was in May of 1976.

If you can help her get rid of this, they will not go on with the suit. Or if you can state that this is Tourette's syndrome they will also stop suit.

We will try to get her into the National Institute of Health Clinical Center. We have to have Drs. write and recommend this. Dr. Shapiro will write also.

He, my husband and I, feel she got so much worse after her experience of living with these people and the beating, that this is in her mind and maybe she resents us for having sent her there. We paid them $100.00 plus per month for her staying there.

To: Florence A. Sharp
November 21, 1970

Dear Florence:

Perhaps you have already seen the child, but in any event, I am referring R. G. to you because I think you ought to be acquainted with this kind of a disorder. The parents have taken her to an unbelievable number of physicians, neurologists, psychiatrists, and psychologists, and have been given the runaround and were never once informed as to her diagnosis. In fact, nobody did diagnose the case. When they called me up from Santa Barbara and told me they had a behavior disorder in a 12-year-old child and wanted to bring her to me, I started to back off on the case. Fortunately, they said the problem centered around the child's swearing and using foul language, so I promptly gave them an appointment, fully expecting that nobody had recognized the condition. The child is suffering from Gilles de la Tourette syndrome. It began when she was about five years old and has resulted in a great deal of handicapping of the child in all of her learning. The poor girl has been spanked, beaten, whipped, and has undergone every conceivable variety of punishment and nobody has had any understanding of the condition. When I interviewed the child separately, she promptly tried me out to see how shocked or distressed I would be and she was really dumbfounded when I showed no adverse reaction. She tried me out a little bit more forcibly and was greatly horrified when I asked her how much it hurt her because of her inability not to say those words. That question enabled her to realize that I had some understanding of her own personal suffering.

To my knowledge, Leo Kanner and I have treated the condition successfully, each of us only once. In the last few years, there has been an interest in attempting to treat it with tranquilizers and to make some study of the condition as a legitimate field of inquiry. At this coming World Congress to be held in Mexico City in 1971 there was a desire to have a session on this condition but the Program plans bypassed any special session. There will, however, be some papers presented on this topic and it is hoped that some of those who deliver papers will get together privately to discuss their separate views. You can write to Dr. F. S. Abuzzahab, Sr., M.D., Ph.D., at the University of Minnesota, who is trying to organize a list of patients by initials and the names of the physicians interested in the condition.

I spent very little time with the girl but I did spend a lot of time with her parents, trying to give them an understanding of the pitiful lack of information about this condition and the need for a complete acceptance of anything and everything a patient does without any effort to correct any of the symptomatic manifestations. A patient simply can't help explosive, bad verbalizations, responses in foul language and the manifestation of any number of unusual and bizarre tics. This girl rocks on the floor, she messes her hair, she waves her hands and the poor kid doesn't want to do any of these things but has no control over them, knows that everybody expects her to exercise control and suffers from the knowledge that she is being offensive against her own wishes, even more than she is being objectionable to others.

In my handling of a similar case, the onset occurred when the boy was about seven or eight, and he had been abused thoroughly, but he did have a doting mother who took pride in teaching him a lot of things before the onset. This girl never had a chance to learn anything that might be useful to her. She has had very little schooling, schoolmates cannot tolerate her and too many teachers reacted as if the child were wronging them beyond any possible endurance and took vengeance on the child. Under California law the school board will furnish the child with a teacher. You will have to make the teacher understand that there has to be a complete acceptance of everything the child does; that there can be no mockery by attempting to show acceptance by using the same language or by imitating the movements. The teacher has to be her own normal self in every way and be completely receptive to everything about the child. In my handling of my patient I had to make certain that my patient did not think that my awkward movements were made as a sympathetic response to his movements. I had to let him know that I was helpless in my way even as he was helpless in his way. Once that point was clarified, I got along with my patient much better.

The usual course for these patients is to become more and more objectionable until they are finally committed to a state hospital where they are soon relegated to the back ward and allowed to deteriorate and they usually die after a few years of hospitalization and their symptomatic behavior also deteriorates into a muttering and groaning and an increasing decrease in activity. I encouraged my patient to do things, but I was very careful in the manner in which I encouraged him. I learned that his mother had taken pride in teaching her baby boy to cook and therefore I quite naturally "bragged" about my ability in cooking.

The boy didn't recognize this as encouragement for him but it really was. The boy's mother had taught him at an early age the importance of interior decorating and then helped him decorate the walls of his bedroom. I naturally reminisced about how I had decorated my room at home on the farm and my room as a student in college. In fact, there were so many things in my past that were in agreement with his past that I was able to establish a common ground of experience. My patient didn't need to know how much fiction there was about my past. I received my patient when he was fifteen years old. It took three years only to get him through the first year of high school and he just barely scraped through with the absolute minimum of credits.

If you accept this girl as a patient, you will have to make the parents understand that they are only hired help with no rights whatsoever and that they follow your orders absolutely. You will have to make the teacher understand that too. The girl does like pets, such as a dog or a rabbit, and she does like to grow things in the garden. She has an inordinate appetite for green bell peppers. If she wants to eat twelve at one sitting, give her the satisfaction of letting her think that she ate two more than you wanted her to. She has to have some rights in rebelling.

I had to let my patient be untidy. He soon discovered that having two fingers dirty was one more than I thought he should have; that if he had all of his fingers dirty, I thought he had just one too many fingers dirty. In other words, you set your expected limit just a little bit under the actual reality. It gives them a marvelous sense of freedom. Thus my patient could be awfully dirty with ten soiled fingers or awfully dirty with two soiled fingers but I never really scolded him. Thus I gave my patient a range of freedom so that he could have as much or as little as he wished, and no matter how little it was, he could have the feeling that I was just a little too prissy, and be comfortable himself. It was a long time before he caught on to this but by then he had established some good standards of his own and had amused himself at my expense.

I think there is eomthing physically wrong with the girl's motor coordination. I don't know whether it is a neurological defect or a learning defect, but whatever it is, there should be no effort made to correct it. The total acceptance of her condition—and let me assure you—will be a most educational experience for you. You will be able to apply these new learnings on your part to a lot of other children's behavior. I think there is some possibility that this girl can be carried through her teens and that in her twenties she can recover from this condition. I can't guarantee this but I know the girl will be a rich source of education for you.

It is most appalling to me to know that this patient was seen by psychiatrists, neurologists, pediatricians, psychologists, psychoanalysts, medically oriented people, paramedically oriented people, and none of them could recognize her condition and all I had to do was hear over the phone was "problem child, she swears" and I made the diagnosis.

I have told the parents that you might be able to accept the patient for therapy. I have also told them that you might be unable to accept her. I also told them that I couldn't take her as a patient and I didn't know of any other possibility of therapy for this patient.

In regard to tranquilizers, I am sending you a folder. This might be useful and you may have to have a physician write a prescription for you, but use it extremely cautiously, starting out with a minimal dose for the first week: That's just one dose, repeated the next week, and observe the effect. Then you might try a minimal dose twice a week for a couple of weeks and then, if it looks safe, try one dose every other day for a week. Withhold the drug and see if there is any reaction of any kind, positive or negative. This drug is the only one I would consider. I think it is perfectly safe to give a half milligram once a week although you might want to use just half of that. Caution is a very important thing.

I don't think you are going to run into trouble with the onset of menstruation. I may be mistaken. I made no inquiries in that regard, but in all other cases I have known, menstruation did not occur. Incidentally, this condition occurs more frequently in boys than in girls. If you take this girl as a patient, she will be a first for the record.

Please feel free to write to me at any time.

Sincerely yours,
Milton H. Erickson, M.D.

The description of Erickson's treatment in his letter to Florence Sharp exemplifies his method of assisting patients to make minimum strategic steps in desired directions. Here, as elsewhere, he demonstrated how these small changes formed links in the chain of therapeutic progress. Also evident is the manner in which Erickson maintained a respect for patients' independent strivings and allowed their needs and values to be expressed (in this case, by rebellion).

To: F. S. Abuzzahab, Sr.
May 13, 1972

Dear Dr. Abuzzahab:

I have just received your most recent reprint, "The Clinical Picture and Management of Gilles de la Tourette's Syndrome," and I think your International Registry will be a most valuable source of understanding in the study of this interesting and rather baffling disorder.

I am herewith sending you some information on an additional patient. Unfortunately, I was able to see this child only once and although I referred her parents to a psychologist nearer to their home since they came from out-of-state, to the best of my knowledge they did not follow up this referral. I will write to the psychologist today to find out if she saw the child since I sent her a long letter of description and advice for follow-up care. The child's initials are R.G. I did not get her exact date of birth, but since I saw her in mid-November of 1970 and she was at that time twelve years old, it was most probably in 1958. She is an only child. The problem had started at age five and although she seemed to be above average in intelligence, she had met with such misunderstandings of her condition that she had been greatly handicapped in her learning, and since age eleven had not attended school. Although she was a typical case of Tourette's syndrome with tics and compulsive hand movements and gesticulations, the problem had been centered about the child's "swearing and use of foul language" and none of the many physicians, neurologists, psychiatrists, and psychologists who had seen the child had recognized the diagnosis.

If the psychologist to whom I referred her has seen the child, I will request her to send you follow-up information.

Sincerely yours,
Milton H. Erickson, M.D.

On September 13, 1976, David M. Friedland, Ph.D., wrote to Erickson stating that he had read one of Erickson's induction techniques in an ASCH publication, and inquired about the rationale behind Erickson's method. He further indicated

*that he was interested in learning more about Erickson's work but was "having
some trouble really getting the feel of it." The following letter of October 19 was
Erickson's reply.*

The case of the 11-year-old enuretic is reported in slightly greater detail in A
Teaching Seminar with Milton H. Erickson *(ed. J. K. Zeig, 1980, pp. 79–84). In
his teaching, Erickson utilized the story as a training case, probing strategies the
students would employ in treating the girl. The case as described in the letter to
Friedland illustrates a number of important generic patterns in Erickson's work.
Note how he met the patient at her frame of reference and began with a challenge
that spurred her motivation. Subsequently, he segued into the discussion of unconscious processes.*

*During the discussion, Erickson built concepts slowly and experientially. He
did not lecture; rather, he provided the gul with reference experiences (examples
of unconscious functions) that stimulated both her understanding and her interests. The logic of Erickson's expostulation was impeccable. But it built slowly,
gaining momentum. By the time the suggestion for control of the symptom was
delivered, it was* fait accompli.

*Note that Erickson's method was not psychoeducational; he did not try to teach
the patient new skills. Instead, he stimulated learnings that already existed and
helped the patient to recombine those learnings in ways that led to therapeutic
change.*

*In a brief reply dated December 28, 1976, Friedland said that he now had a
"better feeling" for Erickson's rationale, and would use Erickson's method to a
much greater extent in the future.*

To: David M. Friedland
October 19, 1976

Dear Dr. Friedland:

I believe that each individual is unique and that in working with him,
my knowledge and potentials are secondary. The subject is primary in all
regards. What the patient or subject wants and can do he really doesn't
know or he would not be seeking help. I can guess, speculate, but I *know*
that I *don't know.*

Hence I establish an interpersonal relationship on a one-to-one basis.
Then I speak, using words that the patient interprets in terms of his own

experience and potentials. Now I will cite a case, and if you study it carefully, you will find that I placed all responsibility for the trance and therapy upon the patient.

An 11-year-old girl came to me with a history of a bladder infection that had persisted for many years, including multiple cystoscopies and the eventual loss of one kidney, a wet bed as soon as she relaxed in sleep, and wet clothes when awake and laughed or was startled. All the neighbors and the schoolchildren knew about it and her siblings called her "bad names." She had been "treated" by doctors, psychiatrists, psychologists, etc., all with no results despite prolonged efforts.

My therapy: "So you wet the bed! I don't know if you want to quit or not. All I know is that you think you want to because it's unpleasant and I think you want to be comfortable. But controlling your bladder is something that belongs to your unconscious mind or the back of your mind. It just happens the way your unconscious mind alternates your feet when you walk or tells you when you are thirsty and tells you without your knowing it how many swallows to take when you are thirsty. In fact, your unconscious mind knows a lot of things you don't know that you know.

"Well, I think that the carpet on the floor, the bookcases, the filing cabinets in this office are unimportant to you, that only your problem is important to you and the control belongs to your unconscious mind, so just look toward that paper weight and don't talk and don't move. You don't even have to listen to me because I am close enough to you that your unconscious mind or the back of your mind can hear and understand what I say. And while I have been talking, your breathing has slowed down, your rate is slower, your blood pressure has lowered and your muscle reflexes have changed, and maybe you will notice a very nice feeling of body comfort, and as you enjoy this, you might as well close your eyes since there really is nothing of interest to distract you from that ever-increasing body comfort. After you have enjoyed that body and mental comfort for some moments I'm going to ask a simple question and your unconscious mind will answer very simply so that I will understand. Now here is the question, 'If you were in the bathroom sitting down and urinating and a strange man poked his head through the door, what would you do?' "

She replied simply with a little body tension, "I'd freeze." I continued,

"That's right, you'd freeze and stop urinating and after he withdrew his head, your unconscious mind would relax your body and start urinating again. But you don't need a strange man looking into the bathroom to make you freeze up and stop urinating. You know how to start, how to stop, start again and stop again, thereby building up your control. And you will have a chance to practice several times a day, and if you forget to practice or are in too much of a hurry to practice, don't worry because once you begin practicing, your control, which never had a chance before, will start and keep on growing and your body will always remind you when you need more practice. Now don't expect a dry bed right away—it may take two weeks for the first one, but after the first one, then more and more often it will happen until you have full control. Of course, it would surprise me if you got a steady dry bed in the first three months but we can both be positive that you will have a regular dry bed within six months. Now enjoy your comfort a while and then you can leave."
END OF TREATMENT

Now if I had been a qualified orthodox psychoanalyst, I could have made a five-times-a-week three-year psychotherapeutic project out of that enuretic eleven-year-old girl. Instead I used one hour to elicit a trance without employing "hypnotic suggestions, instructions or commands." Rather, in a casual, gentle, nonpersuasive, completely confident, expectant voice, I mentioned, just mentioned, various items of lifelong experience. Then I mentioned a capacity for corrective handling of her problem which she had not thought of; gave her simple but not exaggerated hope, then tied that hope to an ever-continuing body function; mentioned the realities involved in recovery; named a highly motivational time limit to her, not easily recognized as such by her; expressed an attitude of absolute confidence concerning her that belonged to me and could not be disputed or doubted by her. Then I dismissed her in a state of comfort and certainty.

Within two weeks she brought me a braided octopus doll to commemorate her first dry bed, probably the first childish gift she had ever given without a shameful inner feeling that she was just a bedwetter.

Within six months she was staying overnight with friends and relatives, even making prolonged visits.

Now in her midteens, she is a well-adjusted girl with no more than memories of a past problem.

She writes to me at Christmastime giving all the news in very much the same fashion as my nieces.

I hope this letter satisfies your requests.

Sincerely,
Milton H. Erickson

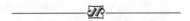

As did many of those who approached Erickson, Leonard Handler asked him about techniques. Clearly, Erickson deemphasized technique but rather, advised students to learn to understand the phenomenology of the patient. This would naturally lead to an appreciation of the evocative nature of subtle suggestions within patients' phenonmenological fields.

Both Erickson's letter and the case he cited point to the economy of his method. He didn't necessarily say profound things in therapy. But he made simple lines of communication come alive within patients by stimulating associational processes that held far-reaching impact.

In a way, Erickson's therapeutic artistry was similar to the work of artist Paul Klee, who painted in simple lines that produce a great impact on the observer. Erickson, like Klee, appreciated the complexity of effect that can emerge from a simplicity of method.

The reprint to which Erickson refers in his letter is "A Field Investigation by Hypnosis of Sound Loci Importance in Human Behavior" (Erickson, 1973). In the case of Fran (pp. 100–105 of the article), Erickson achieved pain control in a "bossy, stubborn, constantly watchful and disputatious" (p. 101) patient through a highly indirect technique involving the removal of guilt. The case exemplifies the efficacy of utilizing patients' motivations and frames of reference to accomplish therapeutic goals through indirection.

To: Leonard Handler, Ph.D.
January 31, 1974

Dear Dr. Handler:

In reply to your letter of January 11, I can offer you only general statements. I have been in a wheelchair since 1965 and have definitely limited my practice. I do see a few patients that are sufficiently interesting and do not require prolonged treatment. My extra energy is taken up at the present time in collaboration with Ernie Rossi, Ph.D., on a two- or three-volume work.

For you to come out to Phoenix might be very satisfying, providing you are willing to cope with the irregularities of my energy output.

Perhaps I can answer your questions in general by giving you this illustration. Most people using hypnosis look upon it as a method of communicating suggestions to a subject and they too often give direct suggestions telling the subject what to do. In my use of hypnosis I do not resort to that sort of suggestion. The operator is the one who indicates that he wants something done and this is to be done by the subject. Furthermore it must be understood that the operator should operate in terms of the subject's frame of reference. To illustrate this much better, a young farmer remarks, "This is a beautiful day." It is because he going on a picnic with his fiancee. On another day the same young farmer can say, "This is a beautiful day," and what he means is the sun is shining, no clouds in the sky, the hay is just right for mowing, and his frame of reference is not himself, his frame of reference is his own personal relationships to his personal obligations. The same farmer can on another occasion say, "This is a beautiful day," and really mean it because the sky is covered with dark clouds, there is a smell of rain in the air, a haze in the barn, and there has been no rain for six weeks. He is using a frame of reference that involves not only himself, his own immediate relationships, but a frame of reference that includes the rest of the world.

One uses words to communicate but if you look at the literature, you realize that the individual relationships between words can convey a special meaning. I learned from Frank Bacon's becoming a star overnight by his stage appearance in a play. He had only one word to say. He came out on the stage and said, "No." I counted the way in which he said "No." There were sixteen different meanings to that word. I attended that play the next night and counted the same sixteen ways in which meanings, commands, entreaties, admonitions, rebukes can be expressed all in the same words. You can address a group and include the entire group if you say, "You come and [pause] you come and you come and (pause) you can join me." It separates the last "you" from the other wonds in a distinctive fashion.

I am including a reprint illustrating how I intentionally got results without any mention of any kind that indicated such results were wanted. In the case of Frank, I merely wanted to illustrate an indirect technique that actually produced a specific memory recovery, and a final therapeutic result.

If you are not acquainted with Jay Haley's books, *Strategies of Psychotherapy*, published by Grune & Stratton, 1963; *Advanced Techniques of Hypnosis and Therapy: Selected Papers of Milton H. Erickson, M.D.*, published by Grune & Stratton, 1967; and *Uncommon Therapy: The Psychiatric Techniques of Milton H. Erickson, M.D.*, published by W. W. Norton and Co., Inc., 1973, you might like to order them.

One additional comment I can make regarding the second paragraph of your letter is this: A patient or subject comes to you and expects to do something. It really doesn't make much difference what you say to them if they, in their own minds, have some clear idea of what they want to do and they ascribe to you some mystical ability. For example: I saw a patient today who wanted some preparation to prevent pain of a dental operation tomorrow. She suffered from arthritis, and two automobile accidents previously and dental surgery previously, and she did not relish the idea of going to the dentist again. I told her an interesting story about my daughter on her vacation that had no connection with pain but rather was a very happy account, and at the end of it while she was still laughing, I remarked, "You enjoyed that story, you can enjoy being without pain, your unconscious knows that," and a trance developed immediately, but then her entire purpose in coming to me was to go into a trance, and perhaps while I was talking about my daughter she was unconsciously saying, "Let's get down to work and get me into a trance." That is usually the effect of an interspersal technique.

I am sorry to be so discursive. Write me again if you wish.

Sincerely yours,
Milton H. Erickson, M.D.

To: Ralph W. August,
March 8

Dear Doctor August:

The hand levitation technique was used extensively by me in 1930 at the Worcester State Hospital in experimental work and lectures given there to the staff and to the staff at the Rhode Island State Hospital for Nervous and Mental Diseases.

I do not know in which of my early publications I first mentioned it, if indeed I did. I had also first used it in my premedic days at the University of Wisconsin during experimental work there in 1923 and 1924. The confusion technique was also worked out at about this same time and progressively modified, but never published in explanatory detail until in our Journal, July 1959, Example 16.*

Hope this meets your needs. In fact, I hope you summarize this information as a footnote.

Sincerely yours,
Milton H. Erickson, M.D.

*I recall now there was an earlier reference to the confusion technique in my article in LeCron's *Experimental Hypnosis*. M. H. E.

From Other Professions

Dentistry

To: Irving I. Secter,
November 5, 1954

Dear Dr. Secter:

I am utterly delighted with that letter that you wrote me. In fact, I am returning it to you, so that you can read it again. Perhaps after reading this far in my letter, you would like to put it aside and read your letter, to see if you can understand it. If you do not succeed, then you can read further in this letter and find out what it was you did so excellently.

As for the automatic writing that you sent me, I was much intrigued by it. You have done both right side up, and upside down and backwards writing. In other words, you are decidedly competent in automatic writing and you need now only practice in the matter of the actual recording of ideas and thoughts.

Incidentally, I should arrive in Chicago on the evening of November 14. Dr. Hirshman, who was at the seminar, wants me to see a number of his patients and I hope that I will have an opportunity to see you then. Therefore, I am suggesting that you keep this letter and return it to me at that time.

As for my notes on the trance I induced in you, if you will read the first sentence of your letter, you will note that it is rather incomplete. And it properly should be. You had to write that letter to me on the 26th of the month. No other day would have been suitable. It could have been October 26, or November 26, or December 26, but it nevertheless had to be the 26th. Furthermore, my notes state that you had to use the word "perform." You will note the use of this word in the second paragraph of your letter. You will also observe that this part of the letter is not written in your usual script. It is a transitional script from your ordinary handwriting to the script that follows on line 4 of that paragraph, where the spacing of the words is re- markable and the actual letter formation is most outstanding. Line 5, which begins "a complete amnesia . . ." is most emphatically written, with special spacing. Note the diminishing script in the terminal two words of that sen- tence ". . . the act." Again your handwriting changed, with particular em- phasis upon "you said." In other words, a posthypnotic suggestion given to you to carry out was to write a letter on the 26th, in which you would use the word "perform" and in which you would express a complete amnesia and, at the same time, would be so carried out that I would recognize the posthypnotic act. I think you will enjoy contrasting your script here and there throughout the letter and how remarkably it changes and not in rela- tion to the interruption by the patient.

Concerning the diagrams, you will note that you drew a line, putting half of each line above and half below the line. Isn't that really what you did in writing your letter? However, we can discuss this in Chicago.

Sincerely,
Milton H. Erickson, M.D.

———————— 𝒥𝓇 ————————

Irving Secter's account of his first meeting with Erickson appears in Ericksonian Psychotherapy, Vol. 1: Structures *(Zeig, 1985, pp. 605–615). This chapter and Erickson's reply were previously published in that book.*

My first opportunity to meet Milton Erickson was in August 1954. He was teaching at a workshop I attended in Chicago. By this time I was already using hypnosis clinically and sharing my experiences with others in a variety of teaching situations. While successful in helping others to develop hypnotic states, I was disappointed that, subjectively, I had never experienced the state myself. I discussed this with Milton and requested that he put me in a trance.

Milton received many requests for personal instructions during workshops. One of Milton's ploys was to defer responding to these requests until only five or ten minutes remained. Then it became a situation of, "If you really want to learn, you had better do it quickly." In my case, a whole hour still remained when Milton came to me and asked, "Was there something you wanted from me?"

What transpired is condensed in the following correspondence. The content of the automatic writing reads:

"Write me something you did posthypnotically." The "write me" is discernible when the paper is turned upside down and read from left to right.

"Something did" can be seen on the second line when the paper is held right side up. There is a pronounced "h" in thing and special "P" where the "g" should be. These of course represent the word "posthypnotically."

Note that the automatic writing was done on September 25, 1954, between 4:40 p.m. and 4:45 p.m. My letter to Milton was written on October 26, 1954.

I still enjoy reading and rereading the letters.

My meeting with Erickson led to our association, which endured for more than a quarter of a century. We taught in more than 100 seminars and workshops. At the same time, I learned from him. He contributed to my progress in both areas. We worked together for the advancement of the American Society of Clinical Hypnosis.

Milton guided research that I conducted, and as a result, he published several of my papers. All of my current clinical interactions are influenced by what he taught me.

I have already described a significant portion of this period in a chapter entitled "Seminars with Erickson: The Early Years" (Zeig, 1982). This present chapter is really a companion piece to the earlier publication. Those whose interest and curiosity have been piqued by this chapter are referred to "The Early Years" (pp. 605–606).

Podiatry

From: K. P. Hardy
December 23, 1959

Dear Dr. Erickson:

Two years ago, I attended your seminar on hypnosis in Seattle, sponsored by the California College of Chiropody.* Since that time I have been using hypnosis in my practice mainly for the alleviation of pain and apprehension and have found it a valuable adjunct.

I have been under criticism by some of my colleagues for certain actions and would appreciate your opinion and advice.

The case in point: a 14-year-old female with multiple verucae [warts; in this case, plantar's warts]. I used injection technique, and after one month, the prognosis was still in doubt. At that time I decided to test for suggestibility in case further injections would be necessary at a later date. I performed a few standard suggestibility tests, and for some reason or other, all were negative and absolutely no response was visible or indicated.

It is accepted by all concerned that the child was never under hypnosis and actively resisted all suggestions.

While admitting the above, some of my colleagues feel that such tests,

---

*At the time, chiropody referred to the treatment of foot ailments. Modern practianers are called podiatists.

regardless of response, constitute using hypnosis and that the following precautions are mandatory:

1. Obtaining parental sanction.
2. Having a third person in the treatment room at all times.

(The above precautions I failed to comply with in this case.)

I feel such precautions are in theory sound, but in practice very difficult, especially when:

a) There is some doubt that further treatment will be necessary.
b) The patient may not be a good subject.
c) There are difficulties such disclosures would present in obtaining true evaluation of suggestibility.

I would appreciate your opinion on:

a) My actions as outlined above.
b) The precautions necessary in general when testing for suggestiblity and when hypnosis is actually contemplated.
c) Whether tests for suggestibility with no response constitute a form of hypnosis.

I wish to thank you most sincerely for your cooperation in this matter.

Sincerely yours,
K. P. Hardy, D.S.C.

To: K. P. Hardy
December 31, 1959

Dear Doctor Hardy:
Speaking as a physician and as a psychiatrist with long and extensive experience in hypnosis, I can offer the following replies to your questions.
1. Obtaining parental sanction for hypnosis is no more warranted than is obtaining parental sanction for any other procedure that in no way

transforms the patient as does a surgical operation. Quite properly a patient comes for expert treatment, not for the decision of what the treatment shall be. They may accept or refuse, but they should not have the privilege of "sanctioning" what gauge needle, what particular treatment, or what maneuver shall be used. They do not understand the problem, nor can it be adequately explained to them.

I know of nobody except the unduly cautious and timid physician and dentist who request parental sanction for hypnosis. Such requests alarm parents who do not understand and thus patients are deprived of benefits.

2. Having a third person present at all times is an old, old demand, but even the Catholic Church no longer demands that for the use of hypnosis. There was once the demand that a chaperon be present at childbirth, but this whole matter of chaperonage of professional treatment of patients is fortunately dying out. Without a third person present, one runs the risk of malicious or uniformed persons gossiping or maladjusted patients making ridiculous charges, but actually any new developments in the healing arts lead to such statements. The widespread use of tranquilizers brought me tales of a ridiculous character, suggesting that the office administration of a tranquilizer should be done in the presence of a chaperon.

In general, I see no need for a third party being present and such is the understanding of physicians and dentists in general. Obstetricians, urologists and gynecologists are in a special category in their relationship, not because they use hypnosis but because of the intimate character of their work.

3. As to the question of a test for hypnosis constituting hypnosis, I doubt if a negative test for urinary sugar constitutes diabetes mellitus. Nor does a negative test for heart disease warrant a diagnosis of heart disease. Also, an attempt to measure a patient's blood pressure and the patient's successful resistance of the test do not constitute a taking of the blood pressure.

As for tests of suggestibility and of hypnosis, I never really use them, except so indirectly that the patient never knows about it. The reason is that I do not wish to give the patient any doubts about his capabilities.

Finally, medical and dental malpractice insurance companies do not require a third person present—such "chaperonage" often prevents or inhibits the patient from responding.

I hope you have no further difficulty.

Sincerely yours,
Milton H. Erickson, M.D.

———————— 𝕁𝕃 ————————

Erickson's response regarding tests of suggestibility, item 3, is consistent with his indirect approach to hypnosis. Erickson believed that almost anyone could profit from hypnosis. That he would assess hypnotic responsiveness covertly reflects the care he took to maintain a favorable set for accomplishment in his patients.

Susceptibility tests were developed by researchers from the traditional school of hypnosis. The theory that underlies such tests holds that hypnotizability is a trait or a skill. Some people possess it, some don't. Further, proponents believe that the extent to which a person possesses hypnotizability can be measured, in much the same way as we measure how fast a person can run a mile. Susceptibility tests contain a series of suggestions to ascertain whether or not subjects can achieve various hypnotic phenomena (e.g., hallucination, catalepsy, amnesia). A score indicating a subject's level of hypnotizability is derived after the test suggestions are administered and responses tabulated.

Susceptibility tests are routinely used in hypnosis research, although their clinical utility is repeatedly questioned. The three forms (A, B, and C) of the Stanford Hypnotic Susceptibility Scales (SHSS) (Weitzenhoffer & Hilgard, 1959, 1962) are the most widely used tests in contemporary research.

Erickson corresponded with several podiatrists through the years, consulting on cases and offering education about potential uses of hypnosis in podiatric practice. He also presented to podiatric groups regarding hypnotic and psychiatric matters, and was much admired in those circles.

From: Jack T. Sanders
May 3, 1960

Dear Dr. Erickson:

It is my pleasure to inform you that the First House of Delegates has elected you first Honorary Fellow of The American Academy of Psychosomatic Podiatry. Your membership certificate will be forwarded to you within a short time, but it would have been a great honor to have been able to present it to you personally. You are, in a large way, responsible for the formation of the Academy, and we hope that within the near future you may become a more intimate part of our programs. Your past help and advice have been most helpful . . .

Sincerely,
Jack T. Sanders, D.S.C.

To: Jack T. Sanders
May 12, 1960

Dear Doctor Sanders:
    Thank you very much for the notice that I have been elected the first Honorary Fellow of the American Academy of Psychosomatic Podiatry. I am very certain that the organization of your chapter will contribute significantly to the further development of podiatry . . .

Sincerely yours,
Milton H. Erickson, M.D.

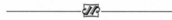

Podiatrists were not accepted as national members of the American Society of Clinical Hypnosis during the early years of the association. Nonetheless, Erickson was supportive of individual podiatrists who communicated with him in his advancement of the sound practice of hypnosis, and a plaque of appreciation from a podiatry association hung on a wall in his office.

From: Wendell B. Reynolds
October 17, 1970

Dear Dr. Erickson:
    For the last seven or eight years I have been a member of the local chapter of the American Society of Clinical Hypnosis. During my membership I have taken several organized courses representing elementary and advanced work in hypnosis. I have utilized many of these techniques in my own practice on both a clinical and an experimental basis. I have

attended several of the lectures given by you in California and have en-joyed listening to Dr. David Cheek.

Not until very recently had I noticed the basic teachings you have at-tempted to divulge to the serious students of hypnosis. One day, while drudging through your text, *Advanced Techniques in Hypnosis and Therapy*, I felt that I found the common thread in the material being presented. After repeated readings, I found many and varied common threads. I am currently engaged in reviewing your writings in the *American Journal of Clinical Hypnosis*, readings which now appear as though I had never read them before. My collection of these journals is dis-appointingly incomplete.

I look forward to again exploring the contents of your text, *Time Distortion in Hypnosis*, and I will again review your commentaries through-out the text *Clinical and Experimental Hypnosis*. I have played and replayed the three lectures of yours that I had the good fortune to record personally, until they are as familiar to me as fine music.

However, these teachings seem painfully incomplete. I am in hope that you can tell me where I can find other tape recordings to supplement those which I now have.

Do you by chance have a list of all of your publications. Do you still lecture from time to time, and if so, would it be possible for me to be a member of the audience? I am currently in correspondence with Dr. Florence Sharp, as I remember that she, at one time, attempted to compile some of your tapes.

I would greatly appreciate any assistance you may give me in my at-tempt to study your teachings in detail.

Very sincerely yours,
Wendell B. Reynolds, D. P. M.

To: Wendell B. Reynolds:
October 24, 1970

Dear Dr. Reynolds:

I am very delighted with your letter, and to know that I had some success in my effort at teaching. I assure you that trying to teach hypnosis is a very difficult thing and I do not blame you for saying, "While drudging through your text," because I assure you that I drudged even more slowly and with much greater difficulty in trying to make it apparent that the essential thing in hypnosis is the communication of ideas on both verbal and nonverbal levels and in a greater variety of ways, direct and indirect. It is one thing to tell a child to go to bed at 8:00 and an entirely different thing to ask the child, "When do you want to go to bed, at a quarter to 8 or at 8:00?" The child gets your message of going to bed at 8 o'clock, but when you ask the child, he thinks he is making the choice.

There is a common saying that any normal six-month-old baby can outsmart his parents, and being the father of eight, I know that is true. Any six-month-old child sees the expression on the mother's face that means, "How on earth can anybody swallow such slop as I am feeding my child?" and the baby reads the expression completely and spits the "slop" out. A mother doesn't know how well the child reads her face. In fact, she doesn't even know that the child can read her face. In hypnosis we want to communicate ideas and understandings, and all ideas and understandings involve a multiplicity of meanings variously coordinated, variously arranged and having many significances.

In Shakespeare one can read the word "fast." A horse can be fast on the race track. He can be fast when tied to a post. A horse can be fast in comparison with a snail. A man or woman can be fast by misbehaving. A person can fast and lose weight. There are innumerable meanings for the word "fast," caused by the tone in which the word "fast" is said, the situation in which the word "fast" is said, etc.

Florence Sharp is the best source of information concerning tapes of my lectures. Personally, I cannot stand to listen to my tapes nor can I endure reading transcripts. I often write a paper, carefully revise it as many as twenty times to make certain that I have put forth my meaning, and once the paper is in print, I hate to read it again. My wife does occasionally ask me to read some paragraphs without telling me their source and I have a son who takes particular pleasure in doing it and more than once I have been fascinated by discovering that somebody really knew what he was writing about, after reading the paragraphs, only to be embarrassed by being informed that I was the author. The book by Shor and Orne, *Selected Readings in Hypnosis*, and Jay Haley's book on *Strategies of Psychotherapy* might be of use to you.

Under separate cover I am sending you some reprints that are not listed in the bibliography of *Advanced Techniques in Hypnosis and Therapy*, which is in the back of the book.

I shall be delighted to hear from you again.

Sincerely yours,
Milton H. Erickson, M. D.

Editor's Note: Jeffrey Zeig once listened to the tape of a lecture by Erickson and asked him if he ever listened to his own lectures. Erickson replied that he did not, stating, "I didn't teach content, for the most part. I taught to motivate [people to learn]."

Erickson placed great importance on allowing people choice and he conveyed this in his language in the first paragraph of his October 24, 1970, reply to Wendell Reynolds. An insignificant facet of the language of influence that is used in hypnosis and psychotherapy is conveying this matter of choice. In turn, the recipient of the communication is allowed to decide the form of the response. Imbedded within this type of communication, though, is the presupposition of compliance. As Erickson pointed out, compliance can be gained while the recipient retains a sense of control.

In the second paragraph of the letter, Erickson underscored the influence that nonverbal messages can have, even those unrecognized by the sender. This is probably in response to Reynolds' statement that the teachings of which he availed himself (lectures, reading, recordings) "seem painfully incomplete." Erickson always insisted that the skillful application of hypnosis involves a complex of linguistic, paraverbal, and interpersonal components. Perhaps he was drawing Reynolds' attention to an area (nonverbal influence) that he sensed Reynolds could bolster to feel more complete in his appreciation of hypnosis.

The third paragraph is somewhat of a non sequitur. Although Erickson on many occasions discussed the multiple meanings of individual words (see, for example, A Teaching Seminar with Milton H. Erickson M. D. *[Zeig, 1980, pp. 173– 174], in which Erickson similarly illustrated "run"), it is likely that he purposely chose the word "fast" here. Perhaps this is an indirect communication to Reyn-*

olds, who seemed to have a tendency to enhance and press, to want to go fast in establishing a connection. Erickson almost certainly knew that Reynolds would read his letter many times; after all, he was attempting to study Erickson's teachings "in detail."

Overall, indirection is the theme that Erickson put forth in this letter. In this and ensuing correspondence with Reynolds, he accentuated variety in hypnotic communication. This was in counterpoint to prevailing trends in hypnosis in the 1960s and 1970s, which were to intensify efforts toward standardization and ritualism. Erickson sought to maintain an individuality of approach and to contravene the homogenization of hypnosis.

From: Wendell B. Reynolds
November 10, 1970

Dear Dr. Erickson:

I was extremely pleased to receive your correspondence of October 24, 1970. I had wondered if I would receive any response at all, and had hoped at best to obtain a bibliography of your publications. Receiving actual correspondence from you was most gratifying.

My work is primarily surgery of the human foot. Over the past fifteen to twenty years, the surgical techniques have been revised and improved until we have a great deal to offer our patients. However, we have one severe stumbling block that diminishes the number of persons willing to accept our help and severely frustrates both the patient and the doctor once surgery has been performed. We find that postoperatively our patients have an inordinate amount of swelling and discomfort requiring a protracted recovery period. Our patients are delighted with the idea of being rid of the annoying discomfort of foot pathology preoperatively, and once recovery is complete, they are equally pleased with the surgical result. However, because the patients are not ill, as they might be during a gallbladder attack, and because they are not disabled, other than the inconvenience of a swollen foot that will not accept the pressure of their ordinary shoes, our patients become extremely impatient, irritable, and demanding shortly after their surgical correction. An equivalent amount of surgery performed on the upper extremity seldom produces this protracted recovery phase because it is not traumatized during ambulation, and it is not held in a dependent position.

However, not all of our patients have this problem. On occasion we find the patient who has no swelling and no discomfort and is able to wear ordinary shoes in a very short period of time. It was those with unusually rapid recovery after foot surgery that made me curious. This curiosity was nurtured by my exposure to hypnosis while in the armed services during the middle forties, and by Dr. Cheek's description of persons in the Orient who, during religious rites, insert needles and knives into their bodies without untoward response, and Esdale's experience before the days of asepsis. It has been my personal observation that patients who suffer little disability postoperatively appear to be persons with little concern for their recent surgery, calm well-balanced personalities, with little anxiety, little apprehension, and little hostility.

It was my hope to find some means of bringing to my "average patient" the opportunity to recover from surgery in a manner similar to those persons having a short recovery. I found that conventional hypnosis, with the usual ritualistic induction and direct overt suggestions of diminished pain and rapid recovery, to be moderately useful. However, the results were not as gratifying to the patient as I had hoped, and frequently the patient rejected this type of assistance. At the hospitals I was cirticized severely for my deviation from "scientific orientation." Most of the courses I have taken and the lectures I have attended have been of little assistance in helping me to circumvent my patients' resistance to the occult and my own lack of acumen in satisfying their needs.

I was indeed "drudging" through your text in an effort to find some clue as to how I might convert the patient with a protracted postoperative recovery into one of rapid and uncomplicated rehabilitation, although perhaps "sifting" would be a better description. While exploring your confusion techniques for perhaps the second or third time, it occurred to me actually that all induction is a confusion technique. It would appear to me that all patients are brought to the point of hesitant wondering what comes next, a moment of partial disorientation, before they alter their state of awareness in an attempt to pay closer attention. If this state of arrested attention and cooperative expectation is indeed the common denominator for trance induction, then the traditional ritualistic approach is unnecessary and the patient's objection to the occult might be circumvented.

Today, while again reading your article in the January 1966 *American Journal of Clinical Hypnosis* concerning the use of the interspursal technique, wherein you discuss the germination and growth of a tomato plant with a patient suffering from terminal cancer, I again must wonder if I might not be able to develop sufficient understanding of the use of hypnosis in an unobtrusive way to assist my patients in recovery from surgery more in keeping with their expectations.

I am certain that you would be able to accomplish these things for my patients, and I most sincerely wish to learn to do these things myself. I will read the books that you recommended, however, I feel that other persons have failed to recognize what you understand so well. In that my work is not as complex as yours, I am in hopes that if I can come to understand even partly some of your teachings, I will perhaps be able to give to all of my patients the rapid and painless recovery that so few of them enjoy presently.

Again, I appreciate very much your correspondence and your recommendation for further readings, and I would be most appreciative of an opportunity to again hear you lecture.

Cordially yours,
Wendell B. Reynolds, D.P.M.

To: Wendell B. Reynolds,
November 21, 1970

Dear Dr. Reynolds:

Your appraisal of hypnotic techniques having in common certain basic factors resulting in "arrested attention and cooperative expectation" is entirely correct. The timeworn ritualistic verbigeration and assumption that the operator or hypnotist actually plays an active part in inducing a trance is also equally false. The operator merely plays a passive role, offering a variety of instructions from which the subject makes his own selection.

Of course, one can wear down the subject (and one's self) by a prolonged utterance of ritualistic verbigeration and bring about a trance state but the subject is left somewhat confused regarding the extent and importance of his responsibility and participation.

These miscomprehensions leave much to be achieved.

Further compounding the difficulties in the use of hypnosis is the assumption that hypnosis can be used to work miracles. To explain, the patient does not want pain or discomfort. The physician does not want the patient to have pain or discomfort. Overlooked by both is the fact that Utopia exists only in the world of wishful thinking. What should be realized by both the patient and the therapist is that it is imperative that some pain and discomfort be retained for absolutely essential protective purposes.

At the present time I am having trouble teaching a Ph.D. candidate with a hereditary neurological disease that numbness is a serious hazard to life and limb. He is a bright boy but his stupidity in this regard is appalling.

With your patients, the problem is to teach them to be sure to retain enough pain and discomfort to enable them to protect fully and happily the surgical gains you have given them. Furthermore, they need to retain enough capacity for pain and discomfort in order to discover the fullest possible use of their repaired foot so that they can discover the areas of disuse, inadequate use and unlearned use so that they can more efficiently achieve full use of the repaired extremity.

In other words, rather than to remove pain, the patient should be thoroughly impressed with the importance of retaining an adequate amount of pain. When you have achieved this, you casually present the idea that, of course, excessive pain, excessive discomfort can readily dispensed with, unless there is a desire to prolong the hardship of being disabled, which does have some false advantage.

I am explaining this entire matter with crude clarity. You present this to the patient with very gentle subtlety. Reorienting the patient from not wanting pain to being concerned about having enough pain has the effect of making it difficult to keep pain. One can have a very great sufficiency with only the slightest trace. All emphasis is placed upon the insurance of securing all the good benefits.

Patients can afford to worry about not having enough pain and the competent operator is always able to verify the smallest trace as an overly large sufficiency and start to worry that it may not last long enough, then to define the longest necessary time in very brief terms, and then to worry that it will not recur sufficiently strong to enable the right brief reflex adjustment, and so on and on.

Words, inflections, pauses, uncertainties are marvelous tools to influence experiential behavior.

Write to me again freely whenever you wish.

Sincerely,
Milton H. Erickson, M.D.

Erickson's first letter (October 24, 1970) to Wendell Reynolds was a mosaic, covering a variety of topics with shifts between a didactic style and an anecdotal tone. The second letter, that of November 21, was more linear and to the point. (As Erickson stated, "I am explaining this entire matter with crude clarity.") On the topic of pain, Erickson wrote from vast personal experience. He suffered chronic pain and learned techniques to manage it and still lead an astonishingly active life. Here, Erickson introduced Reynolds to the approach of guiding the patient's thinking and then providing an unexpected twist; for example, "How much is the right amount of pain for you to have?" The patient, as Erickson stated, is thus occupied with thoughts of retaining rather than discarding pain. (Erickson wrote comprehensively on pain; an entire section of Volume IV, Innovative Hypnotherapy, of The Collected Papers *[Erickson & Rossi, 1980] is devoted to the topic.) Erickson concluded his second letter with a single sentence that repeats the theme of his initial reply to Reynolds: the use of words, inflections, and so on to influence experiential behavior.*

From: Wendell B. Reynolds
May 4, 1971

Dear Dr. Erickson:

In previous correspondence, you have indicated that I might "write freely." I would like to continue to do that if I may. I have recently been grappling with an emotional trauma of my own which has made other persons' problems seem remote. I would like to try to get back to work.

It seems unbelievable that our last correspondence could have been as long ago as November 21, 1970. You will perhaps remember that perhaps the greatest frustration in foot surgery is that the patient considers all operations done on the foot as extremely minor, and assumes that these will heal in an unrealistically short time. Actually, the opposite is true in most cases. Among other reasons, [this happens] because the surgical area is continually being traumatized during ambulation. However, I have noted that with some persons, the inordinate swelling and diminished function noted in so many cases are absent. These persons who escape the generally prolonged recovery time, are persons that, to these unskilled eyes, appear to be exceptionally well-balanced personalities. Generally, they accept the surgical experience without undo anxiety, and leave the process of repair to automatic healing processes while they busy themselves with their daily tasks. I have also noted that the person who undergoes an inordinate recovery period appears to be the anxious, insecure personality who worries and frets about each little sensation and observes, in minute detail, each change that occurs so remarkably slowly during the recovery period.

Because the personality type appears to modify the actual physiological recovery process, and after hearing remarks concerning the work done by Esdale so many years ago, and the observations of Cheek during his early years in China, where persons engaged in self-mutilating processes without penalty, and compounded by the description in your literature concerning the school athlete who virtually bit off his tongue, and recovered without medical attention, I became curious not as to the possibility of performing miracles through hypnosis, but more as to what the patient's emotional tone and basic personality type have to do with the physiology of recovery, and how the better portions of that personality might be emphasized by hypnotic or any other facility that might be instituted by the therapist. This then is my problem: What do the patient's emotional tone and basic personality type have to do with recovery from surgery? How might a better understanding of the personality attached to the surgical area facilitate that person's recovery from surgery? And, of course, equally involved with these curiosities is assuming that benefits involved with these curiosities are to be derived for the patient, and so can I train myself to offer these benefits?

Your last correspondence suggesting that rather than trying to avoid pain, the patient should be encouraged in the knowledge that some pain is desirable and necessary, and converting their attention to retaining sufficient pain for a sufficient length of time is most encouraging. Your remarkable ability to take the patient's objections and utilize them for their benefit is always fascinating. I think that certainly most therapists are over-ly anxious to do what the patient wants rather than what the patient needs.

I don't really know where to start, or if I should start to facilitate my patients' recovery with other than the standard medications "out of a bottle." However, in my readings of your published materials, it has re-peatedly occurred to me that if I had the facility to influence persons as you have, I could surely benefit these people. Inertia is, of course, a sub-stantial force to overcome, and in my efforts to surmount this obstacle, I am currently listening to multiple tapes of your lectures borrowed from Dr. Florence Sharp. Repeatedly your remarkable subtle approach, virtually a conversation with the patient, circumvents the patient's resistance to the occult, and diminishes the hospital's objection to an atypical technique. Time spent with the patient appears to be entirely productive, diminishing the unrelated, and diminishing or eliminating the time-consuming process of subduing the patient.

This note has been, of necessity, somewhat rambling, because my thoughts are somewhat rambling at this point. I am asking myself if I can improve the care of my patients, if the benefits would be worth the effort, and if, in fact, benefits are available. I would greatly appreciate your com-ments and guidance.

Wendell Reynolds D.P.M

To Wendell B. Reynolds
May 15, 1971

Dear Dr. Reynolds:
One of the most important things in dealing with surgical patients is the matter of assuring them that they will have pain because they are willing to believe it. All their lives, experience has taught them that pain is a necessary part of their lives. When you assure them of pain, they are willing to believe you; then you can progress to the matter of how much pain, how long it should last, and you can educate them extensively. The final step is to caution them that they should keep a minimal amount of pain to serve only as a warning to prevent them from placing unnecessary stress on the site of the operation.

In dealing with a cancer patient who was unresponsive to narcotics and who suffered extreme pain, I was very careful, after inducing hypnosis, to start removing pain by having her develop only a numbness of the dorsum of the foot. It was obvious to her that I was disappointed that she did not develop an unbearable itch of the sole of her foot, however, I graciously accepted the numbness of the dorsum of the foot and then proceeded to run the numbness up her leg and across the pelvis and down the other leg. Then I extended the numbness up her sides to her shoulders and down her arms. Then I produced numbness in her back and numbness of her left side. With all the numbness I then placed comfort in its place and I apologized to her for my inability to produce comfort in the area of the mastectomy on the right side. In fact, I left her with a most annoying mosquito bite itch at the site of the operation but freed her of all cancer pain. I had to leave that woman with some distress at the site of the operation because nothing is perfect in this world. I improved her appetite and later on I had to remove some stomach pain by giving her a definite hunger that was easily satisfied by a small amount of food. She remained essentially free of pain except for that mosquito bite, from February 26 to the early part of August.

In removing pain, one cautions the patient to keep enough pain available so that he will not bruise the area operated upon, and explain that pain is primarily a warning signal and when the warning has been properly evaluated it can be dispensed with, but a small amount should be kept to prevent abuse of that part.

I suggest that you work out systematically a wording of this explanation suitable for your personality. I also suggest that you work out a comparable explanation about the nature of swelling, the purpose it serves and the desirability of having no more swelling than is necessary. It is surprising how patients will unwittingly produce an immense amount of swelling to insure attention.

I should be delighted to hear from you again.

Sincerely yours,
Milton H. Erickson, M.D.

On June 11, 1971, Wendell Reynolds queried Erickson about self-punitive patients and indicated his interest in Erickson's technique of "ordeal therapy."

In his reply, Erickson described a method of reframing the self-punitive drives of patients and placing them in therapeutic binds. Moreover, note how Erickson utilized ordeals, presenting them as one step in an elaborate dance. It is not the application of the technique that necessarily leads to symptom amelioration; rather it is the process of providing instructions that helps patients to realize previously unrecognized potentials.

In presenting the ordeal, Erickson was not punitive, but offered it in a clear and firm manner, since an ordeal that is presented punitively may not have as much therapeutic power as one that is presented benignly.

From: Wendell B. Reynolds
June 11, 1971

Dear Dr. Erickson:

I utilized your suggestion of converting the patient's anxiety as to how slowly the wound is healing to one of whether the wound will heal slowly enough for the tissues to do a good job of repair. It works very well.

These patients are now noticing very carefully whether or not enough swelling remains for all the physiological processes of repair to take place. However, I still have patients who appear to be bent on autopunitive measures. These are frequently the patients who have had multiple surgeries or a history of being accident-prone, who seem to be simply punishing themselves repeatedly. On occasions, I have even broached the subject with the patient, suggesting that the prolonged disability might have physiological consequences centered around guilt feelings. Such direct informative measures have been without value. I am curious as to how you would go about teaching the patient to relinquish the habit of repeated and perpetual self-punishment.

I have recently been enjoying my second trip through Jay Haley's *Strageties of Psychotherapy*, recommended earlier by you. The concept that the primary gain of symptomatic behavior, as being the objective of setting rules for the relationship, is a reversal of what I have been taught recently. This had been thought to be a secondary gain, or by-product. As Mr. Haley pointed out, one of the techniques used on the patient is to simply frustrate the doctor into anger, and then the game is over. This type of behavior is reminiscent of the material presented by Eric Berne in *Games People Play*. That we are willing to perpetuate a virtually untenable situation in order that we may predict the outcome even though the outcome may be undesirable is a very interesting concept. Certainly this can be seen in the patient's struggling vigorously to gain control of the therapeutic situation in fields other than psychotherapy. And as in psychotherapy, when the patient gains control of the circumstance, it is surely to be to their detriment. Setting the therapeutic paradox, of course, is a difficult objective.

I enjoyed, in particular, the story about the old gentleman who disliked polishing floors, and in order to overcome his insomnia, was required to polish floors all night rather than sleep [Haley, 1973]. In this general context, with patients who insisted upon being seen an inordinate number of times after their surgical recovery, I began having these persons soak their feet, vigorously apply ointment to the surgical area, and perform various exercises which were modified and made more complicated each time the patient returned to the office. This was very successful in diminishing the number of return visits.

I would appreciate your suggestions concerning encouraging the patient to give up the habitual efforts towards self-punishment, and I look forward with anticipation to your next correspondence.

Sincerely yours,
Wendell B. Reynolds, D.P.M., FACFS

To: Wendell B. Reynolds
July 10, 1971

Dear Dr. Reynolds:

In reply to your letter of June 11, I do not know exactly how to word my answer. One needs to know his patients who insist on autopunitive measures because when you know the kind of thing you are doing, you can suggest the autopunitive measure of healing faster than desired or more painlessly than desired or in better fashion than desired, thus having the surgical healing itself be the punishment because it takes place too rapidly, and too well and too painlessly, thereby cheating them out of self-punishment, and deprivation is the punishment. In the handling of patients with Munchausen syndrome or multiple surgeries I have sometimes convinced them that depriving themselves of an operation is even better punishment than an operation.

I can think of a patient who had twenty-nine major abdominal operations, none of which was indicated. He sought out young surgeons and had read up sufficiently on the symptomology that he coaxed them into doing major operations. After meeting me, having been referred by a surgeon, two years later he was in good physical health but lamenting that he couldn't find an excuse for an operation. However, one has to know your patients and their way of thinking and feeling about themselves in order to reverse the manner of self-punishment. This should be a delightful area of study for you.

Quite some years ago I saw a young woman with warts all over her face, hands, and forearms, hard put to earn sufficient money to see a dermatologist to remove the warts surgically with the electric needle by cauterizing. No matter what measure was employed, the warts invariably returned. Finally a dermatologist sent her to me. I induced hypnotic trance and in the trance state I told her that she was to soak her hands briefly and alternately in very hot and then very cold water for twenty minutes at a time, four times a day, and that she was to apply hot cloths and cloths soaked in ice water alternately to her face four times a day for twenty minutes at a time, and I explained to her that as she did this, she would lose progressively her interest in following these instructions, until finally she would forget about them entirely and would not even realize that she had forgotten about them.

Subsequently she married and her son, at the age of eight, had managed to wet the bed every night for eight years and she had tried every possible kind of punishment and finally she remembered that she once had warts and that I had caused her to lose interest in her warts and she brought her son to me to have me help him lose interest in wetting the bed. I explained to the boy that learning not to wet the bed was difficult after eight years of bed-wetting and I explained that even though he was a very bright, intelligent boy and that he liked solitude and playing by himself, he needed time to learn a number of things and that the best way would be perhaps to copy page after page of a book. Within a few weeks he was going as long as three weeks without a wet bed and then he began wetting now and then, and finally, when he began wetting the bed four nights in succession, the mother brought him back in for another lesson. I am shortly going to call her to find out how her son is doing after his second course of learning. I pointed out to the boy that he must learn to spell a lot of words he never knew how to spell, and before that he had learned to write much better and that he has learned how to write faster and that he has learned to write all day long and that he has learned how to miss having time to play. I found this measure was very successful with chronic bed wetters.

Sincerely yours,
Milton H. Erickson, M.D.

Foreign Correspondents

Julio Dittborn, who died in the early 1990s, was a leading figure in South American hypnosis. In his letter of November 23, 1959, Erickson detailed the remarkable success that the American Society of Clinical Hypnosis enjoyed shortly after its inception. He was obviously disconcerted by the problems that beset the Society for Clinical and Experimental Hypnosis (SCEH) and its international offshoot. Although Erickson despaired of the future of the international society, it has become a prestigious organization. Also, the SCEH has continued even though Erickson questioned its ability to survive financial and political crises.

Eventually, the American Boards of Hypnosis assumed positions of contemporary prominence and status, and today there are active Boards for medical practice, psychology, dentistry, and social work.

The "fraudulent machine" to which Erickson referred was the Brain Wave Synchronizer, described in the next two letters.

To: Julio M. Dittborn
November 23, 1959

Dear Julio,

It has been a remarkably long time since I have heard from you and I regret greatly this lack of correspondence.

You will be pleased to learn of the remarkable development and growth of ASCH. We have approximately 2,000 voting members and over 40 state and regional sections, as well as approximately 1200 affiliate members in foreign countries.

Also, you will be glad to know that we have survived the financial difficulties that so often destroy scientific societies, even after years of difficult existence. In two years time we have accumulated a cash reserve of $20,000.00 and our income for the next year will be over $30,000.00. We are planning to use this reserve for the establishment of fellowships, scholarships, teaching activities, research grants and awards, and the promotion of international exchanges and lectureships.

Our Journal likewise has been remarkably successful and has not only paid for itself but has accumulated cash reserves of $5,000.00. This is most remarkable since scientific journals usually need support for many years. All this serves to demonstrate that our society was fortunate enough to meet adequately a need for the professional scientific world and to develop a Journal that would meet equally well an existing unsatisfied need. We of ASCH feel very pleased at our good fortune and hope that you may share in it.

Unfortunately, even though there is room for two hypnotic societies, the SCEH, of which I am a Fellow, is regrettably encountering more and more difficulties. I was distressed last October to learn how close to bankruptcy SCEH is. It was necessary then to start collecting 1960 dues and asking for contributions and gifts to meet 1959 expenses. This has been the result of hasty and impulsive leadership of SCEH. It has been much too ambitious, has promised too much, and has been struggling so hard to maintain leadership by new ventures that misfortunes are developing one after another.

The so-called "Boards of Hypnosis" were most unfavorably regarded by the American Medical Association in an official announcement last March, and received no credit from either the American Dental Association or the American Psychological Association. This damaged the prestige of SCEH, even though the Society had nothing to do with the boards, which were a private project of the leaders of SCEH.

Then one of their most ardent leaders sponsored a fraudulent machine on behalf of SCEH, misrepresented it to the American Medical Association, which later discredited the machine, and he also published a fraudulent paper in the Journal of SCEH on the machine. Again, more loss of prestige and withdrawals from membership.

Then there was the hasty organization of the International Society with much acclaim and the awarding of many responsible positions in the new "international" society. Then it was discovered that they had very limited funds to support the organization, that it was not an international society but an agreement to have "representatives" of various foreign countries constitute the society until hypnotic societies developed in those countries. For example, one of my friends abroad has been appointed the representative of his country in the "ISCEH" and he is to be the "special delegate" of his society to visit the United States. However, he knows of no countryman of his who uses hypnosis, and he does not know when the "society" will be formed. Not only is there this confusion, but many members of SCEH, in return for their support of ISCEH, were promised the same positions of official importance, and discovery of this led to much resentment among SCEH members.

Then the fact that a number of the long-time members of SCEH have only a B.A. or a M.A. degree, some not even in psychology, has caused much further distrust of SCEH because of the harsh criticism their leaders had given ASCH for admitting men with doctoral degrees and only two years of experience in hypnosis. That criticism of ASCH reacted seriously upon SCEH.

And now it has been learned that Milton V. Kline [the editor of the SCEH-sponsored Journal] has published under the degree of Ph.D. and that his actual degree is that of Ed.D., and this misrepresentation has resulted in more unfavorable reactions.

As it is, SCEH may by some miracle survive, although it is close to bankruptcy, as is its Journal.

I regret this unfortunate state of affairs, but my duties with ASCH have kept me too busy to be of much assistance. Furthermore, the remarkable growth of ASCH has made me most unwelcome to the leaders of SCEH, who see their society losing ground so seriously. I wish that something could be done to salvage SCEH and, if possible, to give it some place of importance. Its leadership has been so poorly advised, and the interests and energy of so many good men have been absorbed by ASCH, that the outlook seems dubious.

I have written you at considerable length because I feel that you should know of the present state of affairs of SCEH and of the growth and development and acceptance by the scientific professional world of ASCH and its Journal. I am distressed that I have not heard from you either personally nor had any editorial communications. I wish very much to know that all is going well with you and that the progress of your work in hypnosis continues.

Sincerely yours,
Milton H. Erickson, M.D.

———————————⟨𝓜⟩———————————

On January 7, 1960, Ainslie Meares, M.D., of Melbourne, Australia, wrote "To the Editor" of the American Journal of Clinical Hypnosis:

> In one of the book reviews of your October issue, I notice that an author is taken to task because he advocates, among other things, that the patient's consent should always be obtained before he is hypnotized, and that he should be given time to consider his decision and if necessary seek advice in the matter.
>
> Your reviewer rather graciously suggests that the author's strange ideas may be due to his geographical isolation.

In closing, Meares asks: "Do your readers really believe that it is proper to hypnotize patients without their full consent? I hope someone will answer me."

Meares was one of the premier practitioners of hypnosis in Australia. He certainly knew, and was known to, Erickson, and his failure to address Erickson by name and the tone of the letter suggest that he was miffed. Erickson, however, was not put off and adroitly answered by providing a compelling argument.

Erickson's discussion of informed consent is as relevant to practice today as it was in the 1960s. Informed consent is required by the ethical standards of the American Psychological Association. It is not similarly specified for other professionals, such as psychiatrists and social workers. According to current APA standards, Erickson's position was not correct. However, his argument had decided merit. For further information about ethics and informed consent, see Zeig (1996).

Of further note is the fact that the review in question pertained to Meares' book Hypnography: A Study in the Therapeutic Use of Symbolic Paintings, *and was written by Bernie Gorton, M.D. The review, which appeared in the October 1959 issue of the* American Journal of Clinical Hypnosis, *was mixed and criticized*

Meares for his limited and authoritarian methods. Gorton was a protege of Erickson's.

The passage to which Meares took offense is as follows:

> This otherwise valuable work contains a number of surprisingly controversial statements that are open to question, and with which this reviewer finds himself in disagreement. Thus the author believes it to be "dishonest" to hypnotize a patient without his knowledge and prior consent: "Patients must be told about hypnosis and [their] consent obtained prior to starting treatmemt . . . one should never proceed to treatment on the same day . . . before treatment is started the patients must be given some sort of estimate of the number of sanctions that might be required and an estimate of the cost. It would be clearly wrong to expect the patient's consent to hypnosis without first discussing these matters." . . . [T]he chief criticism that can be made of this book is that Dr. Meares has not taken the time or trouble to integrate his work with the existing literature in the field of hypnotherapy and general hypnotic technique. It may be that this lack of sophistication is the result of his geographically isolated location. . . .

To: Ainslie Meares
February 23, 1960

Dear Doctor Meares:

You ask, "Do your readers really believe that it is proper to hypnotize patients without their full consent?"

In reply: Hypnosis is a scientific methodology of definite value in the practice of medicine and dentistry. It is not a specialty but a method of procedure to effect desirable goals.

Hypnosis is not something that is done by one person to another. It is a cooperative venture in which the operator instructs and the subject learns to respond. Without cooperation, there can be no hypnosis. Hence, to ask formally that a patient give his full consent is no more than a courteous formality. It is essentially on a par, after completing a physical examination of a patient, with asking his formal consent to instruct him in the care of himself. The fact that the patient seeks out the physician implies that he expects to be treated professionally and in accord with the physician's best skills and knowledge. This implication applies to the administration of narcotics and sedatives which alter the state of the patient's awareness even more effectively and extensively than does hypnosis. Only under most extraordinary conditions would a physician ask a full formal consent as a proper procedure in the administration of a narcotic. The consent is inherent in the situation.

As for the assertion that hypnosis is only a method of choice, the same applies to the question of oral administration, hypodermic injection, intravenous injection, and the choice of a whole range of drugs acting variously and to lighter or greater extent and duration. Should this be a matter of proper consent or should the physician exercise his professional judgment without placing upon the patient a responsibility of decision on a matter on which he is uninformed.

Hypnosis is little understood by the layman. Indeed, a large part of the medical profession is sadly uninformed. To ask an uninformed or misinformed patient for consent for a procedure dependent upon his willing cooperation would be meaningless. Either one would have to educate the patient to an understanding of hypnosis or accept a meaningless response for medical guidance.

As it is, there is much too much pomp and ceremony and meaningless ritual and superstitious practice attached to the utilization of hypnosis. I am of the opinion that the physician handles well the patient when he says: "My examination discloses that you have a bad infection in the throat and that it will respond to treatment with a new drug called combiotic. So will you please bare you arm to the shoulder so that I can inject the medicine."

If the patient bares his arm, I do not feel that the physician should laboriously explain what is meant by "infection," nor do I think he should give an informative account of antibiotic therapy, nor do I think he should properly ask the patient's full consent for the injection. If the patient bares his arm, that degree of cooperation constitutes consent. The request that the patient bare his arm constituted only by remote implication a request for consent. Primarily it was a request for a cooperative endeavor, such as hypnosis is.

However, in case of patients completely uninformed about hypnosis or likely to be distressed by it, explanation should be offered rather than consent sought. Such explanation should be comprehensible to the patient in terms of his own understanding and not necessarily phrased in scientific terminology, possibly completely mystifying in that form. Then, after such reasonable explanation, if the patient cooperates with what he understands, the consent is not only full but proper and manifest.

Sincerely yours,
Milton H. Erickson, M.D.

————————————

Leon Chertok was an eminent French psychiatrist and psychoanalyst. He was also one of the leading figures in twentieth-century French hypnotism. In late 1955, on the advice of Lewis Wolberg, he wrote to Erickson to introduce himself and request a visit. Erickson and Chertok met, in January 1966, when Chertok went to Phoenix to learn about Erickson's methods.

In 1960, one of Erickson's daughters, Betty Alice, was in Paris and visited Chertok. In the summer of that year, Mrs. Erickson sent Chertok a reprint of one of Erickson's papers. In a handwritten letter dated August 10, 1060. Chertok expressed his pleasure at meeting Betty Alice and thanked Mrs. Erickson for the reprint. In a postscript, he mentioned that he was writing a chapter on hypnotic technique and was citing Erickson as describing the arm levitation technique in 1928, but did not have an exact citation—hence, Erickson's reply of September 1, 1960.

Note that Erickson's letter to Ralph W. August, an obstetrician active in the American Society of Clinical Hypnosis, also concerned arm levitation (see page 331).

To: Leon Chertok
September 1, 1960

Dear Doctor Chertok:

The story is simple. In the spring of 1923, I did my first experimental work in hypnosis. Clark L. Hull, then Associate Professor of Psychology at the University of Wisconsin, became greatly interested and suggested that I continue my studies of hypnotic phenomena during the summer and arrange to report upon them at a postgraduate seminar that he would organize in September.

This was done. During that summer, among other things, I became interested in ideomotor activity, including automatic writing. Since the automatic writing had been done by a subject in a trance state, the question arose in my mind about suggesting hand-movement of a writing character to induce a trance. This technique worked with a number of new subjects but automatic writing is almost always a very slow, laborious induction technique. However, it is very easy to suggest that the pencil point will move up or down on the paper and I promptly converted this into hand levitation. I worked out many variations until I realized that ideomotor activity of any type constituted a good induction technique. However, hand levitation, because of the opportunity for visual participation it gives the subject, is probably the best variation.

Additionally, for many years I have used another form of ideomotor activity. The observations leading to this were that when one lectures, often some of the audience, in agreement or disagreement with the lecturer, will unconsciously nod their heads affirmatively, or shake them negatively. This led to my asking naive and resistant subjects questions, which I would explain could be answered only by their "unconscious mind" and that the answer might agree or disagree with what they were thinking consciously. The answer, I explained further, would be in the form of a silent nod or shake of the head and they would have to wait patiently to see in which way their head would move. Then the question would be given, "Does your unconscious mind think that you can learn to go into a hypnotic trance?" A rapid nod or shake of the head is always a conscious response. A slow, gentle nod or shake, sometimes not perceived by the subject, constitutes a direct communication from the "unconscious" and advantage can be taken of it to induce catalepsy and to proceed then to the deepening of the trance.

In a comparable fashion I sometimes tell a naive or resistant subject that levitation of the right hand means "yes," that the levitation of his left hand means "no," and that levitation of one or the other of his hands will constitute the answer of his unconscious mind to a question which only his unconscious mind can answer. Then I can put the question given above, or some other comparable question. Regardless of which hand levitates, the subject goes into a trance state to produce the levitation. This technique is often of value with patients who want hypnosis but resist any effort at trance induction.

Or I may ask the subject to rest his hands passively on his thighs and to wait patiently to see which hand his "unconscious mind" will leviate first. The trance state is concurrent with the development of the levitation and I proceed by demonstrating catalepsy in the other arm and then deepening the trance. This procedure also bypasses resistance to overt trance induction procedures.

Hence, in my personal experience, the hand levitation dates back to the summer of 1923. You will be further interested to know that the first subject on whom it was used was your friend and my sister, Bertha.

As for any early publication of mine mentioning it, I never really considered it sufficiently important. It is only a simple utilization of the old familiar phenomenon of ideomotor activity, extensively reported on as such by a French scholar around 1857. I don't know the exact reference.

I remember the embarrassment of Jastrow, then Professor of Psychology at Wisconsin, discovering that an original study he had published was almost a duplicate of the much earlier French study.

I'm glad that Betty Alice had the opportunity of meeting you. She wrote us a long and happy letter about it.

Sincerely,
Milton H. Erickson, M.D.

————————————ℳℰ————————————

Arm (or hand) levitation is commonly used as a "convincer" technique that allows hypnotic subjects to experience dissociated ideomotor behavior. In this method, the hypnotist offers the subject suggestions that an arm feels light, so light that it will automatically, without voluntary effort, drift upward. When this occurs, the subject directly experiences the way in which hypnosis can nonvolitionally translate idea into physical activity. Erickson often utilized arm levitation as an induction technique. His September 1, 1960, letter to Leon Chertok presents some of the variations he applied. Arm levitation, in one form or another, has been incorporated into several hypnotic susceptibility tests, most notably the Hypnotic Induction Profile (HIP) (see Spiegel & Spiegel, 1978).

Erickson's letter to Ralph August also spoke to the topic of arm levitation. Additionally, he traced the confusion technique to two pieces he wrote. The "earlier reference" to which Erickson referred in the letter's postscript is "Deep Hypnosis and Its Induction" in Experimental Hypnosis *(LeCron, 1952). Erickson's*

1959 article in "our Journal" is, "Further Clinical Techniques of Hypnosis: Utilization Techniques," American Journal of Clinical Hypnosis, 2, 3–21. Later, Erickson wrote "The Confusion Technique in Hypnosis," American Journal of Clinical Hypnosis, 6, 183–207.

Isaac Gubel, an Argentine psychiatrist who founded a hypnosis society in that country, was a corresponding editor of the American Council of Clinical Hypnosis. He was also the founding editor of La Revista Latino Americana de Hipnosis Clinicd, established in 1959.

As noted before, Erickson was vigilant in his defense of hypnosis and dogged in his efforts to maintain respectability for the discipline. When the Brain Wave Synchronizer appeared, Erickson took action to dispel the purported relationship between the device and clinical hypnosis. Two letters follow that exemplify the ends to which Erickson went to keep hypnosis untainted by what he viewed as fraudulent claims. In the first letter, Erickson apparently responded to an inquiry about the machine from a colleague. In the second, he alerted the U.S. Food and Drug Administration to his concerns.

To: Isaac Gubel,
May 11, 1962

Dear Isaac:

The Brain Wave Synchronizer was developed and is manufactured by Mr. S. W. Schneider, who refers to himself as an "engineer," but who, so far as I have been able to ascertain, has no college degree at all. He certainly has no knowledge of neurology, electroencepalography, psychology, medicine, or hypnosis.

Dr. William Kroger co-authored an article with Mr. Schneider which was published by the *International Journal of Clinical and Experimental Hyp-*

nosis in April 1959. This article made many extravagant claims for the device, but in essence described a pragmatically designed device based on a nonexistent etiology which even its enthusiastic promotors admitted lost 70% of its effectiveness when the subjects did not know what it was supposed to do. Dr. Kroger has had no training or background in electroencephalography and neurology, and his statements concerning the numbers of obstetrical patients he claims to have delivered, with or without the aid of the device, have been publicly stated to be significantly inaccurate.

Immediately upon the appearance of this article in print, the Brain Wave Synchronizer was vigorously promoted at an exceedingly expensive price. Questions sent to Dr. Kroger and Mr. Schneider by many physicians requesting references to the many scientific articles which were claimed to have appeared were uniformly ignored or evaded. The same thing is true of questions sent to Dr. Kroger concerning the number of cases he claims to have treated.

The device was originally sold for almost $300.00. Any impressively designed flickering light, implemented by similar appropriate suggestions, would have exactly the same effect at a fraction of this cost, as has been repeatedly shown.

However, backed by their one article, the two promoters repeatedly managed to insert advertisements in ethical but incautious scientific publications. In each case, vigorous protest by physicians, such as the late Dr. Bernard Gorton and Dr. Leonard Ravitz, led to apologies and a withdrawal of the advertisement from further issues of the publications.

Then a question sent to the *Journal of the American Medical Association* was answered in its columns by enthusiastic claims for the device made by one of its promoters. A storm of letters of protest to the American Medical Association followed, which finally led to this official statement.

"In regard to the induction of hypnosis by flashing or flickering lights, I should also like to call your attention to an article by Dr. Hallack McCord in the April 1962 issue of the *American Journal of Clinical Hypnosis*. Dr. McCord points out the hazard of epileptic seizures being triggered in susceptible patients and perhaps mistaken for a hypnotic state."

I hope you will find this information useful.

Sincerely yours,
Milton H. Erickson, M.D.

To: U.S. Food and Drug Administration
May 31, 1962

Gentlemen:

There is an instrument manufactured in Skokie, Illinois, and sold in interstate commerce directly and through agencies, and abroad also, called the Brain Wave Synchronizer.

It is supposed to influence the alpha waves of the brain, is so advertised and is supposed to be used to induce hypnosis for medical purposes.

The American Medical Association has rejected this instrument and competent authorities have termed it fraudulent. In my own personal observation of the machine, I am forced to the absolute conclusion that it does not influence the alpha brain wave and that it aids in no way to induce hypnosis for medical purposes.

A purportedly scientific article was published by William Kroger, M.D., who stated that he had successfully employed the machine experimentally. However, personal knowledge made me aware that Dr. Kroger was not in the city of Chicago long enough in the period of time mentioned to do the extensive work claimed to have been reported upon. Additionally, the Edgewater Hospital in Chicago, where the work was claimed to have been done, refuses to confirm the statements made in the published article.

I have written to Mr. Schneider, whose company manufactures and sells the machine and who advertises that "hundreds of scientific articles" attest to its merits. I have been unsuccessful in soliciting any scientific references whatsoever, except the one unreliable one which I have just described.

I believe this instrument should be investigated as a fraudulent device falsely advertised to physicians and dentists as a valuable adjunct in the use of hypnosis as a therapeutic madality.

Sincerely yours,
Milton H. Erickson, M.D.
Diplomate, The American Board of
Psychiatry and Neurology

The reference cited is the following:
"An Electronic Aid For Hypnotic Induction: A Preliminary Report," *William S. Kroger and Sidney A. Schneider*
Published in:
The International Journal of Clinical and Experimental Hypnosis, *April 1959, Vol. VII, No. 2, pp. 93–99.*

To: Isaac Gubel
November 1, 1970

Dear Isaac:

I'm sorry not to have written sooner but my activities are limited. The anterior poliomyelitis of 1919 resulted in considerable spinal deformity which, because of my vanity in keeping my shoulders level, is not outwardly visible. However, I knew even in medical school that, if I lived long enough, I would have spinal arthritis and be confined to a wheelchair, an event which occurred in 1965. Now I have spinal arthritis, radiculitis, myositis, tenosinovitis, and for good measure, a bit of gout. Fortunately my knowledge of hypnosis enables me to keep pain and distress at a minimum.

I have retired almost completely from practice, seeing only an interesting or former patient now and then, Muscle loss of the right arm and right-sided loss of facial muscles has impaired my speech. Hence, writing and lecturing are no longer possible. But I do have an unlimited capacity to enjoy life and I am getting caught up with the reading that I have promised myself all my life.

My two youngest children, Roxanna and Kristina, are completing college and Betty and I are enjoying our new home. We both are refusing to be "senior citizens" and instead, are doing all the delightful possible things that should be enjoyed in the 30's and 40's and which we had missed doing.

As for activity in hypnosis, I am having a lot of visitors, not only from various parts of the U.S., but from England, Sweden, Czechoslovakia, France, Singapore, etc., and letters from many parts of the world, including even Buenos Aires. This past Sunday, a contestant in the International Shooting Competition who was from El Salvador dropped in to have some hypnotic aid in lessening his anxieties, and yesterday a tennis player in a tennis tournament came in for the same reason.

A former patient and Past President of the American Association of Interior Decorators, as a housewarming gift for us, took over the interior decorating of our new home, and Betty is having a leisurely good time arranging our accumulated possessions acquired over the years from all parts of the world—things that we treasured but whose number we didn't realize until we moved. There is even a taxi horn from Pakistan so I can summon somebody from any part of the house. Among my collection of books autographed to me by the authors there is one included but not autographed since the author died while the book was in press. It is a history of some of the old ghost towns of the West and stories of the pioneers who developed them. I was astonished when I found that one of the chapters was about my father and mother, the mine that my father and his partner had developed and the mining town that had formed about it in the Sierra Nevada Mountain range in the Rocky Mountains where I was born. My mother was also born in a log cabin, but the log cabin in which I was born had for the fourth side the side of the mountain itself and my cradle was made out of a dynamite box. My mother died at the age of 94, my father at 97 1/2 years.

Incidentally, when traveling from Phoenix to Chicago by a jet-propelled airplane, the pilot announced over the loudspeaker that the plane was flying at an elevation of 37,000 feet and that the ground speed was 650 miles per hour. I had the stewardess tell the pilot that he had on board a passenger who had traveled 150 miles in a covered wagon over the Great Salt Lake Desert in Nevada in only three weeks and that that had been a much more interesting trip.

The Ericksons had a family reunion in August 1969 at which all nineteen of my grandchildren were present. Yet unmarried of my eight children are the two youngest of the four daughters.

I wish it were possible for us to visit together in person, and as an inadequate substitute I have written you this rambling letter of reminiscences. If you are ever in the Western part of the United States, it would be a great pleasure to have you visit us. We have a small guest house which is always ready for a stay of one or several days, as many as you could spare.

Dr. Joseph Shibata of Japan sent me a brief account of the Barcelona meeting. I am exceedingly gratified that the meeting was so successful, with such a large attendance and the great interest in the exchange of scientific understandings.

Sincerely,
Milton

Erickson's opinions and counsel were sought by colleagues around the world, and he endeavored to assist professionals in numerous other countries to promote the advancement of ethical hypnosis. As a result, he received many international society commendations and maintained contact with a multitude of eminent professionals overseas. His letter of March 13, 1963, to Raul Eitelberg, a Brazilian dentist, exemplifies his advocacy of hypnosis for bona fide purposes worldwide.

To: Raul Eitelberg
March 13, 1963

Dear Dr. Eitelberg,

In my official capacity for the American Society of Clinical Hypnosis,* it is a pleasure to inform you that hypnosis is regularly employed as a legitimate procedure by dentists in the United States and that it is being taught as a part of the curriculum of the colleges of dentistry in many state and private universities. It would be taught in still more dental and medical colleges if there were available faculty members sufficiently qualified. It may interest you to know that I participated in the first university course given in the United States of America, which was at the University of Wisconsin in 1923. Later I conducted the first course on hypnosis in a medical school, at Wayne State University in Detroit, Michigan, in 1937, and in 1945 it was recommended by the American Psychiatric Association at the Annual Meeting in Chicago, Illinois, that similar courses be taught in all medical schools.

Editor's Note: At the time, Erickson was the editor of The American Journal of Clinical Hypnosis *(1957–1968). He also was the first president of ASCH, which was founded in 1957.*

Scientific progress moves slowly and as yet such teaching is possible only in a few of the schools because of insufficient trained faculty members.

I, myself, have lectured concerning the teaching of hypnosis (as an especially invited guest for that purpose) at more than 25 medical and dental schools and I am only one of many others to so lecture. This should give you some idea of the ever-growing interest in hypnosis as a scientific dental and medical modality.

In September 1958, the American Medical Association went on official record stating that hypnosis was a proper scientific modality for medical and dental practice.

It is used extensively by the dentists who belong to the American Society of Clinical Hypnosis, and there are a number of other official legitimate dental societies throughout the United States separate from the American Society of Clinical Hypnosis that train dentists in the use of hypnosis.

Various court opinions throughout the United States have upheld the use of hypnosis by both dentists and physicians but have discouraged and even penalized its use by nondentists and nonphysicians.

Canada also has passed special laws in various of its provinces restricting hypnosis to dentists and physicians and prohibiting its use for public entertainment. Also, there are independent Canadian societies, medical and dental, all official and legitimate societies, teaching the use of hypnosis for both dentists and physicians.

Out of my experience extending back to 1923, and as a Diplomate of the American Board of Psychiatry and Neurology, and as a former professor of Psychiatry for 14 years at Wayne State University, and as an Honorary Member of several official central societies, I assure you personally that it is my belief backed by extensive experience and by actual observation that hypnosis is a useful scientific modality in the practice of dentistry as well as in medicine.

If you have available a copy of the compilation of reprints by your compatriots Dr. A. C. de Moraes Passos and Dr. Oscar Farina, *Aspectos Atuais oa Hipnologia*, you may find considerable information in that book.

This book offers a summary of the legal situation in Brazil which you can read much better than I can, as well as the official statement of the American Medical Association translated into Portuguese.

There still remains in the United States one society, the Society of Clinical and Experimental Hypnosis, which has some 300 members some of whom are dentists who are not participating in the organized, cooperative council, which is actively forwarding hypnosis as a dental modality. However, I assure you they are not opposed to its use; they are merely promoting their own control of dental use in hypnosis rather than leaving it more properly to the authority of university medical and dental colleges, and the cooperation of all the professional societies in council.

Needless to say, you are unquestionably well acquainted with the dictum of Pope Pius approving wholeheartedly the use of hypnosis in the healing arts.

I am sending a copy of this letter to Lawrence Milton Staples, Doctor of Medical Dentistry. This degree is identical to the more usual degree of Doctor of Dental Surgery, but is bestowed by some universities. He is the man most deserving of credit in promoting the recognition of hypnosis in dentistry and in organizing the Council of Dental Societies to bring about a uniformity of dental hypnotic practices throughout the entire United States. At this time he is its President.

I hope he too will write to you should you wish further information.

Sincerely yours,
Milton H. Erickson, M.D.

To: Alfonso Caycedo
December 10, 1963

Dear Dr. Caycedo:

Your letter confirming my position as a member of the Board of Directors of the International Society of Sophrology and Psychosomatic Medicine is most gratifying. I am very grateful to you for the honor and privilege.

Although the American Society of Clinical Hypnosis has close connections with a large number of professional societies in many different countries, both those that are directly affiliated with us, and those that are associated through La Federación Latino Americana de Hipnosis Clínica,

I myself have been most hesitant about promoting the formation of an international group.

The Society for Clinical and Experimental Hypnosis undertook to launch such an international society several years ago, but did so by merely announcing such a formation and then appointing isolated, single individuals in various countries as the representatives of those countries. Thus in 1960, according to their Directory, the total of worldwide membership, counting Canada and the United States, was only about 230 individuals, 200 of these residing in the United States itself. The control of the so-called International Society of Clinical and Experimental Hypnosis was in the hands of a small group, about 6 men in New York City, who appointed their own personal choices for honorary office, but they themselves constituted the governing group. I am a Fellow of the Society for Clinical and Experimental Hypnosis but I have refused to join the International Society of Clinical and Experimental Hypnosis. It is the very strong feeling of the leading scientific men in America, as well as elsewhere, that an international organization in the healing arts should be democratically initiated, and developed after societies have already been formed in a number of different countries. Hence it was with much pleasure that I read the names of the Board of Directors [of Caycedo's group] and the officers.

The representation is that of the many lands which have been working in this field, and the individuals are selected to coordinate this representation.

The American Society of Clinical Hypnosis has affiliated on equal terms with many different foreign societies, not for immediate gain but to lay a foundation for thinking in terms of a truly international and representative organization which would eventually develop.

It is with much pleasure that I note that the Journal which Dr. Isaac Gubel founded and edits has been offered and accepted as the official organ for the new organization. In the same way, I am offering the *American Journal of Clinical Hypnosis* as a separate official organ for those members and groups which are conversant with the English language, either as their native tongue or in addition to their own language. As you may have noted, Dr. Gubel and I have more than once published simultaneously the same articles so that our colleagues might have the material made available in Spanish or in English.

I am very pleased with the location of the headquarters in Nancy, which is most fitting historically.

You may have noticed that I have often made editorial comments expressing my profound regret that North Americans are so often uninformed about understandings of psychological principles of human behavior and of advancements in psychosomatic medical concepts in Europe, South America, and more distant lands.

My colleague and friend, Gosaku Naruse, Ph.D. and M.D., professor at Kyushu University in Japan, is working toward a bettering of exchange of Oriental and Occidental understandings in psychology and psychosomatic medicines. He has made remarkable achievements toward this goal. I have been appointed a corresponding Editor of the *Japanese Journal of Hypnosis*, and I believe Dr. Naruse would be much interested in joining with us in this international work.

I am now, and have been for some time past, in correspondence with the leaders in hypnosis in England. Their teaching and the growth of their well-organized societies are steadily progressing.

I am also in constant correspondence with the Czechoslovakian Society and they keep me informed on their meetings. Dr. Hoskovec, the founder, recently supplied me with a list of the names and addresses of a large number of the Soviet and Eastern European scientists publishing in this field.

As yet, there has never been an international meeting or congress on hypnosis (I use the word which is widely known in America, although I greatly like the term "Sophrology" because of the meaningfulness of its derivation and its appropriateness) and psychosomatic medicine combined. Such a meeting would be supported, I am confident, by the various psychosomatic societies in the United States.

One thought I would like to emphasize to you is the significance of the World Federation for Mental Health of which the American Society of Clinical Hypnosis is a full Member-Society. I favor greatly following their example by suggesting an International *Federation* for Psychological, Sophrological and Psychosomatic Sciences. This is simply a suggestion. The term "Society" may to some signify a connotation of exclusiveness or geographical limitation. This, however, is a very minor point.

More important, I suggest that the new organization should have as its primary goal the furtherance of knowledge, the exchange of understandings and the open-minded examination of new concepts entering the expanding horizons in a developing and changing world of human values and needs.

I am most eager to hear from you again at your earliest convenience.

Sincerely yours,
Milton H. Erickson, M.D.

───────────── *ℳℰ* ─────────────

In Spain and South America the term "sophrology" was used synonymously with hypnosis. Alfonso Caycedo maintained residences in both Spain and South America, effecting a considerable positive influence for the use of hypnosis in both regions.

In 1964, Jean Lassner, M.D., a prominent french anesthesiologist, organized an independent meeting on hypnosis in Paris, which was attended by many of the luminaries in international hypnosis. Mrs. Erickson reported that at that meeting the Ericksons met Serenc Volggesi, a Hungarian physician who conducted the basic work on hypnosis prior to World War I. He wrote a text on "animal hypnosis" based on studies at the London Zoo conducted under the auspices of Julian Huxley, brother of Aldous Huxley.

To: Jean Lassner, M.D.
October 19, 1965

Dear Dr. Lassner:

I hope very much that the air-mail package you recently received from Chicago will make amends for my tardiness in writing to you. Also, I am asking our printer to send you by air mail the October issue of the *American Journal of Clinical Hypnosis*. I thought it only proper to make the award a part of the permanent literature.

I am most grateful to you for all the courtesies you showed me in Paris. In fact, I wish I could be even more in debt to you for more such pleasurable memories.

Since my return from Paris, I have had recurrent illness, once requiring hospitalization. My diagnoses are sufficiently numerous to make my situation almost humorous: osteoarthritis of the spine from torsion caused by muscle imbalance resulting from anterior poliomyelitis, numerous calcium spurs on the vertebiac causing much painful radiculitis, myositis and tenosynovitis, gouty arthritis, and a reversal (now corrected) of phosphorus and calcium ratios in the blood along with high uric acid, now corrected. I am now ambulatory only in my own home, all other activity is via wheelchair. However, this does not restrict me significantly.

The Eighth Annual Meeting of the American Society of Clinical Hypnosis was most successful. The attendance I believe was between 350 and 400 and the ensuing workshop had an attendance of 200. You will be interested to learn that as a last-minute addition a paper was presented by Dr. Jiri Hoskovec, who had just arrived in the U.S.A. for a year's teaching and study at Lehigh University in Bethlehem, Pennsylvania.

Incidentally, a Canadian journal wishes to publish the paper I delivered in Paris. I stated that I believed you were including it among those you were publishing. If so, assuming that it is not contrary to the prevailing practice in France, could you please send me permission to publish that paper elsewhere?

Many thanks for the periodicals you sent me. I was much flattered by the accounts given of me, and Betty was very pleased, as were my parents, mother aged 93, father aged 96. Their 74th wedding anniversary will be October 21.

We are making plans to visit Spain in 1967 to attend the Fourth World Congress of Psychiatry, and we plan a much longer European stay than we enjoyed this year. [They made the trip.]

One more item: The International Relations Committee of ASCH, at their special session in Paris, voted unanimously to send, if possible, a special mailing of a complimentary copy of the Journal to all the registrants at the International Congress. This mailing could be accompanied or followed by a letter stating that this was being done to acquaint these physicians with the existence and aims of the Society.

Would it be possible for you to send me a list of the names and addresses?

Sincerely yours,
Milton H. Erickson, M.D.

Patients

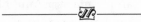

The origin of this September 11, 1962, letter to Mrs. B. is unclear. Perhaps she was a patient, or perhaps the wife of a colleague.

Note Erickson's parental tone. However, he not only instructs but he also chides and encourages. Further, note how Erickson used an indirect style in his writing, as well as in his therapy. Within the context of the letter, he told a story to bring home his point, gently guiding her associations into more constructive arenas.

To: Mrs. B.
September 11, 1962

Dear Mrs. B.:

I hope greatly that by now, with the wedding over, much of the tension is gone.

Now I wish to say something of great importance to you.

Life in itself is hazardous and there is little to be gained by fearing death. So many people waste much peace of mind on what they cannot prevent.

When you married Mr. B. you took him as he was. Had he had a stroke that paralyzed him and made him bedridden for the next 30 years, you would have been a good and faithful wife. But is that the kind of a defect you want in Mr. B.? You would not find fault with it, but you do find fault with lesser faults.

I agree that he is selfish, but so am I and so are you and so is everybody else. Some are more selfish than others. But selfishness and generosity often go together. People have to be taken as they are. Once one tries to take a much desired thing from another human being, a price must be paid, often a price far out of proportion.

Will Mr. B. be killed in a plane accident? The insurance companies assure everybody that the bathroom is far riskier. Will he have to give up driving a car? It's actually far more dangerous than flying.

One of my best friends made her husband give up flying. I got her over it before a divorce occurred. He was killed shortly thereafter on the highway. My friend says, "Thank goodness I got over my phobia, or I would have thought all the rest of my life that if I hadn't, he might have been flying then instead of driving a car. As it was, I was over my phobia and I knew he could choose to either drive or fly, so that it was just fate, not me, that put him in a car at that time."

So, Bend, Baby, Bend.

Yours sincerely,
Milton H. Erickson, M.D.

There is no record of the reason that Erickson began corresponding with the T. family. Obviously, Erickson had a professional relationship with Dr. T., who seems to have been active in the American Society of Clinical Hypnosis.

The letters to the T. family, however, are not professional letters. Rather, they are therapeutic letters, and may represent the earliest use of correspondence as a vehicle to provide comprehensive family therapy. This technique of using letters as part of family therapy has been developed recently by Michael White and his associates in the narrative school of psychotherapy.

The correspondence begins with a letter addressed to Mrs. T. However, it is not only directed to her; but it contains numerous "bank shots" to pool family resources.

To: Mrs. "T."
March 6, 1963

Dear Mrs. T.:

Just a letter to explain things a bit more and to clarify them and to put them down in black and white so that you won't forget and won't change them or leave out a significant part in your memory.

First of all, when some people eat strawberries, they get hives. There is nothing wrong with strawberries, but some people are allergic to them and can develop everything from small generalized hives to huge wheals and urticaria, and even pass out. The same is true of many other good foods.

Now there are a great number of allergies and allergic reactions, and of varying degrees, and those allergies develop in different parts of the body. For example, on the operating table, I saw giant urticaria develop in, and only in, the abdominal cavity during a surgical operation when a certain medication was given. The patient nearly died from that giant urticaria. (Dr. T. can explain these medical terms to you.) Adrenalin saved the patient's life, another surgeon operated on the patient a couple of years later, with the same result.

Careful study of the patient later proved that a certain medication always caused a severe intraabdominal allergic reaction (giant urticaria), but only inside the abdomen.

All this is by way of preliminary explanation so that you and Dr. T. can understand what next I have to say.

It is this, and simply this: Dr. T. is allergic to alcohol. It causes a toxic allergic reaction in his brain. It may relax his muscles, but in his brain, alcohol causes "hives," "wheals," and "urticaria" in the brain tissue. Remember, brain tissue is ectodermal in origin, the same as the skin, the eyes. (Dr. T. can explain.) Most allergic reactions show up in ectodermal tissue, less frequently in endodermal and still less in mesodermal.

When Dr. T. takes alcohol, for which he has very limited tolerance, he gets an allergic reaction in his brain as a result of which he does the things all of you know so well and so painfully. Few doctors recognize this type of allergic reaction.

In some way, unconsciously, Mrs. T., you have recognized that Dr. T. plus alcohol was not the same man as Dr. T. without alcohol. Without alcohol, he had plenty that was good but was too dedicated to medicine and worked too hard and too long, and because he knew he could trust you completely, he kept the practice of medicine for himself and gave you the "practice" of the family. When he didn't drink, he helped with the family, but he didn't get much training or experience with the family because he relaxed with alcohol.

Next question: How long do hives, wheals, urticaria last? I know from experience because of an allergy I have. One miserable little bit of an inconsequential mosquito bite can arouse me from a deep sleep when I am extremely tired, put hives all over my body, which can last for hours, make me sick and nauseated for twelve or more hours. (Frankly, I don't like mosquitos, I'm afraid of them.) Ask Betty how happy I was on our honeymoon because a bee stung her instead of me—it's funny and laughable, particularly her horror when I said with infinite relief, I'm glad that it stung you instead of me. Fine remark to make to your bride on a honeymoon and I had to explain fast that if the bee had stung me, she would have had to have me hospitalized, and who wants a honeymoon in a hospital.

But back to Dr. T. I recognized when I first saw him take a drink a few years ago that I was looking at a man who was allergic to alcohol. But I had had previous experience with alcohol-allergic people, and even other doctors, and you just can't walk up to someone and tell him that he can't handle his liquor. One of Dr. T.'s and my friends is terribly allergic to alcohol in a peculiar way. The first drink makes him the most completely offensive disagreeable man on the face of the earth. I managed to talk him into an experiment because there was something unusual about his offensiveness. In his hotel room I persuaded him to take for his first drink a triple shot, wait about 3 to 5 minutes, and then take a glass of water. If he has been eating just before drinking he has to wait 5 to 10 minutes and then take at least two glasses of water. Doing it that way, he corrects his allergic reaction to one single drink. So now he looks at his watch, orders three shots and two glasses of water, three glasses of water if there is too much ice in the water, swallows the whiskey fast, then at the right time by his watch swallows the water, and then if he wants an occasional additional drink, he can make a night of it. But under no circumstances now will he take a single drink.

But Dr. T. is not allergic that way. One drink, two, three, and his allergic reaction can stay in the hypothalamus and cerebrum (both and always both) for even 24 hours. (I base this on your statements, his statements, [your son's] statements, and my own observations of Dr. T. the next day after I knew he had had liquor the night before.)

Why didn't I do something about it before? Sometimes it only worsens matters to give unasked advice that won't be believed. Now I have been asked and you both have had a few months in which to learn that Dr. T. without alcohol is a far different man than Dr. T. with alcohol.

How long does alcohol stay in the body? It varies. I have a patient who found that the alcohol and alcohol oxidation products would stay in his body from one (1) just one, Tom Collins for 3 weeks. After 4 weeks he could take antabuse safely, but if he took antabuse three weeks after a single Tom Collins or a single shot of vodka or whiskey, a dose of antabuse would lay him up for 3 days.

I don't know how long alcohol and alcohol oxidation products remain in Dr. T. tissues and I am positive that they stay longer than 12 hours. I'm almost certain that I have seen evidence of a stay but this I have no way of knowing for sure.

That is why I say that Dr. T. should say good-bye forever to alcohol—beer, wine, whiskey, all alcohol—even Cheracol cough syrup.

It seems to me I have driven my points home.

Now for you, Mrs. T. People are people and you and each of your children is a separate person.

I do not find fault with you one particle for having protected, sheltered, overmothered, been oversolicitous about your children. Someone had to do something and there was no one to explain to you.

You are to be complimented for what you have done in good faith and successfully.

Now the situation is changed. From now on, Dr. T. without alcohol can be a father, you a mother instead of mother—father—protector—indulger—alibier—and all the other many things that the situation forced upon you.

Right now you are starting under a handicap with [your son] and with [your daughter]—a 15-year-old brat who smokes and you can tell her that is what I called her, a 15-year-old brat who smokes when *I want to call her* a nice, pretty 15-year-old girl who is willing to wait until she is grown up to smoke, instead of using a cigarette *to prove* that she is grown up. She isn't grown up—she knows it, you know it—I know it and only a very stupid damn fool gets taken in by a silly cigarette.

The same thing with [your son]. He's a nice, really nice in the complimentary sense of the word "nice," young 18-year-old gentleman and not really an irresponsible procrastinating brat who pretends he can't tell time and can't read traffic signals and can't study as well as some of his less well-endowed classmates. He knows you know that boys *with less brains* and *less advantages* than he has get better grades than he does. In fact, it takes quite a bit of figuring to let somebody with less brains than one has to let that chap get higher grades. I know another doctor's son, a very brilliant young man—I examined him and I know. There were 1297 others in his class. You know he really had to put his brains in low gear, use poor gas and keep his foot on the brakes to wind up the lowest student in that class of 1298, counting him. That took real brains to do that and yet graduate. When I pointed out to him how thoroughly he had to use his brains to manage successfully to be bottom man in his senior, junior, sophomore years in high school after being top man of the class in his freshman year, he recognized at once that the only person really fooled was himself.

This same boy prided himself on his long, lonesome car drives, his speeding, getting only one ticket—he should have had over 300—and his obsessional interest in a sense of power that he got from driving, recognized at once what I meant by telling him to get an obsessional interest and pride and power from shifting into high gear and pushing down hard on the accelerator in his brain.

Now [your son] has had a semester in which to make satisfactory grades for his fraternity. All I have to say is that if I get to the airport too late to catch my plane, I'll be damned if I will step up to the counter and buy a second ticket for the flight I missed. [Your son] is only one semester late for that fraternity flight. Well, if you want something worthwhile you earn it honestly and if boys dumber than [your son] could do it, he better recognize that his seat on that fraternity flight has been sold out because he chose to be a "no-show."

And now one more parting shot at [your son]. Recently a patient of mine was paroled from prison and he came in to me to visit and to tell me that after 3 years in prison he was convinced that there were a lot of men free and out of prison and had never been in prison who had done things as bad or even worse than most of the convicts. I answered that I agreed with him but would add one thing more, namely, that every convict had worked a hell of a lot harder to get into prison than did equally bad but free men. Then I pointed out to him how hard he had really worked to be absolutely sure of winding up in prison when it would have taken less hard work to stay out.

Then I added that there is damn little competition at the top of the ladder, but plenty at the bottom of the ladder of success.

And now back to you Mrs. T. and Dr. T. Who decides how much allowance, what kind of clothes, parties and activities and interests your children are to have—you or your neighborhood acquaintances? I think the decision should be made through the intelligent guidance of the parents in a family conference. How else can you teach your kids what good judgment and good values are? My son, who is the Acting Dean of Men at a university in Puerto Rico, still remembers how all the older members of the family thought he was too big a boy to be playing with a dolly and he remembers his rage and anger, but he also remembers his own curiosity at the same time why older and wiser people than he could be so wrong. Even then he knew that there was something in that situation he did not understand.

And now we come to [your other daughter], I mean Dumb Bunny. I want her to sit down just for the pure fun of it and prove to me that she is a Dumb Bunny. Personally, I'm willing to bet that she *isn't* a Dumb Bunny and I dare her to take my bet and prove that she is a real honest-to-goodness Dumb Bunny and you better warn her that I am pretty darned hard to fool. She'd better produce genuine proof, not pretend proof, but honest-to-goodness proof that I can believe.

Her father or anybody else calling her a Dumb Bunny isn't proof and any smart kid can get poor grades, so tell her that I'm offering her a bet that she is not a Dumb Bunny, that I always win my bets, and that if she is smart enough to prove she is a Dumb Bunny, she loses the bet because she is smart enough to prove she is dumb and thereby show that she is smarter than I am because I offered the bet.

So now, Dumb Bunny, get to work and do your level best to prove you are a Dumb Bunny. I bet you can't.

Now Mrs. T., my secretary will type this letter. Betty will not read it. But you, Dr. T. [your son] and [your first daughter], the brat who really looks and acts to me like a pretty young lady, can read it and you can discuss it. As for Dumb Bunny, let her read those parts that pertain to her. Certainly as parents you have a responsibility to choose some things that you don't discuss with anyone who has not the background of experience to understand what I mean, as, for example, allergies, urticaria, antabuse, parental responsibilities.

Come to think of it, I'm beginning to realize that after you-all get this letter, I have coming to me a letter from:

1. Dumb Bunny.
2. Anne the Brat.
3. [Your son] who is way over his head in debts of responsibility to himself.
4. Mrs. T. the overworked thinker for others.
5. ALLERGIC Dr. T.

Texas-size letters, too, none of this itsy-bitsy Rhode Island-size letters.

And somewhere, especially in [the first daughter] the Brat's letter, there ought to be some first-class Texas-style name-calling of me to show me that I'm not the only one who can think of names. I'll even settle for a medium-sized squelch if my letter just bores her. Now what could be a sweeter offer than that?

Sincerely yours,
Milton H. Erickson, M.D.

To: Mrs. "T."
March 15, 1963

Dear Mrs. T.:

I received good and sensible and pleasing letters from [the first daughter], [the son], and Dr. T. They were pleasing only because they gave evidence of their own personal recognition of themselves and of their desire to be a source of pride and joy to themselves and others. "To thine own self first be true and then it follows as the night doth the day that thou canst not be false to any man."

I'm very glad Dr. T. took my letter so well—the carbon copy was sent for him to keep in his own secret compartment in his office.

Now comes the more difficult thing, Mrs. T. Make no mistake that I do not understand. I do, I have had much experience that extends back to 1923.

I want you to read what I say carefully and thoughtfully, and as you do so, wonder thoughtfully and carefully if my judgment is correct. Do not declare it wrong, look rather for proof that it is correct.

In order for you to have accomplished what you did you had to exercise phenomenal strength of character. To do this carried with it certain not easily recognized dangers. That is what I wish to bring to your attention now, and Mrs. T., you were a grand trooper to let me talk to you as I did in New Orleans. Few people can take a cold stripping of personal pride as did all three of you.

As a part of the exercise of your strength in holding things together, I feel certain from my own observations that you were forced unwillingly but nevertheless effectively to wear the pants in the home life. Certainly you had to, but you have had no advice or knowledge of when to take off the family pants and wear *Mother's* pretty dresses. Dr. T.'s use of the family pants was so often in the wrong way that the kids came to associate the goodness of the family pants with Mother. That in turn led to expecting necessarily things that should have been demanded from Dr. T. and the force of circumstances led you to overemphasize certain aspects of your character strength.

Now the point I want to make clear is that from now on Mrs. T. with great care and never-ending effort makes her striking, and I mean striking, femininity far more apparent than the family pants. To clarify my point, do you want [your first daughter] to grow up to marry a weakling or do you wish her to copy Mother's femininity and marry a *man*? Do you want your son to marry a dominant wife who will henpeck him into misery, or do you want him to so admire a feminine woman of strength who keeps that strength subservient to her femininity where it will be useful and will bring out indirectly and gently the strength in your son.

You have forcibly held Dr. T. into the role of being a good doctor, but did not know how to force him into the role of a good husband and father.

I hope you understand what I mean and that you will watch matters well with a pretty woman's eyes and the guidance of a purely feminine woman.

Write to me, please.

Sincerely,
Milton H. Erickson, M.D.

From: "Dr. T."
October 3, 1963

Dear Milton,

Mrs. T. and I have been planning for months and months to make the ASCH meeting in San Francisco but now it will be impossible.

College expense for two, [daughter] and [son], has been over twice as much as I had planned for. Both of them matriculated at [a southeastern university]. Write them. They would enjoy hearing from you.

I am doing fine. I am working hard and I am not drinking alcohol. I haven't slipped except the two times Mrs. T. wrote you about in April. I don't want to even slip around and do "closet drinking" anymore. I had no idea how much my friends drank, until I became sober. Within the last five nights Mrs. T. and I have been out three, one night at a country club dance and cocktails, another at an attorney friend's home, where he was entertaining a couple from New York City (plus cocktails), and last night at a neighbor's home for supper (plus cocktails).

Alcohol used to be such a part of my life that I didn't even notice it. I drank Coca-Cola at these outings and kept a clear mind.

Another thing I have found out is that part of my exuberant personality and back-slapping (life of the party) was "whiskey talk." I still feel uncomfortable when I am in the midst of my drinking buddies, but every time I say No! it makes me feel stronger. I feel mighty good now, when I am called back to the hospital on an emergency and do not have to apologize for a "liquor breath."

Naturally, Mrs. T. and my children are doing better. They are closer to me and I feel closer to them. I have asked all of them to forgive me and to not hold on to the past unpleasantness that I have caused them. I realize that this is a big order for them to carry out, and, when I see sometimes that *all* is not forgiven, I try to use all my reasoning and understanding that I have.

I thought that living a more religious life was the answer to my drinking problem and, on October 10, 1962, I rededicated my life to Jesus Christ in my Baptist church. I felt much better after my religious experience and I know I was a better man but—I kept on sipping my Scotch.

I realize now that your interpersonal relationship with me (and Mrs. T.) affected my giving up this bad habit.

Milton, I want to thank you again and again for the good you have done for me.

The next time I see you, I want you to help me out some more though. I have become impotent within the last few months and "that is not like me." I am sure it is psychological, probably from guilt repressions. Whatever the cause, I'll admit I need your help.

Tell Betty hello for me and give our mutual friends whom you see at *our* meeting my best regards.

Oh, I want to be our ASCH delegate at an international meeting in Switzerland in '64.

Regards,
"Dr. T."

To: Dr. and Mrs. "T."
October 16, 1963

Dear Mrs. and Dr. T.:

As you no doubt know, the meeting was saddened by the sudden death of our good friend and colleague, Dr. Troy Shafer. We shall all miss him greatly.

However, although this tragic loss set a sad opening note for the gathering, it was a most successful Annual Meeting, in many ways the best we have had yet. You were greatly missed.

I haven't time to write your son and daughter but our dog, Roger Drasset, very kindly wrote them a nice long letter. Good of him but then he keeps me busy supporting him in the luxury he likes.

So you have found out how completely so many people depend on liquor for the enjoyment of life. I think it is terrible to rely on whiskey talk instead of genuine interpersonal relations and good fellowship.

As for your special problem, I assure you that it is a typical psychogenic one that usually develops temporarily from guilt reactions for past alcoholism. When alcoholism continues too long, it becomes an organic problem. So, instead of getting scared or worried or fearful, patiently wait for a very nice sudden and unexpected surprise. That's what happens.

I'm to be in court in Jackson, Mississippi, on December 3 or 4, or both, as an expert witness. I am going to try to hook that trip up with the possibilities of St. Louis, Memphis, Jackson, New Orleans, Beaumont, Houston and Dallas series of lectures—part going, part coming.

Saturday I leave for Milwaukee for the 72nd wedding anniversary of my parents. Boy, did they really take their time getting around to that:

Did I hear you ask about our grandchildren—only 15 ⅓—8 boys, 7 girls and we don't know about Betty Alice's next—her first was a boy.

Cheerio,
Milton H. Erickson, M.D.

EPILOGUE

Having spent 26 years, or half of my life, studying Milton Erickson, I still find him very much an enigma. To explain, to convey, even to appreciate fully the essence of his work is a difficult task.

There are many lenses through which to examine Erickson. His professional legacy is translucent. It has been mined, although not fully by any means, in the 100 books about him and his derivative work. There are audiotapes; there are videotapes. There is an abundance of material available.

Then there is Erickson the man—heretofore a more elusive territory. The letters in this book shed new light on Erickson's personal and professional life. He emerges as a man of unusual substance and integrity, with the will and energy to persevere. He attacked methodically when he uncovered unethical practices. He was meticulous in his communication. His letters were literary. He was the expert's expert at a very early age. Leaders in many fields—psychotherapy, anthropology, psychology, medicine, hypnosis—sought his wisdom.

Although physically diminutive, Erickson was larger than life. He had many uncanny qualities. He understood the idiosyncrasies of how humans relate and respond. He was thorough and funny, confident and optimistic.

Moreover, he was able to utilize and harness whatever he encountered, wherever he encountered it.

I have studied most of the major therapists of the second half of the twentieth century. I have seen and/or worked with Whitaker, Satir, Minuchin, Cecchin, Madanes, the Polsters, the Gouldings, Masterson, Kernberg, Rogers, Ellis, Beck, Haley, and Bowen, to name but a few. I am grateful to all of them. There is hardly a day in my practice that I do not use methods I have gleaned from their brilliant contributions, and yet I always come back to Erickson. His scope is what holds me; he was able to reach the widest possible range of patients and to affect them most deeply.

I founded the Erickson Foundation in 1979. Dr. and Mrs. Erickson were original Board members; so was my ex-wife, Sherron Peters. The Foundation since has organized countless training programs and workshops. It has spawned more than 80 affiliated Institutes around the world. I lecture internationally, speaking at least twice a month. I have taught in almost 35 countries on six continents. This has been possible because, in 1973, I walked through the front door at 1201 East Hayward Street in Phoenix Arizona, and encountered a man in a wheelchair, limited by polio, but with a limitless intellect and limitless capacity to live life completely.

My associate Brent Geary and I have immersed ourselves in the Erickson letters over many years. We have learned so much. We have merveled at Erickson's richness and depth. We have been moved and inspired. The journey has been eerie and enlightening, like walking through a Roman forum and retracing the steps of those who made history there. Much of the history of twentieth-century hypnosis can be traced in Erickson's letters.

I live in a strange state of hyperkinetic paralysis. I travel, teach, and write, trying to preserve the corpus of Erickson's legacy, and perhaps to add a bit to it in the process. Yet I am paralyzed by the knowledge that I will never complete the task. Some of Erickson will remain obscure. Some of his legacy will be lost. But much of it will live on, through books and videos, through his students and their students and the students yet to come. And now, the first volume of letters invites readers into the private conversations between Erickson and his colleagues and friends. My role? To have offered a glimpse of another side of history.

Jeffrey K. Zeig, Ph.D.
Director
Milton H. Erickson Foundation
Phoenix, Arizona

REFERENCES

Bandler, R., & Grinder, J. (1975). *Patterns of the hypnotic techniques of Milton H. Erickson, Vol. 1.* Cupertino, CA: Meta Publications.

Bateson, G., Jackson, D., Haley, J., & Weakland, J. (1956). Toward a theory of schizophrenia. *Behavioral Science, 10,* 521–564.

Bateson, G., & Mead, M. (1942). *Balinese character: A photographic analysis.* New York: New York Academy of Sciences.

Bateson, G., & Mead, M. (1976, Summer). Interview with Bateson. *CoEvolution Quarterly.*

Berne, E. (1954). *Games people play.* New York: Grove Press.

Brenman, M. (1942). Experiments in the hypnotic production of anti-social and self-injurious behavior. *Journal of Psychiatry, 5,* 49–61.

Brenman, M., & Gill, M. (1947). *Hypnotherapy: A survey of the literature.* New York: International Universities Press.

Cohen, S. B. (1963). Brain damage due to penicillin. *Journal of the American Medical Association.*

Conn, J. H. (1982). The myth of coercion under hypnosis. In J. K. Zeig (Ed.), *Ericksonian approaches to hypnosis and psychotherapy* (pp. 357–367). New York: Brunner/Mazel.

Cooper, L. (1948). Hypnosis: 1. *The Bulletin, Georgetown University Medical Center, 16,* 214–221.

Cooper, L., & Erickson, M. H. (1954). *Time distortion in hypnosis: An experimental and clinical investigation.* Baltimore: Williams & Wilkins.

Cooper, L., & Erickson, M. H. (1959). *Time distortion in hypnosis: An experimental and clinical investigation* (2nd ed.). Baltimore: Williams & Wilkins.

Cooper, L., & Erickson, M. H. (1982). *Time distortion in hypnosis: An experimental and clinical investigation* (2nd ed.). New York: Irvington.

Crasilneck, H. B., & Hall, J. A. (1985). *Principles and applications*: (2nd ed.). Orlando, FL: Grune & Stratton.

Erickson, E. M. (1962). Observations concerning alterations in hypnosis concerning visual perceptions. *American Journal of Clinical Hypnosis, 5*(2), 131–134.

Erickson, E. M. (1966). Further observations of hypnotic alteration of visual perception. *American Journal of Clinical Hypnosis, 8*(3), 187–188.

Erickson, H., Tamlin, E., & Swain, M. (1983). *Modeling and meta-modeling: A theory and paradigm for nursing.* Englewood Cliffs, NJ: Prentice-Hall. (Reprinted 1998. Austin, TX: EST.)

Erickson, M. H. (1935). A study of an experimental neurosis hypnotically induced in a case of ejaculatio praecox. *British Journal of Medical Psychology, 15*, pt. 1, 34–50.

Erickson, M. H. (1938). A study of clinical and experimental findings on hypnotic deafness: 1. Clinical experimentation and findings. *Journal of General Psychology, 19*, 127–150, 151–167.

Erickson, M. H. (1939a). An experimental investigation of the possible antisocial use of hypnosis. *Psychiatry: Journal of the Biology and Pathology of Interpersonal Relations, 2*(3), 391–414.

Erickson, M. H. (1939b). The induction of color blindness by a technique of hypnotic suggestion. *Journal of General Psychology, 20*, 61–89.

Erickson, M. H. (1944). The method employed to formulate a complex story for the induction of an experimental neurosis in a hypnotic subject. *Journal of General Psychology, 31*, 67–84.

Erickson, M. H. (1952). Deep hypnosis and its induction. In L. M. LeCron (Ed.), *Experimental hypnosis* (pp. 70–114). New York: Macmillan.

Erickson, M. H. (1954). Special techniques of brief hypnotheraphy. *Journal of Clinical and Experimental Hypnosis, 2*(12), 109–129.

Erickson, M. H. (1958a). Naturalistic techniques of hypnosis. *American Journal of Clinical Hypnosis, 1*(1), 3–8.

Erickson, M. H. (1958b). Pediatric hypnotherapy. *American Journal of Clinical Hypnosis, 1*, 25–29.

Erickson, M. H. (1959). Further clinical techniques of hypnosis: Utilization techniques, *American Journal of Clinical Hypnosis, 2,* 3–21.

Erickson, M. H. (1963). Hypnotically oriented psychotherapy in organic brain damage. *American Journal of Clinical Hypnosis, 6*(2), 92–112.

Erickson, M. H. (1964a). The confusion technique in hypnosis. *American Journal of Clinical Hypnosis, 6*(3), 183–207.

Erickson, M. H. (1964b). A hypnotic technique in resistant patients: The patient, the technique, and its rationale and field experiment. *American Journal of Clinical Hypnosis, 7,* 8–32.

Erickson, M. H. (1964c). Hypnotically oriented psychotherapy in organic brain disease—an addendum. *American Journal of Clinical Hypnosis, 6*(4), 361–362.

Erickson, M. H. (1965a). Special inquiry with Aldous Huxley into the nature and character of various states of consciousness. *American Journal of Clinical Hypnosis, 1,* 14–33.

Erickson, M. H. (1965b). Experimental hypnotherapy in Tourette's disease. *American Journal of Clinical Hypnosis, 7,* 325–331.

Erickson, M. H. (1966). The interspersal hypnotic technique for symptom correction and pain control. *American Journal of Clinical Hypnosis, 6*(8), 198–209.

Erickson, M. H. (1967). Laboratory and clinical hypnosis: The same or different phenomena? *American Journal of Clinical Hypnosis, 9,* 166–170.

Erickson, M. H. (1973). A field investigation by hypnosis of sound loci importance in human behavior. *American Journal of Clinical Hypnosis, 16*(2), 147–164.

Erickson, M. H., Hershman, S., & Secter, l. (1961). *The practical application of medical and dental hypnosis.* New York: Julian Press.

Erickson, M. H., & Hill, L. B. (1944). Unconscious mental activity in hypnosis—psychoanalytic implications. *Psychoanalytic Quarterly, 13*(1), 60–78.

Erickson, M. H., Huston, P. E., & Shakow, D. (1934). A study of hypnotically induced complexes by means of the Luria technique. *Journal of General Psychology, 11,* 65–97.

Erickson, M. H., & Kubie, L. S. (1939). The permanent relief of an obsessional phobia by means of communications with an unsuspected dual personality. *Psychoanalytic Quarterly, 8*(4), 471–509.

Erickson, M. H., & Kubie, L. S. (1940). The translation of the cryptic automatic writing of one hypnotic subject by another in trance-like dissociated state. *Psychoanalytic Quarterly, 9*(1), 51–63.

Erickson, M. H., & Kubie, L. S. (1941). The successful treatment of a case of acute hysterical depression by a return under hypnosis to a critical phase of childhood. *Psychoanalytic Quarterly, 10*(4), 583–609.

Erickson, M. H., & Rossi, E. L. (1979). *Hypnotherapy, an exploratory casebook.* New York: Irvington.

Erickson, M. H., & Rossi, E. L. (1980a). *The collected papers of Milton H. Erickson, M.D., Vol. 1: The nature of hypnosis and suggestion.* New York: Irvington.

Erickson, M. H., & Rossi, E. L. (1980b). *The collected papers of Milton H. Erickson, M.D., Vol. II: Hypnotic alteration of sensory, perceptual, and psychophysiological processes.* New York: Irvington.

Erickson, M. H., & Rossi, E. L. (1980c). *The collected papers of Milton H. Erickson, M.D., Vol. III: Hypnotic investigation of psychodynamic processes.* New York: Irvington.

Erickson, M. H., & Rossi, E. L. (1980d). *The collected papers of Milton H. Erickson. M.D., Vol. IV: Innovative hypnotherapy.* New York: Irvington.

Erickson, M. H., & Rossi, E. L. (1981). *Experiencing hypnosis: Therapeutic approaches to altered states.* New York: Irvington.

Erickson, M. H., & Rossi, E. L. (1989). *The February man.* New York: Brunner/Mazel.

Erickson, M. H., Rossi, E. L., & Rossi, S. (1976). *Hypnotic realities: The induction of clinical hypnosis and forms of indirect suggestion.* New York: Irvington.

Estabrooks, G. H. (1943). *Hypnotism.* New York: Dutton.

Fisher, C. (1953a). Studies on the nature of suggestion, Part I: Experimental induction of dreams by direct suggestion. *Journal of the American Psychoanalytic Association, 1,* 222–255.

Fisher, C. (1953b). Studies on the nature of suggestion, Part II: The transference meaning of giving suggestions. *Journal of the American Psychoanalytic Association, 1,* 406–437.

Gill, M., & Brenman, M. (1959). *Hypnosis and related states: Psychoanalytic studies in regression.* New York: International Universities Press.

Gilligan, S. G. (1986). *Therapeutic trances: The cooperation principle in Ericksonian hypnotheraphy.* New York: Brunner/Mazel.

Gilligan, S. G. (1997). *The courage to love: Principles and practices of self-relations psychotherapy.* New York: Norton.

Gorton, B. (1959, October). Review of the book *Hypnography: A study in the therapeutic use of symbolic painting. American Journal of Clinical Hypnosis,* 2(2), 102–104.

Grinder, J., DeLozier, J., & Bandler, R. (1977). *Patterns of the hypnotic techniques of Milton H. Erickson, Vol. II.* Cupertino, CA: Meta Publications.

Haley, J. (Ed.). (1967). *Advanced techniques of hypnosis and therapy: Selected papers of Milton Erickson, M.D.* New York: Grune & Stratton.

Haley, J. (1973). *Uncommon therapy: The psychiatric techniques of Milton H. Erickson, M.D.* New York: Norton.

Haley, J. (Ed.). (1985). *Conversations with Milton H. Erickson, Vols. I–III.* New York: Triangle Press.

Hilgard, E. R., Crawford, H. J., & Wert, A. (1979). The Stanford hypnotic arm levitation induction and test (SHALIT): A six-minute hypnotic induction and measurement scale. *International Journal of Clinical and Experimental Hypnosis, 27*(2), 11–124.

Hull, C. (1933). *Hypnosis and suggestibility: An experimental approach.* New York: Appleton-Century.

Huxley, A. (1932). *Brave new world.* New York: Harper & Brothers.

Huxley, A. (1954). *The doors of perception.* New York: Harper & Brothers.

Huxley, A. (1956). *Heaven and hell.* New York: Harper & Brothers.

Kroger, W. S., & Schneider, S. A. (1959, April). An electronic aid for hypnotic induction: A preliminary report. *International Journal of Clinical and Experimental Hypnosis, 8*(2), 93–99.

Kuhn, L., & Russo, S. (1947). *Modern hypnosis.* New York: Psychological Library.

Lankton, S. R., & Lankton, C. H. (1983). *The answer within: A clinical framework of Ericksonian hypnotherapy.* New York: Brunner/Mazel.

Latane, B., & Dorley, J. A. (1969, Summer). Bystander "apathy." *American Scientist.*

LeCron, L. M. (Ed.). (1952). *Experimental hypnosis.* New York: Macmillan.

LeCron, L. M., & Bordeaux, J. (1947). *Hypnotism today.* New York: Grune & Stratton.

Lustig, H. (Producer) (1975). *The artistry of Milton H. Erickson, M.D.* (videotape recording). Haverford, PA: Herbert Lustig, Ltd.

McCord, H. (1962, January). A note on photic stimulation, hypnosis and epilepsy. *American Journal of Clinical Hypnosis, 4*(3), 185–186.

Mead, M. (1928). *Coming of age in Samoa: A psychological study of primitive youth for western civilization.* New York: Morrow.

Mead, M. (1930). *Growing up in New Guinea.* New York: Morrow.

Mead, M. (1935). *Sex and temperament in three primitive societies.* New York: Morrow.

Mead, M. (1977). The originality of Milton Erickson. *American Journal of Clinical Hypnosis, 20,* 4–5.

Milgram, S. (1963). Behavioral study of obedience. *Journal of Abnormal and Social Psychology, 67,* 371–378.

Milgram, S. (1965a). Some conditions of obedience and disobedience to authority. *Human Relations, 18,* 57–76.

Milgram, S. (1965b). The lost letter technique: A tool of social research. *Public Opinion Quarterly, 29,* 437–438.

O'Hanlon, W. H., & Hexum, A. L. (1990). *Uncommon casebook: The complete clinical work of Milton H. Erickson, M.D.* New York: Norton.

Orne, M. T. (1962). Anti-social behavior and hypnosis: Problems of control and validation in empirical studies. In G. H. Estabrooks (Ed.), *Hypnosis: Current problems.* New York: Harper & Rowe.

Pattie, F. (1968, January). Review of the book *Franz Anton Mesmer: Physician extraordinaire. American Journal of Clinical Hypnosis, 10*(3), 225–226.

Reiter, P. (1958). *Anti-social or criminal acts and hypnosis.* Copenhagen: Monkogaard Press.

Rosen, H. (1959). Foreword in L. Cooper & M. H. Erickson, *Time distortion in hypnosis: An experimental and clinical investigation* (p. ix). Baltimore: Williams & Wilkins.

Rosen, H. (1982). *My voice will go with you: The teaching tales of Milton H. Erickson.* New York: Norton.

Rosenbluth, A., Weiner, N., & Bigelow, J. (1943). Behavior, purpose, and teleology. *Philosophy of Science, 10,* 18–24.

Rowland, L. W. (1939). Will hypnotized persons try to harm themselves or others? *Journal of Abnormal and Social Psychology, 34,* 114–117.

Rowland, L. W. (1943). *Hypnotism.* New York: Dutton.

Schilder, P., & Kauders, O. (1927). *Hypnosis.* Washington, DC: Nervous and Mental Disease Monograph, No. 46.

Spiegel, H., & Spiegel, D. (1978). *Trance and treatment: Clinical uses of hypnosis.* New York: Basic Books.

Weitzenhoffer, A. M. (1957). *General techniques of hypnotism.* New York: Grune & Stratton.

Weitzenhoffer, A. M. (1960, April). Unconscious or co-conscious? Reflections upon certain recent trends in medical hypnosis. *American Journal of Clinical Hypnosis, 2*(4), 177–196.

Weitzenhoffer, A. M. (1989). *The practice of hypnotism, Vol. 1.* New York: Wiley.

Weitzenhoffer, A. M., & Hilgard, E. R. (1959). *Stanford hypnotic susceptibility scales (SHSS), Forms A and B.* Palo Alto, CA: Consulting Psychologists Press.

Weitzenhoffer, A. M., & Hilgard, E. R. (1962). *Stanford hypnotic susceptibility scales, Form C.* Palo Alto, CA: Consulting Psychologists Press.

Wells, W. R. (1941). Experiments in the hypnotic production of crime. *Journal of Psychology, 11,* 63–102.

Wolberg, L. R. (1945). *Hypnoanalysis.* New York: Grune & Stratton.

Wolberg, L. R. (1948). *Medical hypnosis.* New York: Grune & Stratton.

Zeig, J. K. (Ed.). (1980). *A teaching seminar with Milton H. Erickson, M.D.* New York: Brunner/Mazel.

Zeig, J. K. (1982). The myth of coercion under hypnosis. In J. K. Zeig (Ed.), *Ericksonian approaches to hypnosis and psychotherapy* (pp. 355–367). New York: Brunner/Mazel.

Zeig, J. K. (1985a). Ethical issues in Ericksonian hypnosis: Informed consent and training standards. In J. K. Zeig (Ed.), *Ericksonian psychotherapy, Vol. 1: Structure* (pp. 459–473). New York: Brunner/Mazel.

Zeig, J. K. (1985b). *Experiencing Erickson: An introduction to the man and his work.* New York: Brunner/Mazel.

Zeig, J. K. (1988). Phenomenological approach to therapeutic hypnotic induction and symptom utilization. In J. K. Zeig & S. R. Lankton (Eds.), *Developing Ericksonian therapy: State of the art* (pp. 353–375). New York: Brunner/Mazel.

Zeig, J. K. (1992). The virtues of our faults: A key concept of Ericksonian therapy. In J. K. Zeig (Ed.), *The evolution of psychotherapy: The second conference* (pp. 252–266). New York: Brunner/Mazel.

Zeig, J. K. (1997). Experimental approaches to clinical development. In J. K. Zeig (Ed.), *The evolution of psychotherapy: The third conference* (pp. 161–177). New York: Brunner/Mazel.